LIBRARIES NI
WITHDRAWN FROM STOCK

AGAINST THE TIDE

D1477421

J. B. Armour in middle age.

10986

U - 285.20924

AGAINST THE TIDE

A Calendar of the papers of Rev J B Armour
Irish Presbyterian Minister and Home Ruler
1869-1914

J R B McMINN

PRONI

1985

C
P.R.O.N.I.
I.S.B.N. 0 905691 10 5

CONTENTS

LIST OF ILLUSTRATIONS

The Players and the Scene

The illustrations are all taken from the originals in the J. B. Armour papers in P.R.O.N.I. (D.1792/C), apart from the Conor portrait which hangs in the session room of Trinity Presbyterian Church, Ballymoney, County Antrim, and is reproduced with the kind permission of Rev. R. F. S. Poots and the kirk session of the church.

AUTHOR'S NOTE AND ACKNOWLEDGEMENTS

James Brown Armour was born in 1841 and died in 1928, therefore the terminal dates of this calendar of his political papers require some explanation. From a number of points of view the year 1869 is a useful starting point, but chiefly because it was on 19 July of that year that Armour was installed as minister of Trinity Presbyterian Church, Ballymoney, and so resumed his intimate relationship with the area of his birth. As far as Armour's involvement in politics is concerned, this did not begin until 1869 and certainly was over by 1914. However, I have included extracts from correspondence prior to 1869 so that readers can gain some insight into his youthful character and personality and also some selected extracts from the post-1914 period in order to highlight his political opinions in old age. I have not included any extracts from Armour's sermons and speeches, or from other miscellaneous material contained in the collection, though I have discussed some of them in the introduction.

Most of the items included in the collection were deposited with the Public Record Office of Northern Ireland by the late J. K. C. Armour, J. B. Armour's youngest son. Following J. K. C. Armour's death in September 1976, further MSS were discovered in his house by his nephew, Rev. J. S. S. Armour, and subsequently deposited by him, through me, in P.R.O.N.I. At his request this material was then integrated into the existing collection and a thorough overhaul of the classification scheme was undertaken. For its imperfections and indeed those of this calendar, I alone am responsible.

I should like to express my appreciation and gratitude to the following people for the help which I received from them in the preparation of this publication: Dr B. Trainor, Dr A. P. W. Malcomson and in particular Mr T. Parkhill of the Public Record Office of Northern Ireland, for providing not only access to the source material in their custody but a great deal of generous advice as well; Dr A. T. Q. Stewart, reader in the department of modern history, the Queen's University of Belfast, for encouraging me to undertake the necessary research for this project; the late J. K. C. Armour of Campbell College, Belfast, for helping me to see his father as a man of flesh and blood; Rev. J. S. S. Armour of St David's Presbyterian Church, St John's, Newfoundland, Canada, for making the Armour additional MSS (now integrated into the main collection) so freely available to me; Rev. R. F. S. Poots and the kirk session of Trinity Presbyterian Church, Ballymoney, for allowing me to consult their records; Dr B. M. Walker, lecturer in the department of political science, the Queen's University of Belfast, for a number of helpful suggestions as to potentially valuable sources; Mr S. Alex Blair, head of the history department, Dalriada School, Ballymoney, for placing his unique knowledge of the history of the Ballymoney and Kilraughts areas at my disposal; Miss C. Doherty and Mr J. Erskine of the Stranmillis College library, for the assistance which they gave through the inter-library loan service; Mrs S. B. McMordie, former librarian of the Presbyterian Historical Society, and Miss Ann Maconaghie of Ballymoney library, for continuing interest and assistance; Mr B. McAleese of the Stranmillis College Learning Resources Unit, for drawing the two maps; Mr J. Burns of the Stranmillis College Learning Resources Unit, for undertaking the photographic work; Dr T. Bartlett, lecturer in history, University College, Galway, for his help with the choice of a title; Miss R. Dickson for typesetting the manuscript; finally, my wife Elizabeth, who not only provided very necessary moral support throughout the months of research and writing, but also read the introduction in draft and made a number of valuable suggestions which were subsequently incorporated into it.

LIST OF ABBREVIATIONS

B.F.P.	*Ballymoney Free Press*
B.N.L.	*Belfast News-Letter*
Col. Con.	*Coleraine Constitution*
I.H.S.	*Irish Historical Studies*
I.N.	*Irish News*
M.N.	*Morning News*
N.C.	*Northern Constitution*
N.L.I.	National Library of Ireland
N.W.	*Northern Whig*
P.A.C.E.	*Protestant and Catholic Encounter*
P.R.O.N.I.	Public Record Office of Northern Ireland

North Antrim in 1885

●	Towns, villages, demesnes
+	Churches
·············	Boundaries of baronies
++++++++++++	William Traill's electric tramway
0 4 miles	Scale

Parliamentary Divisions in County Antrim 1885-1918

(North Antrim, Mid Antrim, East Antrim, South Antrim)

Rathlin Island

Giant's Causeway

Electric Tramway

Ballintoy

Bushmills Ballycastle Ballyvoy

Portrush

NORTH ANTRIM

Derrykeighan Cushendun

Coleraine Dervock Armoy

Stranocum

Kilraughts Cushendall

Ballymoney Pharis Retreat Waterfoot

Loughguile

Knockaholet

Dunloy Cloughmills Parkmore

Finvoy Carnlough

Killagan Newton Crommelin Glenarm

Clogh

Rasharkin **MID ANTRIM**

Broughshane Ballygalley

Cullybackey

Portglenone Larne

Ahoghill Ballymena *Island Magee*

Kells

EAST ANTRIM Ballynure

Randalstown Ballyclare

Toome Doagh Whitehead

Antrim Templepatrick Carrickfergus

Dunadry Whiteabbey

SOUTH ANTRIM

Lough Whitehouse

Neagh Crumlin Legoniel

Dundrod

Glenavy **BELFAST**

Ballinderry

Ballinderry Upper

Aghalee Lisburn

•	Towns and Villages	– – – – – – –	Railways
–·–·–·–	Belfast Borough Boundary	0 10 miles	Scale

J. B. ARMOUR, THE MAN AND THE MYTH

'It is difficult today to picture a sturdy north Antrim farmer having to stand, as Armour saw one stand a century ago, bareheaded in the falling snow before a haughty, cigar-smoking little man—landlord or agent—begging to be allowed to remain on his homestead and begging in vain.'[1] So began an article on James Brown Armour by David Kennedy which appeared in the Protestant and Catholic Encounter magazine of October 1971. The incident which he described is by no means an unimportant one—indeed W. S. Armour in his biography of his father claimed that it was the mainspring of his father's sympathy for the plight of the tenant farmer.[2] However, I refer to it not because of that, but because its emotive language and idealised content are typical of much that has been written by many about Armour. The constant repetition of this kind of interpretation since Armour's death in 1928 has created a myth regarding the man himself and the political and religious context in which he operated in north Antrim. It is interesting to speculate as to how far north Antrim's reputation as the last bastion of Presbyterian liberalism derives from the Armour legend. Armour has indeed for many come to personify non-Unionist politics in the area.[3]

The source of the Armour myth is William S. Armour's *Armour of Ballymoney* which was published in 1934, only six years after J. B. Armour's death.[4] Rarely has a son paid so much filial homage to a father. The explanation lies not only in love and respect, but also in W. S. Armour's own political outlook. He was educated at Campbell College, Belfast, and Jesus College, Oxford (where he was elected president of the Union). In 1910 he took up an appointment in the educational service of the Indian government at Queen's College, Benares, after campaigning for the Liberals in several English constituencies during the general election in January of that year.[5] In the post-war period he returned to Belfast to become editor of the *Northern Whig*, but his political views clashed with those of the management and he moved to London where he continued his career as a journalist and writer in more congenial surroundings. He died in 1940. His political views are set out clearly in a number of books which he published in the 1930s. *Mankind at the watershed*, which appeared in 1936, was essentially a plea for morality in world affairs and a condemnation of the 'Junkers and Tories' whose departure from that morality, he alleged, brought about war in 1914.[6] In this book he roundly condemned European fascist governments and vigorously supported the League of Nation's ideal.[7] He was also the author of two books on the Irish question, and in writing these he was clearly influenced by his sojourn in Belfast. *Facing the Irish question* (1935) traced the roots of the Ulster and Irish problems to the Treaty of Limerick and the establishment of a Protestant ascendancy which, he argued, had yet to be dislodged in the north.[8] He accused successive British governments of submitting to this situation and of continually assuming that Irishmen outside Ulster were disloyal to the crown and the empire.[9] The only solution, he claimed, was the destruction of the ascendancy clique.[10] Similar themes were developed in *Ulster, Ireland, Britain—a forgotten trust* which eulogised the achievements of Ireland after independence.[11] In the book he referred to his years in Belfast:

> Quite unconsciously on my part, I was carrying on an older tradition, which in my father's case was traced back to the eighteenth century. If it reappears in Dublin spontaneously when the bonds are removed, its emergence still awaits opportunity in north-east Ulster, just as surely as streams driven underground come to the surface again.[12]

Much of this had already been foreshadowed in *Armour of Ballymoney* and had revealed itself in his attitude towards his father. Not only did he present a very one-sided view, in that

1. D. Kennedy, 'James Brown Armour' in *P.A.C.E.*, iii, no. 3 (Oct. 1971), pp 8-11.
2. W. S. Armour, *Armour of Ballymoney* (London, 1934), pp 41-4.
3. This is perhaps reflected more in the attitudes of most commentators since Armour's death than in the attitudes of his contemporaries. Obviously the title selected by W. S. Armour for his biography of his father, *Armour of Ballymoney*, is very suggestive indeed. It is but a short step from this to the selection of Armour by F. S. L. Lyons in *Ireland since the famine* (2nd ed., London, 1973), pp 23-4, as the symbolic representative of Protestant Home Rule sentiment throughout the whole province of Ulster.
4. Armour, *Armour of Ballymoney*.
5. *B.F.P.*, 10 Feb. 1910. He spent most of his time campaigning for Basil Williams (Lewes, Sussex).
6. W. S. Armour, *Mankind at the watershed* (London, 1936).
7. *Ibid.*
8. W. S. Armour, *Facing the Irish question* (London, 1935).
9. *Ibid.*
10. *Ibid.*
11. W. S. Armour, *Ulster, Ireland, Britain—a forgotten trust* (London, 1938).
12. *Ibid.*

J. B. Armour in old age.

he discounted anything unfavourable, not only was his use of sources restricted and uncritical, not only did he exaggerate the role which J. B. Armour actually played in political events, but he twisted his father's political views to coincide with his own. A further dangerous feature of his approach can be detected in the final chapter of the biography entitled 'Sundown, splendid and serene', where he related a death-bed vision, which his father experienced during his final, fatal illness in January 1928.[13] From its ambiguous fragments, W. S. Armour went on to construct a concept of religious reconciliation and toleration for the opposite point of view which he claimed would contain the answer to all of Ireland's problems:

> I know he saw something very clearly, and I also grasped what he had been seeing. What I understood was that each side in Ireland must be ready to listen to the other and admit the right of opinion. He had fought his own people for this simple right and had faithfully put before them the rights of Catholics. Now the idea he wanted to leave behind was that Catholics and Protestants alike must show the spirit of brotherliness and hear what the other had to say.[14]

From this it was but a short step to the editorial in the *Irish Times* of 8 September 1969, on the occasion of the celebration of the one hundredth anniversary of Armour's ordination, in which it was claimed that Armour: 'in his passionate opposition to the landlords and brewers, the machine politicians of the Tory party, was as barbed in speech as a young Bogsider. Though he was not a separatist, the devolutionary tendencies of today and the prospect of the E.E.C. bring a new relevance to his concepts.'[15] Inevitably the *Irish Times* chose to emphasise Armour the home ruler, whereas David Kennedy in the 1971 *P.A.C.E.* article stressed Armour the force for reconciliation. 'His prophetic vision illumines the darkness of our present discontent ... . Now more than ever we need an Armour, a man born into one community, yet able to understand the fears and sympathise with the aspirations of the other.'[16] Thus, J. B. Armour's bones have become, in effect, a political talisman.

A contemporary reviewer remarked of *Armour of Ballymoney* that the book was 'not merely of passing interest, it will be a valuable mine for the historian of the eighty seven years which Armour's life covers. The publication of the book is a service to the history of the country.'[17] In the light of Armour's subsequent treatment by historians, one might be excused for suggesting that it has been a mine that has been too accessible and easily worked. Curiously, in spite of its obviously unbalanced nature, it has been accepted by many at its face value. F. S. L. Lyons, in *Ireland since the famine*, cited Armour as 'the famous Presbyterian minister' who was 'a notable example' of those Protestants who took the Home Rule side, stressing of course that such Protestants were always an articulate minority.[18] Patrick Buckland, in his study of *Ulster Unionism and the origins of Northern Ireland, 1886-1922*, goes even further and describes Armour as energetically leading 'the small body of Protestants who were Liberals and home rulers'.[19] J. W. Boyle asserts that Armour gave discreet assistance to R. G. Glendinning in his successful campaign for the North Antrim seat in 1906.[20]

Apart from these brief references to Armour, there are two attempts at a more elaborate analysis which deserve to be mentioned. Oliver McCann's study of the Irish Protestant Home Rule Association between 1886 and 1895 offers an interesting interpretation of Armour's attitude towards Home Rule:

> The Reverend J. B. Armour of Ballymoney is generally and erroneously regarded by historians of this period as typifying Protestant home rulers, however prior to 1891-92 he was totally opposed to Irish self-government and until 1889 he was an ardent Liberal Unionist. There is much to suggest that he would have continued opposing Home Rule if the Unionist and Tory party had been prepared to grant a fair and equitable measure of land reform. It was only when he realised the impossibility of this that he became a convert to Irish nationalism.[21]

13. Armour, *Armour of Ballymoney*, pp 373-4.
14. *Ibid.*, p. 373.
15. *Irish Times*, 8 Sept. 1969.
16. Kennedy, *James Brown Armour*, p. 11.
17. D. O'C., 'Armour of Ballymoney' in *Irish book lover*, xxiii (July-August, 1935), pp 100-1.
18. Lyons, *Ireland since the famine*, pp 23-4.
19. P. J. Buckland, *Ulster Unionism* (Dublin, 1973), p. 31. Significantly perhaps, the Armour papers lodged in P.R.O.N.I. do not figure in Buckland's bibliography, whereas W. S. Armour's *Armour of Ballymoney* does.
20. J. W. Boyle, 'The Belfast Protestant Association and the Independent Orange Order', in *I.H.S.*, xiii (Sept. 1962), p. 141.
21. Oliver McCann, 'The Protestant Home Rule movement, 1886-95' (M.A. thesis, University College Dublin, 1973), pp 134-5.

But, as McCann admits, this interpretation is a provisional and limited one, since he was unable to consult the Armour papers in P.R.O.N.I. (as they were incomplete and had not yet been catalogued).[22]

Armour is seen from a rather different angle by John Megahey:

> Armour was a Presbyterian clergyman ... and he was in fact an old-fashioned liberal for whom Toryism meant landlordism and ascendancy .... Anglicans seemed to have more than their fair share of the important positions in state and society, and Armour and his friends made full use of this fact ... . Again and again the attempt was made to continue that older pattern of Protestant thinking in which the Anglican/nonconformist dichotomy bulked large.[23]

These intriguing suggestions are unfortunately not developed in any detail.

James Brown Armour was born in Lisboy, a townland close to Ballymoney to the west and to Kilraughts to the south-east.[24] The precise date of his birth is unknown.[25] It was certainly sometime in January 1841 and Armour himself always celebrated it on the 31 January.[26] The Kilraughts church baptismal register would seem to suggest, although not very clearly, the 20 January as the correct date.[27] We have W. S. Armour's word for it that even the Armour family bible, while it recorded the event, did not record the date.[28] Armour himself, with his usual penchant for the dramatic, was to claim much later that on the night of his birth 'was one of the wildest storms that ever blew'—an omen he believed for the future.[29]

Lisboy is a townland which lies about a mile from the present Kilraughts Presbyterian Church. Kilraughts itself is a scattered settlement with no obvious centre. An abandoned Anglican church, of which only the shell remains, occupies what is now called old Kilraughts churchyard where Armour's father and mother both lie buried. It was the expulsion of a Presbyterian cleric, Rev. William Cuming, from this church in 1662, following the Restoration, that led to the establishment of First Kilraughts Presbyterian congregation.[30] Their new meeting house in the nearby townland of Carnagheragh was subsequently rebuilt several times, most recently as the result of a serious fire in 1971.[31] There is also a Reformed or Covenanting Presbyterian church where the grave of J. B. Armour's father-in-law, Rev. Alexander McLeod Stavely, is to be found. A shop, a post-office and a group of houses, collectively known locally as 'the road head', complete the settlement as it is today. The farmhouse where the Armour family lived is still to be seen (although greatly altered and extended), as is the Ganaby schoolhouse one and half miles away where Armour received his early education. The latter structure has fallen on hard times and is now used as a farm out-building.

Kilraughts is, and was, a strongly Presbyterian agricultural community of Scottish ancestry.[32] There still is no Church of Ireland congregation, although the basaltic uplands of the Antrim plateau, with their largely Roman Catholic population, lie only a few miles to the east beyond Loughguile. In the mid-nineteenth century most of the farmers were tenants renting their land.[33] However, some of them had considerable holdings—for example William Stewart, one of the principal tenant-right campaigners in the district, lived in 'Larchfield', a fine Georgian farmhouse of some size.[34] James's own father William actually owned sixty acres of land freehold and on his death in 1864 left property valued at over £630.[35] There was something of a radical political tradition in the district—the Hearts of Steel and the United Irishmen had both received local support[36]—and from 1850 onwards the farmers of Kilraughts, led by their

22. Letter from Oliver McCann in J. B. Armour file in P.R.O.N.I.
23. A. J. Megahey, 'The Irish Protestant churches and social and political issues, 1870-1914' (Ph.D. thesis, Queen's University, Belfast, 1969), pp 69-70.
24. Armour, *Armour of Ballymoney*, p. 1.
25. *Ibid.*
26. *Ibid.*
27. *Ibid.*
28. *Ibid.*
29. *Ibid.*
30. S. A. Blair, *Kilraughts: a kirk and its people* (Kilraughts, 1973), p. 26.
31. *Ibid.*, pp 146-7.
32. *Ibid.*, p. 20.
33. S. C. McElroy, *The Route land crusade: being an authentic account of the efforts made to advance land reform by the Route Tenants' Defence Association, the Antrim Central Tenant-right Association and the Ulster Land Committee* (Coleraine, n.d.), p. 30.
34. McElroy, *Route land crusade*, p. 81; *B.F.P.*, 28 Apr. 1892. Stewart in fact rented some 153 acres.
35. Armour, *Armour of Ballymoney*, p. 3.
36. Papers concerning the trial of Richard Caldwell of Harmony Hill, Ballymoney, for treason June/July 1798 (P.R.O.N.I., T.3058); McElroy, *Route land crusade*, pp 7-8; Blair, *Kilraughts: a kirk and its people*, pp 51-3.

minister, Rev. Samuel Finlay, enthusiastically rallied to the cause of tenant-right.[37] Above all there was a fierce pride and a sense of local loyalty. This was the community into which J. B. Armour was born.

Traditionally, Armour's father William is presented as a gentle soul who walked with a limp and was interested mainly in his farm and in his work as treasurer of the congregation,[38] while his mother Jane seems to have been a fairly resolute character.[39] She was a daughter of William Brown of Ballinaloob, a townland through which the main Ballymena-Ballymoney road runs, a niece of Rev. James Brown of Garvagh and was distantly related to the Armour family.[40] Five brothers and sisters survived infancy apart from James—John, Alexander, William, Jane and the crippled Isobel who, it has been claimed, inspired in James at an early age a sympathy for the weak.[41]

Armour's education is not without significance. From Ganaby school he followed its master Mr Warnock, a veritable martinet, when he moved to the Ballymoney Model School which opened in 1854, necessitating a walk of nine miles each day.[42] He then went to the Royal Belfast Academical Institution where he won several prizes in the mathematical department, then headed by Dr Steen.[43] His earliest surviving letters, written to his closest friend and much later political enemy, John Megaw of Ballyboyland (a townland adjacent to Lisboy), date from this period.[44] Their contents mainly consist of church and educational gossip. Though generally approving of the religious revival of 1859 then in progress, Armour expressed grave doubts about some of its more bizarre excesses:

> The revival is progressing in general very well, but there are means used for its extension even by Presbyterian ministers which I think is very far from right ... . I cannot understand the sleeping cases at all, some say that they get a vision from the other world and that they see Christ and the place of woe but I would be inclined to think that it is only imagination and I think that they should be advised not to look for any visions. Another dreadful imposture is a practising [*sic*] in this town, girls painting on their breast the words 'Jesus Christ' and saying it came there when they were in their sleep.[45]

Writing in May 1860, he commented that although the revival continued to make progress, 'there are a great many deceivers. I am beginning to think that the letting of young men speak that knew nothing before has done a very serious injury.'[46] By August 1860 he was beginning to doubt the permanent effect of the revival on some—'the revival sent a great many to learn but a great many have turned'.[47]

In these letters he revealed his concern about falling academic standards and his support for the Queen's Colleges in Ireland. He disapproved of the decision to end the insistence on knowledge of a classical language as a prerequisite for obtaining a degree. 'If a fellow knows a little gibberish of French and some smatter[i]n[g] of German, he may have a degree any time. It is to give the merchants' sons who are too lazy to learn anything that requires work an A.B. and A.M.'[48] He felt that the endowment of the Queen's Colleges was too small and as a result the academic staff were underpaid. He expressed regret at the award of an honorary American doctorate in divinity to the Presbyterian moderator. 'I think it will be possible to get degrees yet without going to college at all.'[49]

Armour was already, as an adolescent, revelling in harmless gossip about individual ministers. In one letter he speculated as to whether Rev. 'roaring Hugh' Hanna would be tempted to move to

37. *Irish Presbyterian*, April 1903, contains a useful biographical study of Finlay by John Megaw; Blair, *Kilraughts: a kirk and its people*, p. 196; McElroy, *Route land crusade*, pp 53-4.
38. J. B. M. Armour, *Notes on the life of the Reverend J. B. Armour M.A.* (P.R.O.N.I., J. B. Armour papers, D.1792/D), p. 1. Hereafter the Armour papers are cited simply as D.1792.
39. Armour, *Armour of Ballymoney*, p. 3.
40. *Ibid.*
41. Armour, *Notes on the life of J. B. Armour*, p. 2, provides a more detailed analysis of the strengths and frailties of J. B. Armour's family than W. S. Armour's biography.
42. Armour, *Armour of Ballymoney*, p. 4.
43. *Ibid.*, p. 5.
44. The survival of this collection is purely accidental. They were given by John Megaw's son, W. J. Megaw, to W. S. Armour while the latter was writing his biography of his father. Some of the extracts which are quoted in the biography differ from the originals and I have therefore used the originals in every case.
45. J. B. Armour to John Megaw, 14 Sept. 1859 (D.1792/A2/1).
46. J. B. Armour to John Megaw, 8 May 1860 (D.1792/A2/3).
47. J. B. Armour to John Megaw, 24 Aug. 1860 (D.1792/A2/4).
48. J. B. Armour to John Megaw, 8 May 1860 (D.1792/A2/3).
49. J. B. Armour to John Megaw, 24 Aug. 1860 (D.1792/A2/4).

Scotland. 'If he goes, Belfast will have lost a clever man.'[50] He was highly critical of most Presbyterian clerics:

> There is no class of men more liable to be Christians in *theory* only as ministers ... . Many choose it [the church] from a desire of show and of having a respectable position in society; others for the sake of the L.S.D., others again for the sake of being called great but the greater number from the ambition of their parents.[51]

He felt that many parents were pushing their sons into higher education, and subsequently the ministry, for their own selfish reasons:

> Perhaps they expect that the Lord will do them good if they have a Levite for their priest ... I rejoice to think that so many are giving their sons an education, but I protest against the goal to which they wish to direct them, very often against their will.[52]

He concluded that 'the majority of the Gen[eral] Ass[embly] are merely theoretical Christians'.[53] This kind of acid criticism was to be one of J. B. Armour's most enduring characteristics. Nor did he restrict himself to denouncing the clergy—the Presbyterian rank and file were also assailed. Writing to his faithful correspondent John Megaw from Queen's College, Belfast, he singled out what he believed to be their greatest fault—a blind and unquestioning attitude in religious matters. They 'take everything as gospel that falls from their pastor's mouth, without even inquiring into the reason of those things for themselves'.[54]

Armour entered Queen's College, Belfast, in 1860 and began an academic career which was neither particularly outstanding nor happy. His first disappointment was his failure to win an entrance scholarship. He tried to account for his lack of success in a letter to John Megaw. Clearly he was disappointed: 'I have been defeated for the first time in my life'.[55] He admitted that he had not been properly prepared for the examination, while arguing that his successful rivals were of a very high calibre. However, this set-back did nothing to deflate his youthful ego. He continued to point out the weaknesses of his fellow Presbyterians. He also denounced life in small country towns, which he believed were like country schools—of very little worth.[56] This denunciation is rather piquant since he was destined to spend the greater part of his life in just such a town. His letters also reveal his interest in the major controversy then raging in the Irish Presbyterian church as to the respective virtues of hymns and psalms.[57] At this stage in his life he had a distinct preference for the latter.

During his two years at Queen's College, Belfast, he studied, as was then usual, a wide range of subjects including Greek, Latin, English, French, logic, natural philosophy, mathematics and German.[58] He found his studies in the first year 'nearly all very uninteresting', though it was only mathematics that he strongly disliked—'the Slough of Despond'.[59] W. S. Armour naturally tried to defend his father's academic record, but even he was forced to admit that 'his reputation was made less by success at written examinations than by the acumen, ability and scholarship he displayed in the classroom'.[60]

One of his major problems was money, or rather the lack of it. Obviously he had missed the scholarship, but his family was by no means poor. However, his father was anxious that he should enter the ministry, though Armour himself was opposed to the idea. Writing to John Megaw, he reminded him that 'this was my resolution from the first and as I grow older and know more of the world, there are matters occurring which render that altogether impossible. It remains for me now to choose some employment which shall ... enable me to repay, to some extent, the money already spent on my education ... . I have resolved to try my hand at an Indian Civil Service appointment.'[61] He felt that it would be dishonest to ask his family for

---

50. J. B. Armour to John Megaw, 1 Nov. 1860 (D.1792/A2/5).
51. J. B. Armour to John Megaw, 1 Apr. 1862 (D.1792/A2/8).
52. *Ibid.*
53. *Ibid.*
54. J. B. Armour to John Megaw, 6 Feb. 1862 (D.1792/A2/7).
55. J. B. Armour to John Megaw, 1 Nov. 1860 (D.1792/A2/5).
56. *Ibid.*
57. See in particular J. B. Armour to John Megaw, 31 Jan. 1861 (D.1792/A2/6).
58. See the certificates of course completion in these subjects in the J. B. Armour papers (D.1792/C).
59. J. B. Armour to John Megaw, 31 Jan. 1861 (D.1792/A2/6).
60. Armour, *Armour of Ballymoney*, p. 13.
61. J. B. Armour to John Megaw, 29 Aug. 1863 (D.1792/A2/10). His father did not die until November 1864.

money since he did not intend to comply with their wishes.[62] As a consequence he was forced to undertake part-time tuition work in order to pay his way, even to the extent of interrupting his studies during the academic year 1862-63 to take a teaching post in a school in Cookstown, headed by John A. Smyth.[63] Even while attending Queen's College, Belfast, and later when he went to Cork, he coached private pupils. The Cunninghams of Glencairn were among those who employed him.[64] This was bound to have eaten into the time which he had available for his own studies. It is therefore to his credit that he was awarded a Peel Prize in classics as a result of his performance in the first examination in arts.[65]

Sir James Dougherty provided W. S. Armour with a rather romantic memoir about J. B. Armour's university career, written from memory shortly before Dougherty's death.[66] It is a nostalgic evocation of Queen's College, Belfast, in the 1860s and W. S. Armour included it in full in his book. In evaluating its contents, one needs to remember that it was written by Armour's closest friend some seventy years after the events which it described. It contains the usual roll-call of distinguished contemporaries and an account of some amusing incidents, but it also provides us with valuable information about J. B. Armour at this stage of his life. The picture which emerges is of a shy, withdrawn young man, slow to make friends and already given to vivid satirical comments and quips about the frailties of his fellowmen. In time this was to become one of his most pronounced and least endearing characteristics. Dougherty did pinpoint his interest in, and sympathy for, those who were down on their luck and this was to be another enduring feature of his life.[67] His aloofness from his fellows was underlined by his total lack of interest in sport of any kind and his unwillingness to make a contribution to the College Literary and Scientific Society, of which he was a nominal member.[68] Two further permanent traits of his character came to the surface in these years—an abhorrence of drinking and of gambling.[69] However, his moral principles were by no means totally unyielding—he expressed strong disapproval of the forced resignation of the popular professor of French who had separated from his wife and was living openly with his mistress.[70]

The Megaw letters contain only a very few comments on contemporary political events. In one of the earliest, Armour expressed his support for Samuel Greer who was standing as a Liberal candidate in a pending by-election for the Londonderry City seat.[71] The Cookstown letters do contain some scattered and superficial comments on the Irish and international scene. He was interested in the American civil war and criticised the Union government for its aggressive policy towards Britain and British shipping.[72] The damage inflicted on the cotton industry by the war had the effect of stimulating the demand for Irish linen, and therefore helped to keep the small farmer in Ulster afloat financially. As a result Armour felt that Cookstown might well be renamed 'Flaxopolis'.[73] His attitude towards the Ireland which lay outside his own province revealed his parochial Ulster Protestant background. It was, he believed, a country of 'Haythens [sic] and Turks, who are beginning to look upon murder as the only effectual means of getting rid of a troublesome bailiff or tyrannising landlord'.[74] He blamed the poverty in the west on laziness and lack of initiative. 'Galway might soon be made as flourishing as Belfast were any pains taken now to improve their trade.'[75] However, its inhabitants seemed intent only on complaining about English oppression and 'brandishing their scythes'.[76] These limited attitudes were soon to be dramatically altered.

In the autumn of 1863, having completed two full years at Queen's College, Belfast, and following the Cookstown interlude, Armour decided to transfer to Queen's College, Cork, to

---

62. Armour, *Armour of Ballymoney*, p. 10.
63. *Ibid*.
64. *Ibid*., p. 9.
65. *Ibid*., p. 19.
66. For a biographical profile of J. B. Dougherty see J. R. B. McMinn, 'The Reverend James Brown Armour and Liberal politics in north Antrim, 1869-1914' (Ph.D. thesis, Queen's University, Belfast, 1979), pp 412-3.
67. Armour, *Armour of Ballymoney*, p. 15.
68. *Ibid*., p. 16.
69. *Ibid*., p. 11.
70. J. B. Armour to John Megaw, 1 Apr. 1862 (D.1792/A2/8).
71. J. B. Armour to John Megaw, 20 Mar. 1860 (D.1792/A2/2).
72. J. B. Armour to John Megaw, 1 May 1863 (D.1792/A2/9).
73. J. B. Armour to John Megaw. 29 Aug. 1863 (D.1792/A2/10).
74. J. B. Armour to John Megaw, 1 May 1863 (D.1792/A2/9).
75. J. B. Armour to John Megaw, 29 Aug. 1863 (D.1792/A2/10).
76. *Ibid*.

complete his B.A. degree course. This decision is at first sight a strange one and unfortunately only three letters written from Cork to John Megaw have survived. These letters do supply a possible explanation. Writing on 4 November 1863, he told Megaw that 'I am 2nd scholar in my third year, which is very well considering that I had never opened a book or made the slightest preparation'.[77] He described his academic competitors in Cork as 'much inferior in attainments to our Belfast men, not from any want of talent ... but rather from indolence and paying too much pains in decorating their exterior'.[78] In short, they were more 'gentlemanly' and therefore presumably less of an academic threat. Many years later in a speech to the General Assembly on university education, he remarked that he had been in Cork 'and there was an atmosphere there, but it was an atmosphere of tobacco smoke'.[79]

The Cork sojourn had a profound impact on Armour's outlook. It widened his experience and it brought him into close social contact with many southern Roman Catholics and nationalists. He was impressed by the fact that in Cork 'there seems to be none of that bigotry with regard to religious principles which ... is too evident in Belfast'.[80] His private pupils included Dr Charles Tanner, a future Nationalist member at Westminster. He was stirred by the beauty of the city and the countryside surrounding it. He shared rooms with another Ulsterman, James Alexander Rentoul, in later life Judge Rentoul K.C. of the City of London Court.[81] Armour himself was subsequently and somewhat cryptically to refer to an attempt by 'a lady of position' to seduce him away from the Presbyterianism of his birth into the Church of Ireland. Had he succumbed, he suggested that he might have become at least 'a chancellor' and perhaps 'developed into a henchman of Edward Carson'.[82]

At the end of the 1863-64 academic year Armour sat for his Bachelor of Arts honours degree. However, he failed the examination, though Sir James Dougherty claimed that a mistake was made in marking his papers which was subsequently hushed up.[83] On the other hand his strange decision to try for his degree in natural sciences, hardly his first love, seems a more likely explanation. He immediately sat the examination for the general degree and thus obtained his B.A. He then returned to Belfast where he tried for his master's degree in 1866, significantly this time in classics, and was awarded second class honours.[84]

We now come to another extraordinary event in Armour's life—his decision to abandon all his previous prejudices and become a minister of the Presbyterian church. He had apparently made up his mind by 1865 to become a barrister, yet he entered Assembly's College, Belfast, instead. Was this change of heart because of his father's influence, powerfully reinforced by a death-bed wish expressed by his brother, Alexander, in October 1865, as W. S. Armour suggested?[85] There is no record of any spiritual experience leading to the decision and J. B. Armour himself never mentioned such an experience. W. S. Armour and J. B. M. Armour were both confident that there must have been some kind of catharsis but could not produce any evidence to justify their statements.[86] Unfortunately, no letters survive for this crucial period of his life and we are left with something of a mystery.

After several false starts elsewhere, including Portglenone, he preached on trial at Second or Trinity Presbyterian Church, Ballymoney, on 4 July 1869.[87] His only rival was James Maconaghy, later to become minister of Fortwilliam Park Church, Belfast.[88] It was Armour who received the call on 12 July, and his ordination by the Route Presbytery as assistant and successor to Rev. John Lawrence Rentoul followed on 19 July.[89] This was destined to be his first and only congregation. It had been founded by seceders in 1748 and had first occupied an old malt kiln in the Roddenfoot area on the southern side of the town.[90] A church was built in

---

77. J. B. Armour to John Megaw, 4 Nov. 1863 (D.1792/A2/11).
78. *Ibid*.
79. *Witness*, 1 May 1908. A rough draft of Armour's speech can be found in D.1792/B.
80. J. B. Armour to John Megaw, 4 Nov. 1863 (D.1792/A2/11).
81. Armour, *Armour of Ballymoney*, pp 19-20.
82. J. B. Armour to W. S. Armour, 30 July 1913 (D.1792/A3/4/21).
83. Armour, *Armour of Ballymoney*, p. 21.
84. Graduation certificate in D.1792/C.
85. Armour, *Armour of Ballymoney*, p. 13.
86. See *ibid*., p. 14 and Armour, *Notes on the life of J. B. Armour*, p. 4.
87. Armour, *Armour of Ballymoney*, pp 23-4.
88. Armour, *Notes on the life of J. B. Armour*, p. 5.
89. Armour, *Armour of Ballymoney*, p. 24.
90. A. H. Dill, J. B. Armour, D. D. Boyle and John Ramsay, *A short history of the Presbyterian churches of Ballymoney* (London, 1898), p. 45.

1813 and a manse in 1845. Armour's predecessor, Rentoul, appears to have been something of a character—an anti-landlord man who had championed the building of a school at Landhead, a zealous advocate of temperance and, above all, prickly and aggressive in temperament, though small in stature.[91] He was remembered as a minister who publicly rebuked latecomers to his services from the pulpit—certainly not an easy man to succeed.

J. B. Armour was one of the last of the commuting ministers to be ordained since dis-establishment was on its way. This was a fact of which he was always intensely proud.[92] Little evidence survives as to his physical appearance in this period. Most surviving photographs and the famous portrait by the artist William Conor[93] all date from his later years, though there is an early photograph to be found in S. C. McElroy's *The Route land crusade*.[94] His hair was black, his features sharply delineated, his poor eyesight required him to wear first a monocle and subsequently a pair of gold-rimmed spectacles and he invariably had a beard.[95] His contemporary nickname, 'the black wolf', perhaps sums up his general appearance best.

He threw himself immediately into the life of both the church and the town. Rev. Rentoul was in poor health and most of his duties fell instantly on Armour's shoulders. The session would only offer Armour a stipend of sixty five pounds, the amount previously paid to his predecessor, lest the latter should be offended.[96] On Rentoul's death in August 1869, Armour insisted that his widow and family should remain in the manse for as long as they wished.[97] He made a major impact in Ballymoney in a relatively short time. As early as 1871 the congregation presented him with an address and the sum of one hundred sovereigns.[98] But, significantly, he was still by no means fully committed to the ministry, continuing to study law for some years in his few off-duty moments.[99] He did manage to find the time to spend several holidays in Europe with friends from his university days, including a trip down the Rhine.[100] He was extremely active in the fields of temperance and education. In 1878 he was appointed principal, and for some years sole teacher, of the newly established Ballymoney Intermediate School.[101] Prior to 1890 he took little part in the General Assemblies of the church except with regard to educational issues. Before 1900 he consistently argued for a non-sectarian educational system, thereafter he was prepared to press for state aid to endow a Roman Catholic university in Ireland.

J. B. Armour did not marry until he reached the age of forty two. The ceremony took place on 19 March 1883 by special licence at the Imperial Hotel, Belfast.[102] His bride was a widow, Mrs Jennie Adams Stavely Hamilton. Her former husband had been her cousin, Dr A. M. S. Hamilton, medical superintendent of Leeds Infirmary. Her father, Rev. Alexander McLeod Stavely, performed the ceremony, assisted by Rev. J. M. Hamilton of Dublin. Rev. Stavely had worked in St John, New Brunswick, for thirty nine years before returning to his native county to become minister of Ballyclare Reformed Presbyterian Church.[103] Whilst in St John he had met his wife, whose family had originally emigrated from Scotland. The Stavely family was steeped in the traditions of covenanting Presbyterianism and was distantly related to the Armours. Jennie already had two sons who were to get on well with their new stepfather. Her background and attitudes were north American rather than Irish,[104] and she undoubtedly influenced Armour considerably. She fought for many years against serious illness[105] and had a strong, vivacious personality.

There are only four letters in the P.R.O.N.I. Armour collection which could be described

91. *Ibid.*, p. 45. See also H. C. Waddell, *Trinity Church, Ballymoney; the bi-centenary book, 1748-1948* (Ballymoney, 1948), p. 19.
92. Armour, *Armour of Ballymoney*, p. 25. Gladstone's act which dis-established the Church of Ireland in 1869 made it optional for Presbyterian ministers either to continue to draw the *regium donum*, or commute this for a lump sum. The vast majority of ministers agreed to commute and voluntarily surrendered over half a million pounds to the funds of their church.
93. This portrait now hangs in Trinity Church, Ballymoney.
94. McElroy, *Route land crusade*, facing p. 56.
95. Armour, *Notes on the life of J. B. Armour*, p. 6.
96. *Session minute book, Trinity Church, Ballymoney, 1863-1924.* W. S. Armour stated that the stipend amounted to sixty-one pounds, but the minutes make it clear that it was in fact sixty-five.
97. This was decided at a meeting of the session on 30 Aug. 1869. See *ibid*.
98. Armour, *Armour of Ballymoney*, p. 25.
99. *Ibid.*, p. 26.
100. *Ibid.*, pp 32-3.
101. Armour, *Notes on the life of J. B. Armour*, p. 6.
102. *Witness*, 30 Mar. 1883.
103. Armour, *Armour of Ballymoney*, p. 51.
104. Both W. S. Armour and J. B. M. Armour stressed this.
105. Probably tuberculosis.

The Armour family outside the manse in Ballymoney (left to right, front row: Isobel Lusk, J. B. Armour, Jennie Armour, Max Armour, Kenneth Armour).

as love letters written to Jennie Hamilton. The first, which has been tentatively dated to 1880, has only survived in part. It suggests that initially Armour was much more enthusiastic about the relationship than Jennie:

> All true joy seems to me to have a rim of sorrow round it ... 'To be or not to be' is a question which other people as well as the Dane have to discuss ... you know the facts on both sides. You have put the question several times, can one be in love twice [presumably a reference to Jennie's previous marriage] ... . You speak of drawing in a certain direction and I can understand the figure keenly, but your friends' chaff about lowering a great clan might make 'the drawing' unfortunate ... I should not like to pull anyone down in life ... . Still as I have not the talents with which my friends credit me and as the present is not bright (at the same time it is not dark), the wisest course is to begin that difficult operation of cutting off the right hand ... . I was out seeing my mother tonight and when she asked me where I was going this year, I replied either to the North Pole or Australia. 'Talk' was her comment. 'I am going to America, I think'.[106]

Clearly, the relationship was far from happy at this point. Jennie's friends seem to have felt that by marrying J. B. Armour, a mere provincial clergyman, she would be marrying beneath her—hence his threat of emigration.

The same theme recurs in another letter dated 3 December 1881. His conscious or unconscious strategy had obviously succeeded, and he took the opportunity to justify himself and the life he had chosen to lead:

> You say truly enough that the world usually takes a man at his own valuation ... [so] what harm does he receive if it passes him by with indifference? I have not been, I would hope, morbidly careful about popular esteem and consequently I am in no way a disappointed man. I have been able to help my friends a little and ... I have received as much kindness from all my friends as any man could wish ... and when one has so many distinguished acquaintances, he ought to be satisfied with the lot in life arranged for him.[107]

Further self-justification is to be found in the third letter which strikes an optimistic note about the future (the wedding was only six weeks away):

> You found me and discovered me to myself ... I see no reason for looking forward with a wry face ... I fear too that I may seem a different man from what many think but I have not assumed many airs and have not posed as anything.[108]

In the event the marriage was apparently a successful one. Jennie bore him three sons—Max, who was to become a Presbyterian minister working first in South Shields and then in Newfoundland, Canada; William, the journalist and biographer; and the youngest, Kenneth, who was to become a teacher of classics at his old school, Campbell College, Belfast. Mrs Armour was a most effective minister's wife, running the manse with the able assistance of the family's faithful servant, Susan Green. The marriage did, however, place Armour in a difficult financial position.[109] He was forced to supplement his income by becoming an intermediate examiner in Latin,[110] by superintending at examinations and, until 1908, by assisting his wife's brother-in-law, Professor MacMaster, in teaching classics at Magee College, Londonderry. During term-time, this required a return train journey of some ninety miles on three or four days of each week.

For my purpose I do not think it is necessary to delve too deeply into J. B. Armour's career as a teacher and a minister. This aspect of his life is treated in considerable, if selective, detail in *Armour of Ballymoney*.[111] His violent temper is left out of the picture and instead we are shown a saintly man who learnt his sermons by heart, who set many young men on the educational road to fame and fortune, who gave away apples and peppermints to children in the street, who entered public houses and extracted those inside who were hazarding their families' incomes—in short the friend and helper of everyone. Not of course that J. B. Armour

---

106. J. B. Armour to Jennie Hamilton, n.d. (D.1792/A2/14).
107. J. B. Armour to Jennie Hamilton, 3 Dec. 1881 (D.1792/A2/15).
108. J. B. Armour to Jennie Hamilton, 31 Jan. 1883 (D.1792/A2/17).
109. Armour, *Armour of Ballymoney*, p. 52.
110. The printed testimonials supporting Armour's application for this position are to be found in the Armour papers (D.1792/C).
111. See especially chapters II, IV, XI, XIV and XV.

wasn't all of these things and more—but there was another side to the man. Even a careful examination of the speeches reproduced in *Armour of Ballymoney*, edited as they are, reveals hints of the intemperate Armour who lashed his critics unmercifully. The few still alive today who remember Armour in his later years, while they are agreed that he was a man who could never be ignored, stress his short temper. One Ballymoney resident, still a leading member of Trinity Church, recalls how, as a young girl in Sunday school, she trembled at times when he exploded with anger, and how her father and the other pupils at the intermediate school were so frightened of Armour the teacher that, when called to the front of the class, they jumped over the top of the desks, rather than use the aisle between them in order to save time.[112] Another Ballymoney resident describes him as 'pig-headed' at times.[113] He ruled his session meetings with a rod of iron and his idiosyncrasy is reflected in the design adopted for the rebuilding of Trinity Church in 1885.[114] The new structure, built with Dungiven sandstone in the decorated Gothic style, looks distinctly unpresbyterian, with its octagonal spire and clock and its then unique pews in the form of a semi-circular amphitheatre (although the interior was more a reflection of Mrs Armour's north American tastes). The church was opened at a special service with Dr John Hall of New York as the guest preacher.[115] A lecture room was added in 1896. Armour was also successful in reconciling his congregation to other changes over the years, such as the introduction of the revised version of the psalms, of hymns, of a harmonium and finally of an organ.

In 1890 there seemed to be a possibility that he might leave his beloved Ballymoney. Dr Witherow, professor of church history at Magee College, died in that year, and a group of friends began to work actively to secure the post for Armour.[116] However, the campaign encountered heavy opposition before and during the General Assembly.[117] He had not as yet put himself beyond the political pale, being still a Liberal Unionist, but he was regarded by some as a radical because of the spire on his church. Others felt him to be unacceptable on personal grounds. So he was defeated, and although there were subsequent tentative proposals regarding congregations in Belfast and Dublin,[118] this was undoubtedly the only point in his career when it was distinctly possible that he would leave Trinity Church.

There are three important aspects of Armour the cleric which overlap with Armour the politician. Let us first of all take Armour's attitude towards the Anglican church in Ireland. For him disestablishment might as well not have happened. He was extremely hostile towards Anglicanism, with regard to its doctrines, its clergy and its role, as he saw it, as part of the Tory/landlord ascendancy. In particular he constantly stressed the sufferings of Presbyterians at the hands of the Church of Ireland establishment. In a remarkable address, delivered at the ordination of his lifelong friend, Rev. J. D. Osborne, in Ballymoney in 1882, he examined the validity of Presbyterian doctrines and of the whole theological foundation upon which Calvinism rested. On the one hand, while he described Presbyterianism as the 'cradle of toleration' and argued that 'wherever Presbyterianism has planted itself there will be free institutions and civil and religious liberty', in the same address he referred to the arguments justifying espiscopacy as being 'reserved for the tag-end of vestry meetings, where bumbledom reigns in its dunderheaded glory'.[119] Armour's views concerning the Church of Ireland emerge even more clearly from a public correspondence with Anthony Traill, Provost of Trinity College, Dublin, and owner of a considerable estate at Ballylough, Bushmills, which arose out of a comment made by Armour about Trinity at the General Assembly in June 1900.[120] Most of the letters in the

112. Letters from Miss Jean Thompson, Ballymoney, in the possession of the author.
113. Interview with Dr W. H. Belford, Ballymoney, 26 June 1976.
114. A detailed account of the planning and building of the new church can be found in the *Session minute book, Trinity Church, Ballymoney, 1863-1924*. See also the article on the architectural features of the building in *Irish builder*, no 26 (1884), pp 211-14.
115. The printed order of service can be found in D.1792/C.
116. See *Testimonials in favour of Rev. James B. Armour, M.A., Q.U.I., a candidate for the chair of church history and pastoral theology in the Magee College, Londonderry* (Ballymoney, 1890).
117. Armour, *Armour of Ballymoney*, pp 58-9.
118. *Ibid.*, pp 59-60.
119. *Ibid.*, pp 44-50.
120. *B.N.L.*, 18 June 1900. The full correspondence is also printed in the *B.F.P.*, 21 June 1900. Armour's original comment about Trinity College, which sparked off the controversy, was to the effect that it was the college where nine-tenths of the country's oppressors had been educated. Traill had then invited him to clarify his statement. Armour responded by claiming that three groups of oppressors had mainly been educated at Trinity—the landlord class, the Anglican clergy and those who administered the law. Traill counter-attacked and sent the correspondence to the press. A final letter from Armour followed which was rather more moderate in tone.

series are taken up with arguments as to whether Irish landlords had been, and were, oppressive towards their tenants, but Armour also attacked the clergy of the Church of Ireland and the Trinity divinity school which nourished them. He argued that the Anglican clergy in general had been hostile to all the measures for the good of Ireland that had ever been proposed:

> Those clerics were so high and mighty and were so oppressive in the past that a tithe bill was passed to restrain their exactions, and they became so superior and so contemptuous to all other denominations that the legislature had to step in and disestablish them entirely.[121]

Apart from a few honourable exceptions, he believed that the clergy of the Church of Ireland had been an obstacle to Ireland's progress. He also regretted the use of the term 'Church of Ireland', implying as it did that there was no other church in existence in Ireland. Traill made a biting reply:

> How you can visit on clergymen of the present day the short-comings or high-handedness of members of an established church in past centuries, I cannot imagine ... . For the title 'Church of Ireland', you have only to consult the act of union ... . It has always astonished me how such a title can act as a 'red rag' to members of your church.[122]

In his final letter, published in the press, Armour protested against Traill sending the unfinished correspondence to the newspapers. He repeated his charges against the clergy of the Church of Ireland.'As a body they opposed Catholic emancipation, the legalising of marriages performed by Presbyterian ministers, the repeal of duties on paper, all the land acts and many other useful measures which were passed in spite of their opposition.' But he qualified his previous statements by stressing that he had not meant to imply 'that the clergy of this church are now the oppressors of our country'.[123] Despite these qualifications, his real feelings had been exposed. Nor was this an isolated incident. As Alan Megahey has indicated, this anti-Anglican attitude was to be employed as a useful weapon by some home rulers in their opposition to Unionism.[124] Armour in his political utterances repeatedly made use of it to try to rally support either for Liberal candidates, or later for the concept of Home Rule.

What then of Armour's attitude towards his Roman Catholic fellow countrymen? This is a complex issue and it needs to be considered along with his developing views on education, since the two are closely interwoven. Many testimonies have been given as to Armour's tolerant outlook, deriving it has been claimed from his student days in Cork.[125]

His consistent support at each General Assembly from 1900 onwards for the establishment of a separate, state-aided Roman Catholic university in Ireland (despite his own personal preference for non-sectarian 'mixed' education) and his support, as a member of the senate of Queen's University, Belfast, from 1910 to 1914, for the continuation of a lectureship in scholastic philosophy are often cited as examples of this breadth of mind. Indeed, they moved W. S. Armour to comment that 'where he [J. B. Armour] differed most strongly from the Ulster of his day was in his realisation of the inherent justice of the claims of Catholic Ireland and in his active championship of its cause'.[126] This comment needs to be set against Armour's forecast in 1909 of a major crisis for the Roman Catholic faith. He based this forecast on his belief that 'Romanism, or for the matter of that high churchism, could not possibly be squared with Christianity as revealed in its outlines in the teaching of the founder of our faith'.[127]

Armour's interest in the educational field was not new in 1900. For several decades previously he had played an active role in the educational debates of the General Assembly. His first major excursion into this area was at the 1882 Assembly when he seconded the report and resolutions of the Committee on Intermediate Education, vigorously supporting the intermediate education act against its critics:

> When you have discounted all its defects you find it has the great merit of bringing educational advantages within the reach of hundreds who never would have had the chance without it. It

121. *B.F.P.*, 21 June 1900.
122. Anthony Traill to J. B. Armour, 13 June 1900 (D.1792/A1/3/39).
123. *B.F.P.*, 21 June 1900.
124. Megahey, *Irish Protestant churches and social and political issues*, p. 70.
125. See for example Armour, *Notes on the life of J. B. Armour*, p. 4.
126. Armour, *Armour of Ballymoney*, pp xv-xvi.
127. J. B. Armour to Jane MacMaster, 12 Jan. 1909 (D.1792/A3/13/11).

has increased by fifty per cent the number of pupils receiving a higher education, and let the Jeremiahs in kid gloves, like Matthew Arnold,[128] and the damaged Solomons, like Mr Mehaffy,[129] say what they will, it has, on the whole, improved the quality of the article.[130]

Armour urged Presbyterians to make more use of the legislation. But perhaps he most clearly revealed his developing educational philosophy when he urged that:

> Instead of wasting energy in clamouring for some theoretic system which might do if all were of our way of thinking, let us use the best opportunity we ever had, and we shall best consult for the perpetuity and power of a church which has always contended for the liberty and enlightenment of the human mind.[131]

A willingness to be flexible and a desire to serve best the interests of his own denomination, as he saw them, are unmistakeable signposts to the future.

On 15 June 1886 he was asked to present the report of the Elementary Education Committee, due to the absence of its convener, Rev. H. B. Wilson, and he seized the opportunity to assail discrimination in education in favour of the Church of Ireland. He broadened out his attack into a general one against the political and social establishment. It was to be a theme to which he would constantly return throughout his life.

> Fair play and even-handed justice in the matter of appointment to place and emolument have never been marks of the episcopal mind, or indeed of any government that has borne sway in our island. We are partly to blame for this ourselves; we have been too 'sheepishly' loyal to the British connection—and our people, while scorning the teaching of rectors and curates on the Sabbath, have been so stupid as to think that they, in matters political, were the only heaven-sent guides to save them from the errors of the Pope and the horrors of the infidel, and follow these blind guides to our loss. This delusion of our folks has contributed largely to bring our country to its present moral muddle. It has helped to buttress up a state of things which is indefensible, has deprived our church of its due share in politics and has tended to rouse the millions of our countrymen against an official caucus which has always claimed the chief seats in every synagogue.[132]

It is not without significance that this speech was delivered in the year of the great crisis over Gladstone's Home Rule bill and although Armour was to remain officially a Liberal Unionist for some years to come, he was undoubtedly foreshadowing his decision to back Home Rule in the 1890s. 'We are in the presence of great and sweeping changes in the government of our country, and I could not fancy that, whatever powers swayed the destinies of Ireland, the members of the Presbyterian church could be worse treated than they have been by the ring ensconced in the purlieus of Dublin Castle.'[133] In the circumstances of the 1880s, he coupled with these views a defence of united secular and separate religious education, unless the 'dragon of denominationalism' should appear, at which time Presbyterians should opt for totally secular education and leave the various churches with the sole responsibility for religious education.[134]

At the 1891 Assembly, while again moving the adoption of the Elementary Education Committee's report, he returned to the now familiar themes. Arthur Balfour's proposal to set up Anglican and Roman Catholic denominational teacher training colleges, he roundly condemned as a betrayal of the National system. He pointed to the fact that many had objected to Home Rule on the grounds that it would inevitably lead to a denominational educational system. Now a Unionist government was proposing to set a dangerous precedent. He saw the issue as a matter of civil liberty and religious equality. He pleaded that 'the Thermopylae Pass of civil freedom' should be defended against 'a new act of uniformity', directed against their cherished principle of united secular and separate religious instruction.[135] Once again he saw Presbyterian weakness and lack of political representation in the face of the enmity of the Anglican establishment as the root of the trouble. Presbyterians had opposed Home Rule in

128. The poet and inspector of schools.
129. Provost of Trinity College, Dublin.
130. Armour, *Armour of Ballymoney*, p. 40.
131. *Ibid.*, p. 41.
132. *Witness*, 18 June 1886.
133. *Ibid.*
134. *Ibid.*
135. *Ibid.*, 9 June 1891.

1886 but they had been duped and betrayed:

> The prancing colonels, the blustering captains, the squirming majors, the sons of old manu-facturers, the worn-out officials of corporations, landlords professing conversion—all spouted like squirrels from one ecclesiastical bag—in 1886 ready to save Ireland, and we, because the crisis was sudden and the question was vital, rather than divide what was wanted to be an expressive vote on a great issue, accepted this. And I am not here to say '*peccavi*'. But with three or four honourable exceptions they have turned out the enemies of our church, the weakness of the Union, the silent foes of our educational policy.[136]

He saw the Balfour training college proposals as 'new rivets to make the chains of your bondage more secure and new instruments of torture'.[137] He argued that the only way to shake off these chains was to elect Presbyterian members to Westminster.[138]

Given Armour's educational views, it is in some ways surprising to turn to the university issue as it developed from 1900 onwards. Ever since Sir Robert Peel's government had been in office, the problem of higher education in Ireland had defied all the efforts of successive well-intentioned English ministers to solve it.[139] As Gladstone discovered in 1873, the root of the problem lay in the unwillingness of the Roman Catholic hierarchy to accept anything less than effective control of a university to serve the needs of the Irish Catholic population. Tinkering with existing institutions, such as the Queen's Colleges, proved to be of no avail. This had become increasingly clear to both Lord Salisbury and his nephews, Arthur and Gerald Balfour. Legislation seemed imminent and from 1900 to 1908 the General Assembly debated the issue annually when its Committee on Higher Education presented its report. Armour invariably spoke, always with biting humour and sarcasm, and his contribution rapidly became an essential part of the predictable ritual. His role was almost at times that of the court jester. Indeed, the anonymous author of 'Assembly notes' in *The Witness* described his performance of 1906 as 'the tit-bit of the meeting ... Mr Armour is a gentleman of unbounden humour, I do not know that he takes himself seriously on the education question, and I am afraid the Assembly does not ... . He may have added to the gaiety of the Assembly, but he contributed little to its wisdom or its dignity.'[140] His stinging attacks on 'doctors of divinity whose ancestors came from the ark',[141] and on the 'troglodytes'[142] generally, were offensive to many of his victims, as the editorial writer of *The Witness* pointed out:

> Mr Armour in effect says that all the people in the Assembly who do not agree with him are fools where they are not mountebanks, and he claims to make his deliverance under the divine right of his private judgement ... . Is it not possible that he may be wrong instead of them ... is it not possible that all the wisdom of the church is not concentrated in his own brain?[143]

He himself admitted in 1908 that he might, in the course of the debate, have said bitter things 'but a voice crying in the wilderness must always be strident'.[144]

It is not necessary to trace the twists and turns of the university controversy. However, J. B. Armour's views do require some explanation. How could he justify abandoning his life-long antagonism towards denominational education, an antagonism which the majority of his fellow Presbyterian clerics continued to display despite his verbal assaults?[145] In his speeches he tried to account for his change of heart, particularly at the 1900 Assembly where he first made his new views public. The origin of these views is to be found in that early speech of 1882 when he had urged an undogmatic, flexible approach to education and support for whatever was in the best interests of the Presbyterian church. He reminded the 1900 Assembly that the university issue seemed about to be settled on denominational lines, therefore, it was futile to continue outright opposition:

136. *Ibid.*
137. *Ibid.*
138. *Ibid.*
139. See T. W. Moody, 'The Irish university question in the nineteenth century' in *History*, xliii (1958), pp 90-109.
140. *Witness*, 15 June 1906.
141. *Ibid.*
142. *Ibid.*, 19 June 1903.
143. *Ibid.*, 15 June 1906.
144. *Ibid.*, 1 May 1908.
145. The strength of the pro-Armour group in the Assembly varied from year to year. His most successful year was 1903 when his amendment was lost by 108 votes to 148.

> As one who would like to see our church put on an equality with all other churches in regard to university education, I would be glad if you would boldly face the music, give up your fireworks about undenominational education, cease crying for the moon and make the best of an awkward situation which you have helped to create. On paper and in the resolutions of the Assembly for the last thirty years, you have been undenominationalists, but in fact in political life you have thrown over the principle ... . You have no moral grounds for opposing Lord Salisbury and Mr Balfour for they propose to do for Ireland in the matter of education what with your sanction and consent they have done for England[146] ... . In my simple-mindedness I always thought that a principle like the moral law was true and binding everywhere and that men were bound to uphold it everywhere and against all-comers.[147]

This was hardly an accurate statement of his own position since it was he who had changed his opinions, but then he believed his new views were those most likely to benefit the Presbyterian church. The report's suggestion that Trinity College, Dublin, should be nationalised, he denounced as 'an illusion'.[148] It was also undesirable since it was the institution where nine-tenths of the oppressors of Ireland had been educated.[149] He warned his audience that they were spurning Balfour's offer of an Ulster university as part of the package:

> For years we heard nothing but the greatness of Ulster, its wealth, its intelligence, its go-aheadness, and Belfast was spoken of as if it was a new Jerusalem, a new Jerusalem, I admit, erected largely by jerry-builders. Now the turn has changed, and when Mr Balfour proposes to take your greatness at your former estimate you turn round and say: 'Mr Balfour, we are miserable sinners, not worthy of a university. We are provincial. We are parochial, and Belfast the once glorious is a mushroom city. Its citizens neither care for, nor are worthy of, any place save the beggar's seat at the gates of proud Trinity ... . If Birmingham, the borough of Joseph,[150] deserves and demands a university for itself, I refuse to regard Ulster as inferior to the borough of Joseph.[151]

The university log-jam was finally broken in 1908 with the introduction of the Irish universities bill. In consequence, a special meeting of the General Assembly was held on 29 April 1908 and the official resolution condemned the bill.[152] Armour proposed an amendment which is a useful synthesis of his views on the university question.[153] The amendment expressed general support for the bill, apart from the inadequate protection which it offered for the existing university privileges of Magee College, Londonderry, which were to be put in the hands of the senate of the proposed Belfast university (hence his inclusion of proposals to safeguard Magee's position). He justified his support for the bill on the grounds that it would provide for a just settlement of a problem which had helped to create 'racial and religious separation',[154] and in doing so would satisfy the grievances of the majority, while maintaining the principle of religious equality. He also applauded the provision for self-government for the university of Ireland and the proposal to establish a university in Belfast, which would be under the control of Ulster people and would be 'without embarrassing connection with other institutions whose ideals are different from their own'.[155] In Belfast at least, the non-denominational principle would be maintained.

In the event the Assembly accepted neither the official resolution nor Armour's amendment, but instead a compromise resolution proposed by Rev. William Park. Armour's speech was probably best remembered for his concluding suggestion to the Assembly to send a message of reconciliation to the Irish Roman Catholic population. 'You and we differ in our ideal of education. We cannot pursue it together, but we give you your claim and we send you the word—"Though we disagree, may God be with you and God's blessing be with you now and

---

146. This was a reference to the fact that the Assembly had become devoted supporters of Unionism, and that the Ulster Unionist members at Westminster had given their support to Balfour's education act of 1902 which had increased financial aid to denominational schools (these in England were mainly Anglican).
147. Armour, *Armour of Ballymoney*, p. 148. For a more developed version of this argument see J. B. Armour to Jane MacMaster, 20 June 1903 (D.1792/A3/13/6).
148. *Ibid.*, p. 150.
149. This was the remark which sparked off the debate with Anthony Traill.
150. Joseph Chamberlain.
151. Armour, *Armour of Ballymoney*, p. 151.
152. *Witness*, 1 May 1908.
153. *Ibid.*
154. *Ibid.*
155. *Ibid.*

for ever".'[156] This astonishing proposal was not taken up but it does underline Armour's generous approach to the whole university problem. Nonetheless, this approach needs to be set in the context of his flexibility in the educational field and, even more importantly, in the context of his desire to look after the best interests of his church, as he saw them, along with his desire to seize the attractive possibilities contained in the proposal for a new Belfast university.

The new Queen's University of Belfast, having been established by the legislation of 1908, duly came into being, supervised by a group of commissioners. As Moody and Beckett have pointed out, the process was one of gradual transformation rather than dramatic change.[157] The new university faced many problems, especially in view of the initial hostility towards it from various quarters such as the General Assembly of the Presbyterian church. Armour found himself treading familiar ground at the 1909 Assembly, as he opposed a resolution from the special commission on the new institution.[158] Yet again sectarian animosity seems to have been at the root of its views and Armour was once more cast in the role of championing Roman Catholic interests. The commission report, presented by Professor Todd Martin, objected to the appointment of four Roman Catholics, as such, and two Methodists, as such, to the first senate of the new university. It also condemned the proposed acceptance of scholastic philosophy as a subject in the university. Armour expressed his surprise at having to speak on the university issue yet again; he had believed that even 'cart ropes' would not have drawn him to it. His course for the last seven years had been vindicated, he felt, by the legislation of 1908. He expressed his regret that the majority of Assembly members were not prepared to accept their defeat graciously and to accept the new situation realistically. He stressed that the six offending senators were only a small minority of the whole senate and that scholastic philosophy would obviously be studied in a critical fashion. Despite his arguments, the report was adopted.[159]

The commissioners who had been appointed to get the university off the ground were anxious to attract Roman Catholic students and the appointment of the Roman Catholic members of the senate was a step towards that end. It was these senators who approached the commissioners in April 1909, by letter and by deputation, with four major proposals—the appointment of a professor in scholastic philosophy; the creation of a second chair in history and English literature; the bringing of the Mater Infirmorum Hospital into association with the university; and the appointment of a professor of Celtic languages and literature. Their purpose was to 'induce large numbers of students to become members of the university who otherwise may go elsewhere'.[160]

The hospital question was left to the senate for decision by the commissioners (in the event the Mater Infirmorum was recognised as a teaching hospital and a member of its staff was appointed annually to membership of the faculty of medicine); the second chair in history and English literature was not conceded; a lectureship in Celtic was established but, despite the urgings of the Gaelic League who even offered financial assistance, the senate turned down the suggestion that a chair be created. A lectureship, but not a chair, in scholastic philosophy was agreed to and a Roman Catholic priest, Rev. Denis O'Keefe M.A., appointed to it.[161]

There was immediate public opposition, some undoubtedly inspired by sectarian animosity but some by concern at what seemed to be a departure from the non-sectarian principles on which the new university had been founded. As Moody and Beckett put it: 'Protestant opinion generally in Ulster had accepted the Irish universities act reluctantly and had considered as its main redeeming feature that the Belfast university should at least be strictly non-sectarian'.[162] The legality of the lectureship was challenged by three appeals, as provided by the 1908 act, to the universities committee of the Irish privy council.[163] These appeals were made by two Presbyterian clerics, Rev. J. J. Magill and Rev. J. MacDermott, and by the marquis of Londonderry. They were dismissed after a three day hearing in October 1909. Moody and Beckett, arguing from the Chief Secretary Augustine Birrell's reminiscences, suggest that this was a result

156. *Ibid.*
157. T. W. Moody and J. C. Beckett, *Queen's Belfast, 1845-1949: the history of a university* (2 vols., London, 1959), i, 413.
158. *Witness*, 18 June 1909.
159. *Ibid.*
160. Moody and Beckett, *Queen's Belfast*, i, 407.
161. *Ibid.*
162. *Ibid.*
163. W. S. Armour erroneously states that only two appeals were made. See Armour, *Armour of Ballymoney*, pp 199-200.

of government policy rather than 'strict legal interpretation'.[164]

The matter did not rest there and the controversy continued into the following year, by which time Armour had himself been appointed by the government to fill a vacancy on the senate. The issue marred the very first meeting of convocation on 16 April 1910. The attack was spear-headed by a leading Unionist politician and Presbyterian layman, Thomas Sinclair, supported by Professor Benjamin Moore. A resolution, proposed by Sinclair, included a condemnation of the scholastic philosophy lectureship as 'an innovation which, in our opinion, is calculated to destroy the character of the university as a non-sectarian institution', and contained an appeal to the senate to reject any attempt to enlarge the sphere of scholastic philosophy. The principal speakers against the motion were Armour and R. M. Henry. Their amendment asked that the issue be postponed until reports on it could be prepared.[165]

Armour's speech was, as usual, full of biting quips. He denounced 'the mad Mullahs' and those 'who seemed to have scholastic philosophy on the brain' and regretted that such 'an honourable man' as Sinclair should have stooped so low as to join them. He argued that the issue had been decided by the privy council and that meant they would have Home Rule in that particular university if they decided to defy the council's decision. He claimed that underlying the opposition to scholastic philosophy were prejudices against the whole concept of the university and against Augustine Birrell. He denied that scholastic philosophy was especially sectarian and pointed out that the refusal of one lectureship to a Roman Catholic would look very bad, since a Presbyterian had been appointed to the southern university. He reminded convocation that the university was designed to serve Ulster as a whole and that practically one half of Ulster was Catholic. The real promoters of sectarianism, he felt, were those who were opposing a measure which was necessary to reassure Catholics that their faith would not be undermined if they attended the university. He concluded by drawing attention to the fact that University College, Galway, and University College, Cork, had already established chairs in philosophy as well as scholastic philosophy and that University College, Dublin, was expected to follow suit—surely then they should reciprocate. Despite an appeal by the chancellor, the earl of Shaftesbury, for a postponement of a decision on the grounds that the matter had already been decided and this was 'the last kick of the football when the match is over', the Sinclair resolution was carried by 238 votes to 52.[166]

W. S. Armour gave the impression that although the convocation decision went against scholastic philosophy, all was not lost since the decision had no effect. 'The senate stood firm and the lectureship in scholastic philosophy remained without, as far as can be ascertained, doing any harm to anyone.'[167] This is a serious over-simplification of the ensuing situation. Moody and Beckett make it clear that 'the majority in the senate was already of much the same opinion on this topic as the majority in convocation and was determined to confine scholastic philosophy within the narrowest possible limits'.[168] An effort by Rev. Denis O'Keefe to offer three 'separate options' in his subject was defeated in the senate in June 1910 by fourteen votes to thirteen (of which Armour's was one).[169] For many years to come all efforts to expand the subject were persistently blocked, although at least the single lectureship did survive.

Nor did the General Assembly allow the matter to drop before yet again making its position clear. On Tuesday 14 June the Assembly debated the report of the Committee on University Statutes and Students which denounced scholastic philosophy in the usual terms as 'a grave infringement of the non-sectarian principle on which the Queen's University is professedly founded'. Professor Todd Martin and the Right Hon. Thomas Sinclair spoke in favour of the report while Rev. J. D. Osborne opposed it. When Sinclair described the supporters of scholastic philosophy in the senate as pawns of the Catholic bishops, Armour was forced to defend himself. His speech contained the usual arguments for a generous approach, and he said that the Assembly 'wanted to allow no one to enter the Queen's University unless they signed the thirty nine articles of Scotch philosophy'. Osborne could only rally fifteen votes for his amendment, while fifty three voted against it.[170]

164. Moody and Beckett, *Queen's Belfast*, i, 409.
165. *B.N.L.*, 18 Apr. 1910.
166. *Ibid.* W. S. Armour's figures are 238 to 56. Armour, *Armour of Ballymoney*, p. 204.
167. Armour, *Armour of Ballymoney*, p. 204.
168. Moody and Beckett, *Queen's Belfast*, i, 410.
169. *Minutes of the senate of the Queen's University, Belfast*, 9 June 1910.
170. *Witness*, 17 June 1910; *General Assembly minutes*, xi, 1179-85 (1910).

One cannot doubt J. B. Armour's sincerity and constancy on the scholastic philosophy issue, working as he was on behalf of the Roman Catholic population. However, W. S. Armour exaggerated the importance of the issue itself. Not only did he wrongly assume that his father carried the senate with him on the matter, he implied that it was mainly through his father's efforts that Roman Catholics were able to attend the university.[171] But, as Moody and Beckett have shown, the issue was largely a symbolic one. Less than twenty students took the subject between 1910 and 1925 and many Roman Catholics still had reservations about the new university. As late as 1923, Cardinal MacCrory, Roman Catholic archbishop of Armagh, described the university as having 'a non-Catholic atmosphere' and declared, along with the other northern bishops, that no teacher trained in Queen's would be appointed to elementary schools under their control. There was of course a partial acceptance of the university by Roman Catholics nonetheless. Moody and Beckett see this as due not only to the token goodwill gesture with regard to scholastic philosophy, but also to the improved economic position of northern Roman Catholics, which resulted in a greater demand amongst them for university education, and to the establishment of the lectureship in Celtic.[172]

Indeed, W. S. Armour's view of his father's role in the senate between 1910 and 1914 was somewhat flattering. He saw him as a key figure wielding enormous influence. 'As personal friend of many of the Protestant members and with the confidence of the Catholics, he was in an exceptionally favourable position.'[173] Certainly he worked hard to defend the university's interests during the crisis created by the announcement in 1909 of the forging of a link between Magee College, Londonderry, and Trinity College, Dublin, which he believed was an attempt to torpedo Queen's.[174] He did his best to publicise the new university, speaking for example to the Londonderry County Council on its behalf.[175]

He was active on a wide range of policy matters such as matriculation standards, which he felt were too high, the conditions attached to, and the value and number of, scholarships and the need to spend more money on facilities for arts as well as science subjects.[176] He favoured the taking of the master of arts degree by examination as well as by thesis, supported evening classes in commerce and stressed the need to continue to restrict the minimum age limit for entrance to seventeen.[177] However, many of his causes were lost ones. He supported R. M. Henry in his unsuccessful effort to establish a chair in Celtic studies.[178] At the onset of the Home Rule crisis in 1912 the senate held a special meeting and Sir Samuel Keightley and Armour failed to persuade it 'to deprecate any proposal which would result in isolating the university from the main current of national life and development'.[179]

There is a revealing postscript to Armour's senatorial term. The nominated or charter senate ceased to hold office in October 1914 and the first elected senate took over on 1 November 1914. Of its thirty-six members, twenty were survivors from the first senate, but J. B. Armour was not amongst them.[180] He had hoped to be elected as one of the eight representatives of convocation, but his support evaporated and his political views doomed him. Those elected were, ironically, as Armour pointed out, opponents of the 1908 legislation. 'Every mother's son of them fought bitterly against the establishment of the university, and now they are anxious to be chauffeurs of the educational motor.' It was then suggested that Birrell might choose him as one of the four crown nominees, but Birrell and his advisers felt it necessary to nominate four Roman Catholics, since predictably the convocation had elected none.[181] Armour was not Protestant enough to suit most Protestants, nor yet was he a Roman Catholic. There was simply no room for him in a university senate which so accurately mirrored the polarised island.

Apart from his activities in the educational sphere, there is other important evidence as to Armour's relationship with the Roman Catholic community which requires examination.

171. Armour, *Armour of Ballymoney*, pp 214-5.
172. Moody and Beckett, *Queen's Belfast*, i.
173. Armour, *Armour of Ballymoney*, p. 215
174. See interview with Armour in *B.F.P.*, 12 Aug. 1909.
175. *Ibid.*, 28 Nov. 1912.
176. On the scholarships issue see J. B. Armour to W. S. Armour, Mar. 1911 (D.1792/A3/2/10).
177. Armour, *Armour of Ballymoney*, pp 215-7; *Senate minutes*, 7 Apr. 1911.
178. Moody and Beckett, *Queen's Belfast*, i, 412.
179. *Senate minutes*, 28 Nov. 1912.
180. Moody and Beckett, *Queen's Belfast*, ii, 453-4.
181. Armour, *Armour of Ballymoney*, p. 219.

Individual Roman Catholics did from time to time give their opinion of him. Rev. John McErlain, Ballymoney's parish priest, provided him with a testimonial when he applied to become an intermediate examiner in 1882, and he remarked that he saw no reason why he as a priest should not take an interest in Armour, 'a respectable clergyman of this town'. He stressed Armour's abilities as a teacher of classics which eminently qualified him for the position of examiner.[182] Joseph P. O'Kane of Ballycastle, writing to the *Northern Whig* in February 1909, was lavish with his praises:

> His whole life has been one long sermon of toleration to Irishmen of all classes and creeds and Ireland has no more distinterested son. Long 'ere the advice had been given to 'bridge the Boyne', and thus banish sectarian animosities and induce Irishmen to unite for a common motherhood, Mr Armour had preached the doctrine by the more persuasive eloquence of his example.[183]

His death in 1928 evoked similar tributes, for example from the two local Roman Catholic clergy in Ballymoney, Rev. J. O'Neill and Rev. H. E. Plunkett,[184] and also from the Nationalist party leader, Joe Devlin, who sent a telegram to Mrs Armour which read:

> A great light has gone out in Ulster. We have lost the bravest, most consistent, truest of the sons of our northern land. We shall rarely meet his equal. I feel poorer for the loss of a dear and valued friend.[185]

The *Irish News* echoed these sentiments in its obituary.[186]

Some of the later tributes need to be weighed very carefully. By 1928 Armour had been out of active politics for at least fourteen years and the accounts of his career which appeared in the press on his death were at times both romanticised and inaccurate. The *Derry Journal*, for example, claimed that 'all through the long struggle for Home Rule, through all the storm and passion and bitter controversies of the 'eighties and 'nineties and up to his death, he held firmly to his political faith of self-government for Ireland'.[187] This conveniently ignored Armour's opposition to Home Rule between 1886 and 1892 and it presented his conception of Home Rule in a rather ambiguous way.

There are a number of further inconsistencies in the accepted version of J. B. Armour's relationship with his Roman Catholic fellow countrymen. He and the North Antrim Liberals in general were assailed on a number of occasions for their isolationism with regard to political co-operation with Roman Catholics.[188] There is also the rather curious minuet Armour began to dance in 1910 with the Independent Orange Order,[189] which, although it was more politically independent than the official order, was not behindhand in denouncing Roman Catholics.[190] Not only did Armour consent to allow the new organisation to hold services in his church, but he was also the anonymous author of the sermons delivered at these services by Rev. Heney of Mossside. He wrote to his son William on 7 July 1910: 'I have been under fire in the house for over a week in consequence of the service to be held on the evening of the 10th in the church ... for the Independents ... . I had suggested the subject, what is Protestantism, what are its principles and why are we Protestants?'[191] He is even more explicit on 13 July, again writing to William. 'Heney's sermon approved itself to the brethren and the strangers. It raised more money for the order than any address has done ... . The hands were the hands of Esau but the voice was Jacob's ... . The sermon must take its place as to authorship with the letters of Junius.'[192] Finally, the famous meeting in Ballymoney Town Hall in September 1913 to 'protest against the lawless policy of Carsonism' is, in its Protestant exclusiveness, symbolic of the isolationist approach of both Armour and his North Antrim political allies. After all it was Armour, as he admitted to his son, who quietly vetoed Sir Roger Casement's suggestion that

182.   John McErlain to J. B. Armour, 27 Sept. 1882 (D.1792/A1/3/3).
183.   *N.W.*, 6 Feb. 1909.
184.   Armour, *Armour of Ballymoney*, p. 382.
185.   Armour papers (D.1792/C).
186.   *I.N.*, 27 Jan. 1928.
187.   Armour, *Armour of Ballymoney*, pp 388-9.
188.   See *B.F.P.*, 20 and 27 Oct. 1892.
189.   W. S. Armour totally ignored this episode.
190.   See Boyle, *Independent Orange Order*.
191.   J. B. Armour to W. S. Armour, 7 July 1910 (D.1792/A3/1/10).
192.   J. B. Armour to W. S. Armour, 13 July 1910 (D.1792/A3/1/11).

some Roman Catholics should be invited to take part.[193] This may of course simply have been good tactics, since the purpose of the meeting was to demonstrate that not all Protestants were loyal Unionists.[194]

Thus, the evidence with regard to J. B. Armour's attitudes towards, and relationships with, Roman Catholics is to some extent inconclusive. Certainly, there are a few episodes in his life which do not square with the traditional interpretation. Further than that the evidence does not allow one to go. But, in fairness to Armour, it must be said that he cannot be placed in the same category as some of his Liberal colleagues in North Antrim such as John Megaw and S. C. McElroy, who were to end their lives as anti-Catholic Unionists.

The final point that needs to be made about Armour the cleric is that above all else he was theologically orthodox. In no sense can unorthodox religious views be said to have led to unorthodox political views. In his address at J. D. Osborne's ordination in 1882 on the validity of Presbyterian orders and on the grounds on which their ecclesiastical polity rested, he made his attitude to critics of official Presbyterian theology very clear. 'To a type of critics among our own ranks—to these atrabilious Jeremiahs and gelatinous Christians I have only this to say—keep your halfpenny rattle of an opinion. It is worthy of the religious babyhood from which you are never likely to emerge.'[195]

Armour's ordination in 1869 coincided with a major new phase in both north Antrim and Ulster politics. In Ulster generally the years after 1869 witnessed a revival of enthusiasm for the Liberal party, fuelled by disestablishment and discontent amongst tenant farmers about the limited benefits of Gladstone's land act of 1870.[196] In north Antrim the Route Tenants Defence Association was born at an open-air meeting in Ballymoney's Market Square on 19 November.[197] An impressive Liberal challenge, albeit an unsuccessful one, was mounted by Sir Shafto Adair against the Conservative candidate, Captain Seymour, in the Co. Antrim by-election of that year.[198] This set-back was temporary and the Liberals grew in strength in the ensuing years but, as in Ulster as a whole, the Liberal renaissance had apparently collapsed by 1885. This very distinctive phase in the history of Liberalism in north Antrim and Ulster corresponds with an equally distinctive phase in J. B. Armour's political career.

W. S. Armour gave a somewhat vague account of his father's political activities during this crucial period from 1869 to 1885. 'Throughout these years he [J. B. Armour] frequently appeared on tenant-right platforms and was regarded as a tower of strength.'[199] But Armour cannot be described as one of the founders or principal leaders of the tenant-right movement in the area. He was not at any time an office-bearer in a tenant-right organisation, and indeed there were other local Presbyterian clerics who were as active as he—Rev. Samuel Finlay of Kilraughts, Rev. J. S. Mairs of Dunloy and Rev. Archibald Robinson of Broughshane are obvious examples.[200] His role seems to have been essentially that of a supporting speaker. Perhaps this is what S. C. McElroy meant when he wrote that Armour 'brought a tongue of fire to the cause'.[201] Press reports of meetings of the Route Tenants Defence Association rarely covered his speeches in detail, a privilege reserved for the more prominent figures. But he was present at a considerable number of these meetings, such as those on 18 April 1870, 12 February 1873, 12 February 1878, 14 April 1881 and 3 April 1884.[202] Undoubtedly he sympathised with the

193. J. B. Armour to W. S. Armour, Sept. 1913 (D.1792/A3/4/27).
194. I am grateful to Professor D. W. Harkness for elucidation on this point.
195. Armour, *Armour of Ballymoney*, p. 45.
196. B. M. Walker, 'Parliamentary representation in Ulster, 1868-86' (Ph.D. thesis, Trinity College, Dublin, 1976), pp 543-4.
197. McElroy, *Route land crusade*, p. 31.
198. Walker, *Parliamentary representation in Ulster*, pp 221-2. Adair polled 2,377 votes as against Seymour's 5,770.
199. Armour, *Armour of Ballymoney*, p. 36.
200. See McElroy, *Route land crusade*; *Minute book of the Route Reform Club and the Route Tenants Defence Association, 1886-1902* (P.R.O.N.I., D.1426); *Ballymoney almanack*, published annually by the *B.F.P*
201. McElroy, *Route land crusade*, appendix. McElroy's book is both verbose and eulogistic—the praise which he heaped upon his co-workers in the campaign for land reform was invariably lavish.
202. *Ibid.*, 20-1, 23, 32-3, 42. See also *B.F.P.*, 21 Feb. 1878 and 21 Apr. 1881.

tenant farmers' cause; indeed there were few public figures in the area even amongst Conservatives who did not at least pay lip service to it.

Two of his speeches on the land issue are worthy of closer examination. In February 1877 he spoke at a meeting of the Dervock Presbyterian congregation, called to discuss the eviction from his farm of their minister, Rev. Alexander Field. He had been evicted from the farm at Knockanboy, Dervock, by his landlord, Samuel Allen, and two other tenants had suffered the same fate. Ultimately all three were able to prove the existence of the Ulster custom on the estate and, under the terms of the 1870 land act, Allen was forced to pay £885 in compensation to Field. In his speech Armour spent some time justifying the intervention of the church in social questions, of which the land was one, citing St Paul as his authority. 'When a great social question arises now, we who claim to be messengers from God to men will be cowards if we hide ourselves behind the hedge of the miserable sophism—"This does not come within the scope of our calling." ' He reminded his audience that at least their pastor had received compensation under the provisions of the 1870 act, 'for which he has to thank the great states-man—Gladstone, who has been maligned by a horde of sycophants and a tribe of sympathisers with tyrany, social and territorial'. He drew their attention to the fact that poorer men than Field had been treated equally harshly. He then proceeded to define his own attitude towards the land problem and landlords in particular:

> I have never in my life said a hard word of landlords as a class. They have acted, as a class, as honourably as any class with the same unlimited powers could possibly have acted ... . But the fact is they have had far too extensive powers—powers which a few have misused, and which are not compatible with those rights which the tillers of the soil possess in equity and ought to possess by law. And if you wish to know what ought to satisfy us on this question, it might be said in a sentence and it is this—take the mode in which such kindly, generous and just landlords as Mr Leslie or Ford-Hutchinson have treated their tenantry, lop from it a few excrescences on which they would not insist, make that the law for all and you settle this question for ten generations.[203]

This was hardly the language of social revolution.

The Dervock speech contrasts rather oddly with the much quoted 'eviction' speech, delivered at a meeting sponsored by the Route Tenants Defence Association on 23 January 1880 in Ballymoney Town Hall. S. C. McElroy, analysing the speech in one of his editorials, was most complimentary: 'No speech was listened to with such breathless attention as that of Rev. J. B. Armour. His eloquence held the audience spell-bound.'[204] This was the first meeting to be organised in the area following the onset of the severe agricultural depression of 1879-80. Its purpose was once again to put the case for further land reform and, more specifically, to promote the candidature in the forthcoming general election of the Liberal, Charles Wilson, who had unsuccessfully contested the county in 1874. It was also hoped that the meeting would be a demonstration of solidarity with afflicted farmers in the south and west. There was a large number of speakers—Thomas McElderry of Ballymoney, who chaired the meeting; Samuel Black of Randalstown (though because he was suffering from a cold his speech was in fact read by S. C. McElroy); Thomas Houston of Carnmoney; Charles Wilson, the prospective candi-date (who was something of a disappointment since he had little to say and said it badly); Thomas Dickson M.P. of Dungannon; Thomas MacKnight, editor of the *Northern Whig*; Daniel O'Rourke, a Belfast solicitor; William Gray, a farmer from the Lisburn area; and Armour himself, who gave what was in effect a personal testimony as regards the land question. He explained how he had been first made aware of the injustices of the land system when, as a boy, he had witnessed an old farmer begging his landlord to allow him to retain his farm, but to no avail. The story was told in vivid and highly emotive detail—the old farmer, poorly clothed, with his bald head exposed to the falling snow—the landlord standing smoking his cigar, the reins of his well-covered greyhounds in his hands.

---

203. *B.F.P.*, 15 Feb. 1877. W. S. Armour included extracts from this same speech in his biography, but I have relied on press reports for the text since the version given by W. S. Armour appears to be inaccurate. See Armour, *Armour of Ballymoney*, p. 30. The landowners referred to in the speech were James Edmund Leslie, owner of the Leslie Hill estate of 7,428 acres adjacent to the town of Ballymoney, and William Ford-Hutchinson, owner of the Stranocum estate of 2,730 acres. See U. H. Hussey de Burgh, *The landowners of Ireland* (Dublin, 1878), xiii.

204. *B.F.P.*, 29 Jan. 1880. See also P. Bew and F. Wright, 'The agrarian opposition in Ulster politics, 1848-87' in S. Clark and J. S. Donnelly, Jr., *Irish peasants: violence and political unrest, 1780-1914* (Manchester, 1983), pp 210-1.

> I vowed that, if ever God gave me an opportunity, I would use what little strength was mine to drive a nail in the coffin of a system which, in the way it was administered, was not only a negation of justice, but which so battered the moral qualities out of men that they could not look their fellow-mortals in the face without their hat in their hand.

He then condemned the tyranny of landlords and agents, self-proclaimed saviours of society 'whose faces are never seen except on a rent day or when an election comes round'. He criticised the 'robbery' of the system and argued that the British constitution would hardly collapse, or the Russians march into Co. Antrim, if reforms were introduced. But even so, he sounded a note of caution:

> We want no man's property. We want no violent retaliation for the despotism of years, we want only that rents be fair, that the terms of tenure shall be such as, in the increased competition between the markets of the world, Irishmen shall not be so weighted by feudal restrictions and social bonds that they will break down in the struggle for existence.

These are clearly the words of a moderate, despite the emotional overtones. Indeed, he studiously avoided recommending specific remedies to his audience, other than that they should vote Liberal in order to help turn out the Conservative government, 'the most immoral and incapable that ever frittered away the force of a great nation'. Anyone who believed that the Conservatives could reform the land system 'is the most credulous and gullible of mortals'. He dwelt at some length on the impact of distress in the south and west as well as the lack of prosperity nearer home. Charity would achieve little, he believed, the only real remedy was 'a change in the land tenure'. He also appealed to farmers to treat their labourers fairly and he concluded by reminding his audience that anyone who voted Conservative would be branded by posterity as a traitor, 'an abettor of a system which consults for the luxury of the few at the expense of the many'.[205]

During these years Armour's devotion to Liberalism and to Gladstone as the epitome of moral action in politics cannot be doubted. He had, of course, been loyal to the Liberals ever since his youth. The fate of the Christians of the Balkans at the hands of the heathen Turks in particular aroused his indignation. An allegedly non-political protest meeting to denounce the Bulgarian atrocities was held in Ballymoney Town Hall on Monday 11 September 1876, chaired by J. Leslie Beers J.P., chairman of the town commissioners. It was Armour who proposed one of the resolutions passed by the meeting. 'We are met here tonight', he said, 'not in the interests of party politics, but in the more sacred cause of humanity which has been outraged by atrocities and barbarities which ... stand unparalleled and alone.' However, despite his protestations as to the non-party character of the gathering, he went on to issue a warning to the government that it must change its policy or be overthrown by the country.[206]

Armour lent his support to Liberal candidates at elections during these years, though his role, as in the land reform movement, was essentially a secondary one. His election campaign speeches underline the aggressively Presbyterian character of his Liberal creed. On 5 February 1874, in urging a Ballymoney audience to vote for Charles Wilson, he asked how as Presbyterians 'could they conscientiously support those who tried to prevent them from burying their dead'?[207] In May 1885 he spoke at Kilraughts in support of the Liberal, W. P. Sinclair, whose by-election victory proved to be the swan-song of Liberalism in Antrim, at least in the short term. In this speech he defined the principles of Liberalism as 'a love of liberty—the liberty to stand in things secular and stand in public and private according to a man's own convictions of what is right, a belief in progress and the dignity of human life, an abhorrence of class legislation and selfish interests and a desire that justice shall run through all laws'. But he also listed in order of priority the reasons why he believed that his audience should vote for Sinclair. Firstly, he was a Presbyterian; secondly, a Liberal in politics; thirdly, a man who would not be bought or bribed; and fourthly, he supported the claims of the labourers.

> For a hundred years the representatives of Antrim have been confined to a church which is only a minority of the community, and while they have been babbling about equality they

205. A very full account of both the meeting and J. B. Armour's speech is given in a pamphlet subsequently published by the Route Tenants Defence Association, entitled *The Irish land question* (P.R.O.N.I., McElderry papers, MIC. 57). See also *N.W.*, 24 Jan. 1880.
206. *B.F.P.*, 14 Sept. 1876. Beers, who chaired the meeting, was in fact a leading local Conservative who subsequently left Ballymoney and entered the prison service as a governor.
207. *Ibid.*, 12 Feb. 1874.

have never said—why, we will let you have one of your own party represent you ... . You have been hewers of wood and drawers of water too long.[208]

Armour's political involvement between 1886 and 1914 falls into four distinct phases, the first of these covers the period from 1886 to 1893. For a number of years after the introduction of the Home Rule bill he was an unmistakable Liberal Unionist and a member of the North Antrim Liberal Association, which, despite its misleading name, was the local Liberal Unionist organisation. At some point between 1886 and the general election of 1892 he became a convert to Home Rule. The reasons for, and the precise date of, this conversion are open to question. Unfortunately his surviving correspondence is not particularly helpful. Virtually no letters written to him survive for the years 1886-1890, though there is a useful series written by James J. Shaw from 1890 onwards which throw some interesting light on the background to the 1892 election. No letters written by Armour relating to this vitally important period of his life have come to light at all. However, the rough draft of a letter, dated 26 March 1893 and written to an unknown correspondent, does deal with the matter in retrospect:

> I did not like the Bill of '86 [*ie* the Home Rule bill] and opposed it principally on the ground that the Irish members were to be excluded from Westminster which gave foundation for the cry which did duty in Ireland, as elsewhere, that the Irish were seeking separation from the United Kingdom ... . The retention of the Irish members at Westminster will prevent the other possible danger—namely religious persecution on the part of the majority.[209]

However, it should be remembered that this letter was written after the publication of Gladstone's second bill which included a provision for the continued representation of Ireland at Westminster by eighty members. Armour's conversion to Home Rule certainly came before the election of 1892 and cannot therefore be related to the improvements made to the form of government which was offered to Ireland in the second bill. It is true that during the crisis concerning the 1886 bill, Gladstone made a vague promise that if it passed its second reading, an amendment allowing for continued Irish representation at Westminster might be accepted.[210] In the event the bill did not get that far, and during the ensuing years in the political wilderness, Gladstone, although remaining committed to the principle of Home Rule, never spelt out in any detail the precise form which a future bill would take, even during the 1892 election campaign.[211] Armour's conversion cannot therefore be explained by any shift in Liberal policy and it is necessary to delve more deeply in order to discover his possible motives.

Oliver McCann has of course suggested that it was Armour's all-consuming desire for land reform which led him to become a home ruler.[212] Certainly, he remained very interested in the land issue throughout this Liberal Unionist interlude. At a meeting of the North Antrim Liberal Association on 31 March 1887, he urged that the Liberal Unionists should not remain passive but should organise meetings throughout the constituency to 'show that though they had no intention of becoming Tories, they had just as little intention of supporting the outrageous proposals of the home rulers'. He expressed himself in favour of remedial land legislation.[213] At a meeting of the reactivated Route Tenants Defence Association on 1 November 1889, he welcomed the re-emergence of the organisation as a non-political platform for land reform. He supported resolutions calling on the government to introduce compulsory purchase legislation and called for meetings to be held throughout Ulster to echo this demand. He said that he wanted to see every farmer in the Route district the owner of the soil which he tilled. The Ulster tenant farmers, he believed, wanted no man's money and they did not say that the landlord had no interest in the soil. He himself was willing that bygones should be bygones, but only on condition that the landlords themselves became bygones.[214] So clearly he was unhappy with the progress of the Unionist government since 1886 in the area of land purchase. However, to suggest without qualification, as McCann does, that this disappointment drove him into the Liberal camp is to overlook the fact that, following the failure of the Home Rule bill in 1886

208. The original of the speech has survived (D.1792/B).
209. J. B. Armour to an unknown correspondent (draft copy), 23 June 1893 (D.1792/A2/22).
210. E. J. Feuchtwanger, *Gladstone* (London, 1975), p. 248.
211. For a fuller discussion of this point see F. S. L. Lyons, *Charles Stewart Parnell* (London, 1977), pp 440-51.
212. McCann, *Protestant Home Rule movement*, pp 134-5.
213. *B.F.P.*, 7 Apr. 1887.
214. *Ibid.*, 7 Nov. 1889.

with its accompanying abortive land purchase proposals, Gladstone and the Liberals had become decidedly lukewarm on the subject of land reform. This coyness drove their devoted Ulster supporters, such as S. C. McElroy, to despair at times.[215]

Therefore, it is to yet another possibility that we must turn. Armour's abandonment of Liberal Unionism must be seen against the background of growing Presbyterian and Liberal Unionist restiveness, particularly in North Antrim, over the Conservative/Anglican monopoly of parliamentary seats. This restiveness began in 1887 with the selection of Charles Lewis as the Unionist candidate. The sitting Unionist member, Edward Macnaghten, had been appointed a lord of appeal. The Liberal Unionists had then unsuccessfully attempted to nominate Sir George Trevelyan. He was regarded as being far too radical by local Conservatives and they cleverly out-manoeuvred the Liberal Unionists, foisting upon them Charles E. Lewis, a lawyer and former member for Londonderry City who was widely regarded as an enemy of land reform.[216] Indeed an independent, though by no means liberal, Unionist ran against him— William Traill, the manager of the Giant's Causeway electric tramway and a brother of Anthony Traill, the Trinity College provost.[217] Lewis was elected with a sizeable majority.[218] By 1890 it was common knowledge that ill-health would prevent Lewis from defending his seat. But once again the wishes of the Liberal Unionists were ignored, and in 1891 the delegates of the North Antrim Constitutional Association selected Charles Connor, a successful businessman and mayor of Belfast.[219] He was regarded as an able man, though within a short time his major business interests foundered, but he was hardly a popular choice—an outsider who was a non-Presbyterian and a director of the Bushmills distillery. Worse than Connor himself was the manner of his selection. Five names had been considered, none of them of Liberal Unionists, by the hundred or so delegates at the meeting.[220] The Liberal Unionists, after the 1887 debacle, had already made moves to have a candidate of their own selected. In the autumn of 1890 there had been press reports that James J. Shaw, a Dublin-based Presbyterian barrister and an old friend of Armour, would be their choice.[221] Shaw was quick to issue a public denial that he was as yet in the field, stressing that only the Unionist constituency party in North Antrim had the right to select a candidate. Some of the reports had implied that he had been chosen not by local Liberal Unionists, but by the government committee of the Presbyterian church. This Shaw denied, insisting that under no circumstances would he consent to being the candidate of one particular denomination. 'If I ever stand it will be as a Unionist.'[222]

Shaw's letters to Armour provide us with an insight into this complex situation. They show that, in spite of his public denials, Shaw remained very interested in North Antrim. Obviously the premature reports of his impending candidature were a source of considerable embarrassment. Writing to Armour on 3 November 1890, he expressed his belief that the initial leak 'was meant to do mischief'. Negotiations between the two Unionist factions had begun at the local level and Shaw was hopeful that the Conservatives might suggest putting two names before Lord Salisbury and Lord Hartington to enable them to arbitrate. He urged Armour to accept such an offer. if made, since he was sure that 'our claims could be regarded far more favourably in the larger circle of political life than in the narrower. If the Conservatives do not make the proposal *I think you ought*.'[223] Shaw was an ambitious man who seems to have been interested in the seat simply to further his career. On 27 November 1890 he appealed for Armour's help in securing a land commission vacancy, emphasising how poorly treated Presbyterians had been in the judicial field.[224] Even Connor's nomination did not kill his ambitions. He continued to urge Armour on, supplying him with arguments to use against the local Conservatives, who were

215. See McElroy's editorials in *ibid.*, 22 and 29 Apr. 1886, 23 July 1891 and 28 Jan. 1892.
216. *Ibid.*, 20 Jan. and 3 Feb. 1887.
217. See Traill's election address in *ibid.*, 10 Feb. 1887.
218. He had a majority of 1,332 over his nearest opponent S. C. McElroy (Gladstonian Liberal).
219. *Col. Con.*, 7 Mar. 1891.
220. Apart from Connor the others were George Hill-Smith, a Belfast barrister: Colonel McCalmont of Abbeylands, Whiteabbey; Sir Charles E. G. Phillips of Picton Castle, Wales; and Dr Anthony Traill of Ballylough, Bushmills.
221. *B.N.L.*, 24 Oct. 1890.
222. *Ibid.*, 28 Oct. 1890. The 'government committee' referred to was a purely unofficial body set up during the meeting of the General Assembly in June 1890. It should not be confused with the official Committee in Correspondence with Government. It consisted of clergy and laity who were interested in promoting the representation of Ulster constituencies at Westminster by Presbyterians.
223. J. J. Shaw to J. B. Armour, 3 Nov. 1890 (D.1792/A1/3/10).
224. J. J. Shaw to J. B. Armour, 27 Nov. 1890 (D.1792/A1/3/11).

claiming that the unilateral nomination of Shaw the previous autumn by the Liberal Unionists had freed them from any obligation.[225] They also argued that the Liberal Unionists were far from being in the majority in the constituency. Shaw suggested that Armour and his friends should threaten to run their own candidate as a protest, and that they should appeal to the national leadership and 'have influence brought from above to bring the local Tories to reason'.[226]

On 13 March Shaw wrote from Downpatrick, where he was presumably attending the assizes, in order to indicate that his hat was still in the ring. He asked that the Liberal Unionists in the constituency hold a conference to decide the matter. If they felt they could not elect a candidate of their own, they should let the matter rest. 'If on the other hand they think they have a fair chance, let them say whether they still think I am their strongest candidate and I will let them know at a very early period whether I can undertake the contest under the altered **circumstances**.' He also suggested that they find out whether there was likely to be a Nationalist candidate, since that could be a vital factor in coming to a decision.[227] Back in Dublin by 13 April, Shaw had finally made up his mind as to his attitude. If there were to be two Unionist candidates, he felt that he could not stand. The only hope was pressure from the Unionist leadership to force the local Conservatives to abandon Connor, and Shaw was anxious that the issue should be brought to their attention. He himself would try to help with this. In the meantime he was prepared to be adopted as the Liberal Unionist candidate, but he would not run against another Unionist. Possibly a compromise could be arranged, whereby at least the Liberal Unionists would be promised the reversion of the seat in exchange for accepting a more agreeable Conservative than Connor. Shaw made no secret of his ambitions:

> You can easily see that for me as a Unionist to be the instrument of a Unionist split would be almost equally fatal whether I succeeded or failed. On the other hand if I could secure a safe seat as the representative of a united party it would be the making of me.[228]

The final letter in the series reported a meeting that Shaw had had with F. E. Ball, acting as a representative of the Unionist leadership in London, who had been alarmed by the chain of events in North Antrim which they feared might easily be repeated elsewhere. Shaw claimed that he had warned Ball that Connor would have to be withdrawn, since the Liberal Unionists would otherwise run their own candidate. Ball allegedly agreed, especially since Connor was such a poor speaker 'and they have enough of that sort', and assured Shaw that his chiefs in London would much prefer him. Shaw had then unveiled his compromise scheme and was hopeful that Ball had taken the bait. However, in retrospect he felt angry that the whole affair had been mismanaged. Premature alarms in the press had given the game away, whereas quiet action might have produced a successful result.[229] In the end Connor's candidature was allowed to stand and Shaw was bought off with a county court judgeship.

The selection of Connor, 'the square man in the round hole'[230] as Thomas MacKnight called him, irritated Armour greatly, and when the Shaw episode had ended in disaster, he and some of his Liberal Unionist friends in North Antrim deserted the Unionist camp altogether. A subcommittee of the Route Tenants Defence Association was set up, with Armour as one of its members, to obtain an independent candidate.[231] The result was the selection of W. H. Dodd, a lawyer and a close friend of Armour ever since their university days.[232] It is possible that Dodd's name was suggested by Armour and he was widely blamed for Dodd's candidature, though he was by no means the only person involved.[233]

However, the Connor affair was merely the last stage in a gradual process of alienation and disenchantment. Throughout the 1880s Presbyterians generally had been complaining loudly about discrimination against them, not just in the matter of parliamentary representation but

225. See for example a letter from J. S. Cochrane, a local Ballymoney Conservative, in *N.W.*, 9 Mar. 1891.
226. J. J. Shaw to J. B. Armour, n.d. (D.1792/A1/3/12).
227. J. J. Shaw to J. B. Armour, 13 Mar. 1891 (D.1792/A1/3/13).
228. J. J. Shaw to J. B. Armour, 13 Apr. 1891 (D.1792/A1/3/14).
229. J. J. Shaw to J. B. Armour, 21 Apr. 1891 (D.1792/A1/3/16).
230. Thomas MacKnight, *Ulster as it is, or twenty-eight years experience as an Irish editor*, 2 vols. (London, 1896), ii, 269.
231. McElroy, *Route land crusade*, pp 50-1; *B.F.P.*, 31 Mar. and 14 Apr. 1892.
232. For a biographical profile of W. H. Dodd see McMinn, *Armour and Liberal politics in north Antrim*, p. 412.
233. No detailed record of the sub-committee's deliberations has survived. It was set up at a meeting of the Route Tenants Defence Association on 25 Mar. and consisted of Armour, Rev. J. S. Mairs, James Cameron and S. C. McElroy. It reported back to a further meeting of the association on 7 Apr.

in the whole area of public appointments.[234] After the 1886 split had divided the Liberal party irreparably, the high-handed treatment meted out to Presbyterian Liberal Unionists by their new Conservative allies made the complaints even louder. Armour's General Assembly speech of June 1886 on education is a good example of the kind of approach taken by many Presbyterians.[235] The Liberal Unionists therefore watched their new allies with a sharp eye and the Lewis affair worried them. W. S. Armour suggested that his father's change of heart concerning the government of Ireland and the merits of the Conservatives came as early as 1887, as the result of listening to Joseph Chamberlain and Jesse Collings speak at a major Unionist demonstration at Coleraine in October.[236] This may have been the case, but there is no evidence to support such a view.

In 1889 Armour contributed a series of anonymous leading articles to *The Witness* and these provide useful evidence as to how his views were evolving, especially an article in the issue of 8 February. The land question, he felt, was no longer a serious problem as a result of the legislation of successive governments:

> We live at present under a new and better order of things. Landlords and tenants all over the country, through the instrumentality of the land courts, have come to terms, save on thirty or forty estates where the landlords are exacting and obdurate, or the tenants wretched and unreasonable ... . It is not the landlord class, but the exceptional men among them—the Clanrickards, the Vandaleurs and the O'Gradys—who are at the bottom of the mischief.

However, the Presbyterians of Ireland had still much to complain of:

> Home Rule to most of them does not look more beautiful now than it did in 1886. But it need not be concealed that the more intelligent Liberals will have greater difficulty in joining the Conservative ranks in the future than they have had in the past ... Presbyterians, whether rightly or wrongly, have a growing conviction that they do not get fair play from those who stand at the head of affairs. They obtain an abundance of fair words when they attend *levees* or go on deputations to the viceregal lodge. But when any substantial office had to be conferred, it seldom comes the way of a Presbyterian ... . Even a police constable finds it impossible to obtain the promotion to which he is entitled by good service and seniority, except an appeal is made to the public through the newspapers, or a deputation is sent to the Castle. We need scarcely say that Presbyterians feel this treatment deeply. One of them said in our hearing not many days ago, with an exaggeration which served to show how keenly he felt on the matter—unless home rulers cut our throats, they could scarcely treat us worse'.[237]

On 16 August 1889 he contributed a leading article bewailing the lack of Presbyterian representation in Ulster and especially in Belfast.[238] He asked whether the Presbyterian mechanics, merchants and ministers of Belfast were 'content to be hewers of wood and drawers of water to others'. This lack of representation, he believed, was due both to Anglican intolerance and Presbyterian apathy:

> We are asked in this nineteenth century to acknowledge the right of members of one sect to be the almost exclusive legislators for the British empire ... . The sacred cause of Unionism is made at the present day a stalking horse to cover a multitude of political hypocricies.

If there was to be a rift within Unionism, then the responsibility would rest with those who 'take advantage of the political crisis to grasp all the nuts and throw the shells to the Presbyterians'.[239]

In December 1889 rumours of the impending retirement of Lewis from his North Antrim seat drove Armour to take up his pen once again. Lewis's departure would lead to the reduction of the existing Presbyterian representation by half, therefore Armour argued that he would have to be replaced by another Presbyterian. If a non-Presbyterian succeeded him, 'it will be a fatal

---

234. See McMinn, *Armour and Liberal politics in north Antrim*, chapter 3.
235. See above.
236. Armour, *Armour of Ballymoney*, p. 77.
237. *Witness*, 8 Feb. 1889. The views expressed in this article concerning the land question would seem to undermine Oliver McCann's interpretation of Armour's conduct with regard to Home Rule.
238. There were at this time only two Presbyterian members sitting for Ulster constituencies—Sir James Corry and Sir Charles E. Lewis.
239. *Ibid.*, 16 Aug. 1889.

mistake which will be regretted bitterly a fortnight after it has been committed'. A fairer Presbyterian representation was necessary if only because 'the majority of the clerics of the Church of Ireland are suspected of hankering after a ritual quite out of keeping with Reformation principles'.[240]

Despite these early intimations, Armour's apparent apostasy, when it became public knowledge during the course of the 1892 election campaign, drew down much criticism on his head. This was despite the fact that many other Presbyterians were saying very similar things. Even the moderator, Rev. R. McC. Edgar, in his closing address to the 1892 General Assembly in Dublin, had argued that if he were sure a man was a good Presbyterian, 'I would not be so particular about his politics'.[241] The difference was that Armour was prepared to act on such sentiments, but most Presbyterians and their newspaper *The Witness* were not. In its editorials during the campaign *The Witness* made its position perfectly clear towards W. H. Dodd, Thomas A. Dickson and Professor J. B. Dougherty, the three Presbyterian independent candidates. Although acknowledging that they were 'excellent men', it warned that the defence of the union was more important than local irritations, and urged Presbyterians to be wary of deceptive lures such as land purchase schemes and suggestions for lower rents:

> A successful member of a self-seeking profession, an experienced wire-puller in back offices of cabinet ministers and a stray professor who eats the bread of the Presbyterian church are asking God-fearing men to strike this corrupt bargain, are offering wealth and free farms in return for votes for Mr Gladstone in his Home Rule frenzy.[242]

It is hardly surprising therefore that during the campaign intensive efforts were made to discredit Armour, now regarded by many Unionists as an ungrateful renegade. These efforts must of course be seen in the context of Armour's continuing association with the Liberal Unionists until the very last minute. As late as 19 May 1892 he was present at a meeting of the North Antrim Liberal Association in the Temperance Cafe, Ballymoney.[243] In a speech at Ballymacwilliam on 29 June 1892 Armour publicly committed himself to Dodd's cause. During this speech he read two letters from other Presbyterian clergymen—one written to him by Rev. J. D. Osborne of Rutland Square Church, Dublin, and one sent to Dodd by Rev. J. C. Johnston of Dublin—both expressing support for Dodd's candidature.[244] The speech itself was largely a rehearsal of the by now familiar reasons as to why Armour had decided to abandon the Liberal Unionists. The Unionists, he suggested, had used the crisis in North Antrim to maintain their supremacy and 'like the Bourbons they have shown that they have learned nothing and forgotten nothing'. Since he was speaking to an audience of farmers, he devoted considerable attention to the weaknesses of Unionist policy on land reform. In particular he dwelt on the unfairness of the judicial rents in Ulster and the need to promote a generous measure of land purchase. The selfishness of the ascendancy class towards 'the hewers of wood and drawers of water' was attacked with customary vigour. As to Gladstone's proposals, he entreated them to recollect with gratitude his Irish measures in the past and give him at least a chance to develop his self-government scheme, which could not become law before a further election at which the electorate could pass judgement on it. He claimed that Dodd's opponents wished to perpetuate 'the worst form of home rule—the home rule of the grand jury system, which is taxation without representation; the home rule of big rents; the home rule of representatives in whose selection you have no voice, whose principles are the principles of ascendancy for a class and degradation to all creeds save one'.[245]

The reaction of local Liberal Unionists was both immediate and violent. One of their leading figures, William Hamilton J.P., was quick to brand Armour as a traitor. He condemned his allegedly dubious conduct in the matter of J. J. Shaw's abortive candidature, arguing that Armour had continued to mislead his fellow Liberal Unionists into thinking that Shaw would be their candidate long after he knew that Shaw was more interested in a judgeship. He blamed Armour for going behind their backs and stage-managing Dodd's nomination by the Route

---

240. *Ibid.*, 27 Dec. 1889.
241. *B.F.P.*, 23 June 1892.
242. *Witness*, 1 July 1892.
243. *B.F.P.*, 26 May 1892.
244. See appendix A for the full text of Osborne's letter.
245. *Ibid.*, 30 June 1892.

Tenants Defence Association. He also accused Armour of suppressing the full text of Osborne's letter, claiming that Osborne's reservations about some of Dodd's political views had not been made public.[246] In a subsequent letter to the press Armour denied all of these allegations, and argued that it was Hamilton who was not being truthful.[247] Osborne himself later confirmed Armour's version, namely that the political reservations in the letter had all been made public and that only irrelevant personal remarks had been excluded:

> This deplorable accusation is absolutely baseless. It arises out of an entire misrepresentation of my words. So far were Mr Dodd and his friends from wishing to suppress the fact that I did not entirely agree with him in his political position that it was in order that that very fact should be known that I was requested to allow my letter (a private one) to be published. Mr Dodd wished to show that although I differed from him, I should yet feel it my duty if I were an elector in North Antrim to give my vote to him. That I know is the position of many besides myself and will be, I hope, the position of many more in the constituency before polling day arrives.[248]

Although Armour was thus vindicated, the accusation had done some damage to his own reputation and that of W. H. Dodd. Indeed it was Dodd himself who took an active hand in persuading the *Northern Whig* to insert a correction and apology after he had shown the original of Osborne's letter to them, but this apology did not appear until after the election was over.[249] However, the *Belfast News-Letter*, which had also carried Hamilton's charges, proved to be more obdurate and Dodd, having retired for a rest to Port Salon in Donegal after his defeat at the polls, was not well placed to use his legal expertise to force them to recant. He advised Armour to be satisfied with the apology in the *Northern Whig* and simply let the matter drop.[250] William Hamilton himself remained unrepentant and publicly stuck to his original position.[251]

An even more damaging attack was made on Armour during the course of the campaign. This took the form of the re-publication of a violent anti-Home Rule broadsheet, allegedly written by him to discredit a land reform meeting which had been held by the Route Reform Club on 3 November 1887.[252] This handbill had originally made its appearance on the morning of the meeting. It was to haunt Armour for the rest of his political life, so it is worth examining its history in some detail. Its purpose is clear enough. It was intended to undermine the newly-founded Route Reform Club and its principles, by associating it in the public mind with the horrors of Gladstonian Home Rule. Its language and style are crude and straight-forward, but its authorship is something of a problem. Despite its vulgarity, it has features which are reminiscent of Armour's own style. The author is evidently an advocate of temperance; the terms 'wire-pullers' and 'troglodytes' are used; he is unhappy about judicial rents and some of his phrases have a familiar ring, such as 'these Ethiopians have not changed their skin', or the description of the legal profession as 'lawyer loons'.

Certainly some contemporaries were confident that Armour was the author. A correspondent signing himself 'A Route Liberal', writing to the *Ballymoney Free Press*, concluded that 'it was only when I came to look at it more closely that I discovered, what does not appear on the surface, that it is the work of men whom we have been accustomed in the past to consider political friends'. He was even more specific when he said that 'the identity between the sheet issued two years ago by the authority of the presbytery (but known to many at the time to be the work of one member of it, not the moderator) and the latest production of the kind from Dalriada must be apparent to anyone'.[253] Further letters to the local press made similar points. The *Morning News* took up the story and rather inaccurately claimed that the authorship of the pamphlet 'has been avowed by no less a person than a candidate for a professor's chair in connection with the General Assembly whose claims were ignored'.[254] A similar charge was

246. *Ibid.*, 7 July 1892; *Col. Con.*, 9 July 1892.
247. B.F.P., 7 July 1892; N.W., 9 July 1892.
248. B.F.P., 7 July 1892. The letter was read out in full at meetings addressed by Armour at Dunloy and Dirraw.
249. W. H. Dodd to J. B. Armour, 3 Aug. 1892 (D.1792/A1/3/21). See N.W., 13 Aug. 1892.
250. W. H. Dodd to J. B. Armour, 17 Aug. 1892 (D.1792/A1/3/22).
251. B.F.P., 1 Sept. 1892.
252. The original 1887 broadsheet has not survived. However, it was re-published in both 1892 and 1894 in order to discredit Armour and a copy of the 1894 edition can be seen in the local history collection in Ballymoney Library (U/A B.M.O. 1315106). The full text is given in appendix B.
253. B.F.P., 17 Nov. 1887. Oliver McCann, *Protestant Home Rule movement*, pp 134-5, confidently asserts that Armour was the author, but provides no supporting evidence. The 1885 broadsheet, which the correspondence referred to, was an appeal to the Presbyterians of north Antrim to vote for W. P. Sinclair in the by-election of that year.
254. B.F.P., 24 Nov. 1887, carries a reprint of the *M.N.* editorial.

made in a lengthy ballad, published in the *Ballymoney Free Press*, entitled 'The Unionist handbill':

> Yet, after all I think this holy howl
> Was largely due to Rev. Blattergowl,
> Now surnamed Troglodyte, who wields the pen
> When met in council Gotham's wisest men.
>
> But let us tell you, times may yet be worse,
> If 'loyal' patriots from the public purse
> Are not rewarded, is the almighty dollar
> To go to rebels; while a polished scholar
> Is forced with sighs to move the ambient air,
> Heart sick with waiting for 'a vacant chair'.[255]

Armour appears to have made no attempt to answer these insinuations in 1887, hoping perhaps that the matter would soon drop out of sight.

However, the revival of the controversy in 1892 did move him to take action. The broadsheet reappeared in that year with Armour's signature appended and this signature was clearly bogus. Armour was therefore on strong ground when he denounced it as a forgery. His denials did not end the affair however, and the broadsheet was to bob up to the surface again on occasions when his political opponents were particularly enraged, or felt that it was necessary to discredit him. The broadsheet was re-issued on 6 September 1894 in the wake of his General Assembly pronouncements on Home Rule. This time the signature did not appear, but instead a few apposite paraphrased lines from Robert Burns (this was a most appropriate device since Armour had a great fondness for Burns' grace):

> Oh wud some power the giftie gie us,
> To see ourselves as ithers see us;
> It wud from money a blunder free us,
> Like those of a turn-coat Preacher.

The disputed broadsheet made its final appearance on 6 January 1911 when the *Northern Whig* published it in conjunction with a feature on Armour.[256] He protested to the editor, securing a promise never to publish it again, then sought legal advice from J. L. Brown K.C. A copy of his initial letter to Brown, dated 23 January, has survived. He asked for Brown's advice as to whether he had grounds for taking action against the newspaper and gave him an interesting account of the broadsheet's origin:

> In 1887 some four or five gentlemen wished to publish a manifesto in view of a public meeting to be held and they asked me to sketch something for them which I did and sent it to them. They corrected and added sentences to it and held a meeting I believe at which I was not present and resolved to publish it—which was done. That was my connection with it. I did not regard it as mine as I have never published anything that I regarded as mine without putting my name to it.[257]

Therefore, Armour, on his own admission, had been involved, but obviously was not the sole or final author. This would explain the style in which the document was written and the familiar phrases which it contains. It is also clear from this letter that one of the 'gentlemen' in question was William Hamilton, who had been the prime mover in the Osborne affair, and it was he, according to Armour, who was responsible for the reappearance of the broadsheet in 1892 and 1894. The success enjoyed by Hamilton's strategy was considerable—he fastened a can to Armour's tail which the latter never really managed to remove.

In the face of this hostility and criticism, Armour felt it necessary during the course of the 1892 campaign to put his views on record in an interview with the *Ballymoney Free Press*. This interview provides a further useful insight into his motives. Much of what Armour had to say had been said already. He rehearsed the reasons why he, as a Liberal Unionist, had gradually become alienated from Unionism—the selection of Sir Charles Lewis in 1887; the unsuccessful efforts of local Liberal Unionists to have J. J. Shaw nominated in 1891; the refusal of the

---

255. *Ibid*. The ballad is given in full in appendix C.
256. *N.W.*, 6 Jan. 1911.
257. J. B. Armour to J. L. Brown, 23 Jan. 1911, draft copy (D.1792/A2/37).

Unionists to submit to the arbitration of Lord Salisbury and Lord Hartington; the selection of Connor; Connor's unsatisfactory views on the land question; the failure of the Tories to introduce an effective land purchase scheme; Connor's association with the 'drink traffic'; the likely removal by Gladstone of the worst feature of the Home Rule bill of 1886—the exclusion of Irish members from Westminster; Armour's feeling that some change in the local government of Ireland was bound to come anyway and that Gladstone should at least have the chance to develop his scheme, especially since it could not become law without a further general election; and of course the unfair treatment of Presbyterians by the Unionist party:

> The wire-pullers never omit an opportunity of flouting the Presbyterians and though I have never advocated representation by churches, yet the deliberate attempt made throughout Ulster to keep the Presbyterians in political degradation shall have my determined opposition. If Unionism means what the past and present tactics of the party indicate—the ascendancy of a sect, I cease to respect it and to attempt to buttress up what has no right to exist.[258]

This was a cooler expression of his own attitudes than that to be found in his public speeches, where the Liberal Unionists were dismissed as 'mere circus riders in the Tory hippodrome'; the city of Belfast condemned as 'the necropolis of Liberalism'; Dodd, Dickson and Dougherty described as 'the Uhlans of the conquering host'; and an appeal made to Presbyterian voters to 'make this election the Sedan of the Tory faction' in order to 'save your church'.[259]

The whole episode had taken a great deal out of Armour both mentally and physically. Following the declaration of the poll, he had to take to his bed, and it was from there on 17 July that he poured out his innermost feelings to his 'daughter dear', Jane MacMaster, the sister of Professor James MacMaster, his wife's brother-in-law. Since he had no daughters of his own, Armour treated Jane, who never married, as a member of the family. She had entered the nursing profession and trained at St Thomas's Hospital in London, later becoming matron at the Salisbury General Infirmary (1898-1905) and subsequently at the North Staffordshire Royal Infirmary, Stoke-on-Trent, until her retirement in 1930. Her relationship with her adopted 'father' was a very close one, and he regarded her as having a kindred spirit to his own—hence the confidences. The letter in question has only survived by accident. Armour, upset by the events surrounding the election, was unable to sleep. He dreamed continually of making speeches and used the letter as 'a safety valve'. He urged Jane to burn it after she had read it.

'I have been through Hades for the last fortnight and now I have got back to purgatory', was how Armour summed up his feelings. He praised his wife for her stoicism and feared that his behaviour would result in her being irritated in the future by the 'gad flies of social life', whom he compared to swarms of clegs—not deadly, but annoying nonetheless. He believed that 'every "cad" and every Liberal Unionist from Dan to Beersheba' were preparing to destroy him and he had already had to endure 'a good deal of Billingsgate'. William Hamilton's conduct over the Osborne letter had particularly angered him, but he felt that events had shown him to have been in the right. He feared that he had annoyed some members of the congregation but was unrepentant:

> I have fallen on evil days and evil tongues, but I feel free and I have no regrets and am untroubled in my conscience about cutting my connexion with a party that I served to the best of my small ability and which is proving itself a party of spite, vulgarity and meanness.[260]

Dodd was in the event decisively defeated,[261] but at the national level the Liberals were more successful, and Gladstone set about the task of forming a government. Armour took the opportunity of writing to James Bryce to press his friend's claims to be the new solicitor-general for Ireland, stressing Dodd's devotion to Gladstone's Irish policy and the value of his recent efforts in North Antrim. But once again it was Dodd's Presbyterianism that was his chief recommendation. 'To conciliate the Presbyterians, the appointment of Mr Dodd, who is a thorough Presbyterian, would be a wise stroke of policy.'[262] But it was not to be.

258. *B.F.P.*, 30 June 1892.
259. *Ibid.*, 7 July 1892.
260. J. B. Armour to Jane MacMaster, 17 July 1892 (D.1792/A3/13/2).
261. He polled 2,027 votes as against Connor's 4,666. See B. M. Walker, *Parliamentary election results in Ireland, 1801-1922* (Dublin, 1978), p. 325.
262. J. B. Armour to James Bryce, 9 Aug. 1892, draft copy (D.1792/A2/18).

The election invariably had an effect on Armour's own position in Ballymoney. Some members of his congregation must have been annoyed by his conduct. The dangers of the situation were clearly illustrated by the case of Rev. J. D. Craig Houston of Hydepark, Co. Antrim, who had written to the *Daily News* announcing his conversion to Home Rule.[263] Writing to Armour on 3 August, he admitted to having lost some thirty people from his services. 'I have kissed nobody's wife and I have forged nobody's hand, and yet if I had done any or all of these things, the indignation of some people against me could not have been greater.' He congratulated Armour on having 'weathered the storm', and on having suffered few defections.[264] But in reality the storm had yet to break.

The year 1893 was in many respects the climax of Armour's political career. On Wednesday 15 March 1893 a special meeting of the General Assembly took place in May Street Church, Belfast. It was called for the purpose of 'considering the dangers by which the civil and religious liberties of members of the church are menaced by proposed legislation, and to determine what action should be taken thereon'. The moderator, Rev. Robert McCheyne Edgar, who presided, began the proceedings by explaining how and why the meeting had been convened. Normally a special Assembly would only be called if four or more presbyteries made a request to the moderator, but this had not happened in this instance. The moderator explained his conduct by pointing to the imminent threat posed by the second reading of the Home Rule bill. This, he said, had convinced both him and the Committee on the State of the Country to act immediately. The Assembly then unanimously approved the moderator's decision and went into committee to consider the many memorials and petitions to be laid before it. However, after lunch the Assembly publicly debated eight resolutions prepared by the Committee on the State of the Country. The burden of these resolutions was to reaffirm loyalty to the queen, generally to express a determination to maintain the union, specifically to reject the government of Ireland bill currently before parliament for a variety of stated reasons, to urge the abolition of dual ownership of land in Ireland, to support reform of the system of local government in Ireland, to encourage Presbyterians to remain calm and treat all their fellow-countrymen with forbearance and goodwill and finally to suggest that Sunday 26 March be set aside by all Presbyterians as a day of prayer to invoke divine aid in averting the current dangers. These resolutions were to be laid before the prime minister, various other leading politicians and both houses of parliament. They were proposed by Rev. Petticrew and seconded by Armour's erstwhile friend, John Megaw.[265]

It was then in the crowded church that J. B. Armour emerged on to the Ulster political stage as a major figure, when he rose to propose an amendment to the official resolutions. From this moment on Armour was to be regarded as a leading Protestant champion of Home Rule—indeed his amendment and speech were printed in pamphlet form by the *Irish News* and this was to achieve a considerable circulation.[266] But a close examination both of the amendment itself and of his speech reveals no really new thinking. He had little to say about the positive virtues of Gladstone's proposals. His chief justifications were negative, and in particular he concentrated upon the well-worn argument that Presbyterians had been unfairly treated under the current constitutional arrangements—though this was an obvious ploy to use before a wholly Presbyterian audience. He tacked on to this the usual pleas on behalf of the tenant farmers, which the proposers of the official resolutions had also included, and he made an effort to dispel the fears expressed by Unionists about Ireland's potential future under a Home Rule government. The first sentence of his amendment fairly summed up the substance of his case:

> Whereas, under the existing system of government in Ireland, the offices and honours of state have practically been monopolised by a small section of the community, and the members of this church have been excluded from that share in the administration of public affairs to which they are justly entitled, the General Assembly of the Presbyterian church is of the opinion that a thorough reform, which will give to Ireland such a measure of self-government as is consistent with the unity of the empire, the supremacy of parliament and the protection of minorities is desirable and necessary.

263. *Daily News*, 29 June 1892.
264. J. D. Craig Houston to J. B. Armour, 3 Aug. 1892 (D.1792/A1/3/20).
265. The full text of the official resolutions can be found in appendix D.
266. The full text of J. B. Armour's amendment can be found in appendix E.

J. B. Armour addressing the Presbyterian General Assembly.

In his vigorous speech he acknowledged that he was taking a different course from that of many in the Assembly, he asked that he should be extended the right of free expression and he reminded the Assembly of the political degradation experienced by Presbyterians during the previous century:

> The whole weight of officialism was directed during all this century against their civil interests more than against any other religious denomination in this land. To start public life in Ireland as a Presbyterian was to start with a dead weight around the neck; was to proclaim one's self as a political leper; was the passport to political degradation and insult.

Armour pointed to the fact that many families had been forced to renounce their Presbyterianism in order to make their way in the world. He made it clear that he saw the Home Rule bill as an instrument designed by God to smash the existing discriminatory system:

> The resolutions are the policy of a man who commits suicide for fear of death. You profess to be afraid that your people will be deprived of their civil rights. I tell you that under no government conceivable or imaginable could they have fewer civil rights than they have had in the past ... . I traverse the policy of the resolutions because it is a policy which ties this church to a party which has been, more than any other, the cause of Ireland's misgovernment, which has opposed every reform with persistency, which has filched from you almost all share in the representation of Ulster, which has filled your land courts with administrators of the land laws that are robbing and wronging your people, which has given you no share in the government of your country and which has always had to surrender, and in surrendering has served its friends and wronged you.

He reminded the Assembly too of the support for Home Rule amongst English and Scottish nonconformists and of the mistaken belief of many Unionists that Gladstone could not and would not win another election. As to prophecies of financial disaster and discrimination under Home Rule, he believed them to be wildly wrong. 'The principle of Home Rule is a Presbyterian principle', and the bill was the work of 'the only genius in state-craft we have had in these lands for centuries', who deserved their gratitude for the numerous benefits which he had conferred upon them in the past. However, it should be emphasised that despite some misleading statements, Armour was not giving his unqualified support to Gladstone's bill. He accepted that it would require modification and he was simply advocating that the Assembly give it a fair trial.

He then proceeded to deal with the land question, arguing that the sympathy with the tenants expressed by the proposers of the official resolutions was pointless and irrelevant. By opposing Home Rule they were saving the landlords and thus saddling the tenants with impossible rents. He criticised the landlord class, 'the curse and scourge of Ireland', in scathing terms, and suggested that if the Ulster tenants 'never paid a penny of rent or a shilling of purchase money they would break no divine law'. This comment provoked a torrent of heckling. After it had somewhat subsided, Armour went on to argue that the tenants needed a 30 per cent reduction in judicial rents, followed by compulsory sale on the basis of those reduced rents. He concluded by appealing to the Assembly to abandon its negative policy and warned that if they did not do so, then 'this Assembly will be known as the Assembly which, in its unreasoning passion against Mr Gladstone to spite the majority of our countrymen, sold its people into bondage and, through a senseless fear of Romanism, sacrificed the power and progress of true Presbyterianism in Ireland for generations'.

At various times during the speech Armour had had to face a barrage of interruptions and points of order and the uproar grew worse as the debate continued. Many members became anxious to put the resolutions to the vote in order to go home. Armour's amendment was seconded by a lay elder, John Steen of Portstewart, and was also powerfully supported by Professor J. B. Dougherty. Both Steen and Dougherty stressed the dangers of the church becoming so closely involved in politics. Dougherty also questioned the circumstances in which the Assembly had been called, arguing that, as no presbytery had requested it, there was no evidence of widespread concern about the Home Rule issue except in Belfast. Towards the end of his speech Dougherty was constantly heckled and called to order. He responded by asking those who agreed with his views to abstain from voting as a protest. With the exception of one person, they duly did so when Armour's amendment was put to the vote. The official resolutions were then carried unanimously after a discussion which had lasted for five hours. The clerk refused to agree to Professor Dougherty's request that he should record the fact that many had declined to vote because of the stifling of discussion.[267]

Armour's stand attracted much publicity. Many wrote to him congratulating him upon his speech and sympathising with him in view of the social ostracism which was likely to follow. Some of his correspondents shared his essentially narrow Presbyterian attitude towards Home Rule. Rev. Thomas Macafee of Ardglass, for example, was of the opinion that:

> If our church had not wholly parted from its traditions and given up its proper position, it would have passed your amendment unanimously. Anyone can understand why landlordism and episcopacy should struggle earnestly to retain the remnants of their ascendancy, but why the Presbyterian church should unite with them in the struggle is more than I can understand.[268]

Armour's replies to these congratulatory letters reveal something of the difficulty of his position. He referred to bitter things being said against him, to the fact that some were attempting to enforce a new Presbyterian doctrine of obedience to Unionism and to a boycott directed against him by most of his clerical colleagues.[269] But he believed that his speech had been worthwhile and that the Assembly had been a useful platform. He felt that his opponents had discredited their cause through their attempt to restrict discussion and that support for Gladstone's policy had been increased. He even thought, somewhat optimistically, that but for the application of pressure and the absence of a secret ballot, his amendment would have passed.[270] His opponents did not agree with this assessment however. *The Witness* believed that of some 750 members present at the Assembly, 700 were in favour of the official resolutions and only five—Armour, Dougherty, J. D. Craig Houston, Matthew Kerr and a single elder, John Steen—were definitely against. The Unionists in the Assembly saw Dougherty's abstention proposal as a useful device to conceal the real size of the tiny minority who were in revolt.[271]

Armour also took comfort from the fact that he had always kept politics (at least of the Irish variety) out of his pulpit and that as a result his congregation remained loyal, even though some of its members were staunch Unionists.[272] W. S. Armour claimed that only two or three members left his father's church at this time.[273] Certainly the congregational statistics in the table below would seem to bear this out.[274]

Table One—Congregational Statistics for Trinity Church, Ballymoney, 1870-1914

Year	Number of families attached to congregation	Number of communicants	Number of elders	Sabbath collections for the year
1870	130	290	7	£25 2 3
1880	140	236	4	£30 7 8
1890	170	248	7	£49 4 2
1900	170	252	7	£67 12 5
1910	175	240	6	£57 11 10
1914	172	230	5	£58 15 2

In the crucial decade 1890-1900, when Armour openly identified himself with Home Rule, the number of elders remained static as did the number of families, while the number of communicants actually increased and Sabbath collections substantially improved. It was only during the crisis provoked by the introduction of the third Home Rule bill that there was any reduction in the size of the congregation, and even then it was hardly very significant.

267. *General Assembly minutes*, viii, 470-4 (1893); *The Irish Presbyterians and the Irish question: The necessity for Home Rule maintained, the Presbyterian Unionists answered. Eloquent speech by Rev. J. B. Armour, Ballymoney, delivered at the special meeting of the General Assembly, at Belfast, on March 15, 1893.* (Belfast, 1893); *Witness*, 17 Mar. 1893.
268. Thomas Macafee to J. B. Armour, 22 Mar. 1893 (D.1792/A1/3/23).
269. J. B. Armour to J. W. Kirk, 18 Mar. 1893, draft copy (D.1792/A2/20).
270. J. B. Armour to T. A. Dickson, 31 Mar. 1893 (D.1792/A2/21).
271. *Witness*, 17 Mar. 1893.
272. J. B. Armour to J. W. Kirk, 18 Mar. 1893, draft copy (D.1792/A2/20).
273. Armour, *Armour of Ballymoney*, pp 114-5.
274. I have compiled this table from the annual congregational statistics submitted to the General Assembly and printed in the Assembly minutes.

The Home Rule issue came up again when the General Assembly met in the normal way in June. The report of the Committee on the State of the Country endorsed and reaffirmed the March resolutions and deplored Gladstone's refusal to receive a deputation from the Assembly. A critical amendment was proposed by John McElderry (an elder of Trinity Church, Ballymoney) and seconded by Rev. J. D. Craig Houston. J. B. Dougherty and Rev. Matthew Kerr gave it their support but Armour did not speak, although he was present. This time the matter was brought to a vote. The report, with the March resolutions appended, was carried by a very large majority.[275] At first glance this seemed to be a disastrous defeat for Armour and his friends, but his own analysis was rather different. Writing to an unidentified correspondent, he stressed that the resolutions had taken the Home Rule party by surprise, that the roll had been called to intimidate those who were against the resolutions and that out of some 750 members present only approximately 320 actually voted. He concluded from this that although the majority of Irish Presbyterians was opposed to Home Rule, there was a strong and growing minority in favour of it. He saw Belfast, 'the temple of the rankest Toryism', as the major centre of Presbyterian Unionism. Undoubtedly these claims were partly wishful thinking on Armour's part, but in one respect at least this letter contained an astonishingly accurate prophecy. Home Rule, he argued, was bound to come in some form, even if the Liberal government then in power was removed from office:

> If the Tories come back to power they will either grant it in a form which will mean that their friends—the landlord party and ascendancy party—will have the management as of old and the old sores will not be healed, or they will by bribery on the education question stave it off for a few years and then it will come *too late* and in a form which will be revolutionary.[276]

Armour and his chief allies now decided that it was necessary to provide a focus for Presbyterian Liberal sentiment. They were also anxious to counteract the impression created by the two Assemblies of 1893, that the Irish Presbyterian church was wholly opposed to Gladstone's Irish policy. Lacking any formal organisational machinery, they decided to organise a memorial to be signed only by Presbyterians which would be sent, with a covering letter, to Gladstone to assure him that not all Irish Presbyterians were his political enemies. The prime movers were Armour and Dougherty and it was they who drafted both the memorial and the covering letter, although the latter was signed by Rev. J. D. Craig Houston, John McElderry and John Steen as well.[277]

The memorial, addressed directly to Gladstone, consisted of two paragraphs. In the first the memorialists expressed their gratitude to Gladstone for his past services and their sympathy with him 'in his present efforts to secure the better government of Ireland'. In the second paragraph they pressed for an immediate downward revision of judicial rents and the implementation of compulsory purchase on the basis of the revised rentals.[278] Dougherty, despite his fair words on behalf of the tenant farmers at the March General Assembly, did not seem to be particularly enthusiastic about urging their demands. 'I should be satisfied with the first paragraph alone but I suppose our agricultural friends would not. The second par[agraph] might be made shorter perhaps, but I think it desirable to rub in "revision of judicial rents" as compulsory sale is played out.' The expectations of the memorial's architects were modest, Dougherty believing that around 1,000 signatures would represent 'a great success'.[279] In the event they obtained 3,535[280] and there is evidence in the considerable correspondence relating to this episode, that but for social and political pressure there would have been more.

The method employed to collect the signatures was haphazard—basically Dougherty and Armour sent copies of the memorial for signatures to everyone whom they believed to be sympathetic. As the covering letter to Gladstone said, there was no public solicitation and

---

275. *General Assembly minutes*, viii, 556-9 (1893); *Witness*, 13 June 1893. Altogether 226 ministers and 78 elders voted for the report and resolutions; 9 ministers and 2 elders voted against. There was thus a majority of 293.
276. J. B. Armour to an unknown correspondent, n.d., draft copy (D.1792/A2/22).
277. The evolution of the memorial can be followed in a number of letters written by Dougherty to Armour. See for example J. B. Dougherty to J. B. Armour, n.d. (D.1792/A1/1/5 and /6).
278. There are two copies of the final printed version of the memorial in the Armour correspondence (D.1792/A2/24A, /24B). The full text is given in appendix F.
279. J. B. Dougherty to J. B. Armour, n.d. (D.1792/A1/1/6).
280. J. B. Dougherty, J. Craig Houston, J. B. Armour, John McElderry and John Steen to W. E. Gladstone, 1893 (D.1792/A2/25).

undoubtedly many districts were neglected. However, to suggest that the entire thing was 'spontaneous'[281] was perhaps misleading—it was clearly orchestrated by Armour and Dougherty. The signatories were promised that their names would not be published. This made it possible for some to sign who might otherwise have been unwilling to do so.[282] Even so, family or business pressure dissuaded others.[283]

It would be wrong to suppose that all of those who signed were fully committed to the principles embodied in Gladstone's 1893 Home Rule bill,[284] even if Gladstone himself chose to interpret the document in that way.[285] The reference to the future government of Ireland in the memorial was a vague one. Some of those who signed were probably influenced by their interest in land reform and by a feeling of gratitude towards Gladstone. They may not necessarily have fully endorsed Gladstone's Home Rule proposals.[286] Some others were no doubt motivated, as *The Witness* declared, 'by hatred of the old episcopal ascendancy, otherwise they would not have signed at all'.[287] However, to suggest, as some Unionist critics did, that many of the signatures were bogus, protected as the memorial was by a cloak of anonymity, would seem to be unfair. That there were some 3,535 male Presbyterians in Ireland who had not, as Thomas Dickson put it, 'bowed the knee to the Baal of Toryism'[288] is probably true. Indeed if we set this figure in the context of Oliver McCann's estimates of the total number of home rulers in Ulster at this time, it seems to be perfectly reasonable. He has calculated that in the general election of 1886 some 2,500 Protestants voted for Gladstonian Liberal candidates in six Ulster constituencies; he estimates that in 1887 there were between 5,000 and 10,000 Protestant home rulers in Ulster; that by 1893 this figure had increased considerably, so that there were some 5,000 in Belfast alone and in the rest of Ireland at least 10,000.[289] Nonetheless, extensive efforts were made in 1893, both inside and outside the house of commons, to discredit the Presbyterian memorial. The issue was raised on four separate occasions in the commons by various Ulster Unionist members. They concentrated their attack on the signatures to the document, alleging that some who signed it were not in sympathy with its objectives and that others were not Presbyterians at all. Gladstone was pressed either to publish the names, or agree to refer the document to the committee on petitions for further investigation. The prime minister refused to give way to these demands and expressed his continuing confidence in the good faith of those who had organised the memorial and those who had signed it. 'Further than that I cannot go, and I must leave the matter to be fought out between the respective parties outside the walls of this house.'[290]

The events of 1893 had shown just how weak in the organisational sense Ulster Liberalism had become, even though it was enjoying something of a resurgence in numerical terms.[291] In addition, the announcement at the beginning of 1894 by the Liberal government's Irish chief secretary, John Morley, that a parliamentary inquiry would be held to investigate the working of previous land legislation, further underlined the need for a united front on the part of like-minded Liberals. Consequently, on 2 February 1894, a conference, attended by 190 Liberals and nationalists, met in Rosemary Street Lecture Hall, Belfast, under the chairmanship of Thomas Dickson, to concert action to organise Irish 'Liberal and radical' opinion. In the event little was immediately achieved beyond the adoption of a series of resolutions supporting the 1893 Home Rule bill and various proposed social reforms in Britain and endorsing the familiar farmers' demands regarding judicial rents and compulsory purchase. The conference also

281. *Ibid.*
282. See letter from J. B. Armour to W. E. Gladstone of 29 Aug. 1893, printed in full in Armour, *Armour of Ballymoney*, pp 123-5.
283. See for example, Robert Macauley of Mullaghduff to J. B. Armour, n.d. (D.1792/A1/2/28); T. Irwin of Newry to J. B. Armour, 6 June 1893 (D.1792/A1/2/2); William Craig of Newtownards to J. B. Armour, 19 June 1893 (D.1792/A1/2/8).
284. See for example, A. [McCaldin ?] of Banbridge to J. B. Armour, 14 July 1893 (D.1792/A1/2/24).
285. 'I have received with pleasure the address from 3,500 Presbyterians, favourable to Home Rule for Irish purposes in Ireland'. W. E. Gladstone to J. B. Armour, 12 Aug. 1893 (D.1792/A1/2/29).
286. See for example, John Orr of Saintfield to J. B. Armour, 10 June 1893 (D.1792/A1/2/4); R. Cooper of Balloo to J. B. Armour, 17 July 1893 (D.1792/A1/2/25).
287. *Witness*, 18 Aug. 1893.
288. T. A. Dickson to J. B. Armour, 15 Sept. 1893 (D.1792/A1/2/30).
289. McCann, *Protestant Home Rule movement*, pp 42-5; 95-6; 140.
290. *Hansard 4*, xvi, 528-9, 646-7, 769, 973-4 (18, 21, 22 and 24 Aug. 1893). See also W. E. Gladstone to J. B. Armour, n.d., in Armour, *Armour of Ballymoney*, p. 125.
291. T. A. Dickson to J. B. Armour, 15 Sept. 1893 (D.1792/A1/2/30). 'I feel that in Ireland we Gladstonian Liberals have no platform.'

established the Ulster Liberal Land Committee.[292] A further conference on 8 March, whilst approving of John Morley's recently introduced land bill, also passed a resolution proposing the setting up of a body to be called the 'Ulster Liberal and National Union'.[293] The *Irish News* hailed these developments as the 'Ulster Presbyterian awakening':

> The Ulster Tory landlords must be by this time beginning to realise that the game they have played so long and so successfully of preserving their privileges by the dissensions of the tenant farmers is up ... . The murmurings abroad among the Presbyterian tenantry mean something more than may appear to the superficial observer. The men who for eight years fought hard and bitterly against the Irish policy of their former chief Mr Gladstone are rapidly awakening to the fact that Home Rule has become inevitable, and that Home Rule, look at it as they may, will not at least mean to them dilapidated homesteads and interests confiscated by the landlord champions of the union.[294]

Armour, although a member of the Ulster Liberal Land Committee, does not appear to have taken an active part in these meetings, but Rev. Richard Lyttle of Moneyreagh enlisted his support subsequently. Lyttle stressed that an election was pending and argued that the recent Presbyterian and Unitarian memorials on Home Rule and the activities of the Liberal Land Committee 'should furnish the bones of an organisation'. He believed that a target of 10,000 members would be perfectly realistic.[295] The organisation finally got off the ground in March 1895, with William Killen and Rev. Richard Lyttle as its secretaries and Armour as a member of the executive council.[296] An Irish Women's Association had already been formed in November 1894 and Mrs Armour became its first president. The association was linked with the Women's Liberal Union of Great Britain and it established branches in Belfast, Dungannon, Londonderry and Omagh. Mrs Armour in her inaugural address stressed that their purpose was 'to show that we are not afraid of Home Rule, but that we believe it to be the right of the Irish people—an ideal worthy of our efforts to gain and the stepping-stone to many social reforms'.[297] The association was however destined to be short-lived.

J. B. Armour contributed to the brief renaissance of Ulster Liberalism in other ways. He offered his services to the Home Rule cause in Great Britain[298] and took part in a by-election campaign at South Hackney in May 1894.[299] During the same year he also spoke at many meetings in Ulster, primarily to audiences of tenant farmers, for example at Ballynure, Co. Antrim, on 5 April. Here several hundred local farmers gathered to hear a number of speeches on the current state of the land question, most of which dealt with the proposed Morley committee of inquiry. The meeting provoked considerable opposition—two Orange bands played outside and the windows of the hall were smashed by stone-throwers. When the meeting ended the speakers had to run a gauntlet of stones and verbal abuse from a mob, said to have been mainly employees of the Ballyclare Paper Mill, and Armour's hat was struck by a stone.

In his speech Armour praised the framers of the resolutions for recognising that:

> There are other provinces in Ireland as well as Ulster: that the inhabitants of the provinces are not necessarily blood-thirsty savages, animated by the continuous passions for robbing and massacring Ulster folks, and that there are wrongs to be redressed and rights to be established, as well beyond as on this side of the Boyne.

He argued that the gains made by Ulster farmers were largely the result of the efforts of those in the other provinces. He delivered his usual attack on the political reactionaries of Belfast, as well as paying a lavish tribute to Gladstone and his successor Lord Rosebery. He claimed that Gladstone's retirement had not resulted in the destruction of Liberalism. He stated his belief that the proposed inquiry would reveal that the 1881 land act's intentions had been frustrated by the prejudice of the courts. He denounced the efforts of the Tories at Westminster

292. *B.N.L.*, 3 Feb. 1894. The principal members of the Ulster Liberal Land Committee were Thomas Dickson, Thomas Shillington, J. B. Dougherty, Samuel Young, Thomas McClelland and Francis Shepherd.
293. *Ibid.*, 9 Mar. 1894.
294. *I.N.*, 21 May 1894.
295. Richard Lyttle to J. B. Armour, 26 May 1894 (D.1792/A1/3/29).
296. J. B. Dougherty had a very low opinion of Lyttle's abilities. See J. B. Dougherty to J. B. Armour, n.d. (D.1792/A1/1/8).
297. *I.N.* 3 Nov. 1894. See also the prospectus for the new organisation (D.1792/C).
298. J. F. X. O'Brien to J. B. Armour, 22 June 1893 (D.1792/A1/3/27).
299. *I.N.*, 5 May 1894.

to make the terms of the inquiry as favourable as possible to the landlords. He condemned the Liberal Unionists, 'the decoy duck of the Tory party', for their land policy, and in particular for their expressions of satisfaction with the land courts. He appealed to his audience of farmers to present their case effectively to the Morley committee. As to the future, he repeated his belief in the need for compulsory purchase preceded by the reduction of all judicial rents, especially necessary in view of the twenty five per cent decline in agricultural prices since 1881 and the accompanying twenty five per cent increase in wages. He expressed his sympathy with the evicted tenants of the other provinces. He repeated his belief that only through the Liberal party would genuine land reform come and also his conviction as to the inevitability of Home Rule:

> It should come, and is coming as certain as that tomorrow's sun will rise ... . I am sure that
> a race of Presbyterians and Protestants worthy of the best traditions of our faith will arise in
> the near future, with their minds cleared of Unionist cant and blood purified from the rust
> of serfdom—and that they will claim to dwell in the land, not under the protection of the
> Saxon, not by permission of the Celt, but in virtue of the services they will render to a country
> which we love.[300]

Another similar meeting was held on 6 September 1895 in Ballymoney Town Hall, with Armour himself in the chair. His own speech and the speeches of W. H. Dodd and J. B. Dougherty were primarily concerned with the findings of the Morley committee. The majority report was given a qualified welcome and the hope was expressed that the anomalies revealed would be corrected by legislation on the part of the Liberal government as rapidly as possible. The necessity of maintaining the Liberals in power was stressed. One of the resolutions passed by the meeting regretted the failure of Gladstone's government of Ireland bill. There was also an eloquent plea by John Pinkerton M.P., the Nationalist member for Galway City, for co-operation between the forces of parliamentary Nationalism and Ulster Liberalism.[301]

This meeting was regarded as highly successful. Ulster Liberals believed that it represented yet another step towards a major political break-through and that the revelations of the Morley committee would be of further help.[302] However, the North Antrim Liberals, including Armour, were sorely disappointed by the refusal of John Morley to come north to speak to them.[303] John Pinkerton warned Armour in advance that he was likely to refuse and would thus miss a 'golden opportunity'. 'One meeting in Antrim would count for more in changing the political current than twenty in the south. If Mr Morley gave the northerners a chance of seeing and hearing him we could almost carry Ulster.'[304] The Ulster Liberals certainly believed that the Unionist opposition to the Morley committee would be a source of embarrassment to the Liberal Unionists.[305]

Their hopes were soon dashed. The general election of 1895 provided an opportunity of testing the solidity of the Liberal revival which had been at least partially inaugurated by Armour's stand at the March 1893 General Assembly. The Liberal and National Union of Ulster published a manifesto addressed to the electors of Great Britain, stating the case for Irish self-government and asking them to assist in putting an end to 'a vicious system of government that for nearly a century has impoverished our countrymen, overcrowded your labour markets and is depriving Great Britain of a valuable market for her wares'. Only by this means would Ireland become 'a profitable, helpful and really integral portion of the British empire'.[306] The Ulster Liberals contested four seats—North Derry, South Derry, North Tyrone and South Tyrone. There were allegations by Tim Healy that the Irish National Federation had, in effect, sold these seats to the Liberals, since the latter were not having to confront National Federation candidates.[307] Armour campaigned on behalf of Thomas Shillington in South Tyrone and

---

300. *Ibid.*, 6 April 1894.
301. *Ibid.*, 1 Sept. 1894.
302. W. P. Blair to J. B. Armour, 5 Sept. 1894 (D.1792/A1/3/32).
303. *Address to John Morley from the residents of Ballymoney and district, Sept. 1894* (D.1792/A2/30A-B).
304. John Pinkerton to J. B. Armour, 20 Oct. 1894 (D.1792/A1/3/33).
305. J. B. Dougherty to J. B. Armour, n.d. (D.1792/A1/1/8). 'Our Liberal Unionist friends won't like this tender subject to receive too much attention.'
306. The full text can be found in McCann, *Protestant Home Rule movement*, appendix V, pp 155-6.
307. See F. S. L. Lyons, 'The Irish parliamentary party and the Liberals in mid-Ulster, 1894' in *I.H.S.*, vii (March 1951), pp 191-5.

W. H. Dodd in South Derry, but to no avail since only Charles H. Hemphill in North Tyrone was able to win by a narrow majority of ninety one votes over his Unionist opponent, W. Wilson.[308]

The Ulster Liberal leaders remained optimistic, ignoring the fact that such success as they did achieve was dependent on the support of the Nationalists.[309] Even more significant was the defeat of the Liberal party in Great Britain and the ensuing decade of Unionist supremacy. The revived hope of Home Rule, so apparently potent in 1893, now withered completely. Liberalism in Ulster went into an eclipse from which it would not emerge until after 1900, and then only in the guise of the Russellite land purchase movement. It is of course doubtful whether the Liberal revival of 1893-95 was as impressive as it seemed. Those Presbyterians who supported it were less concerned with the virtues of Home Rule than they were with their own selfish grievances. As Oliver McCann has written: 'these people were prepared to accept any form of government, so long as their needs were satisfied'.[310] Even W. S. Armour admitted that his father was at no time 'a nationalist in the sense in which those steeped in Celtic traditions were. Refrains like "A nation once again" would have no appeal for him.'[311] Many of the farmers who attended the meetings of 1894 and 1895 were more interested in land reform than they were in self-government. As J. B. Dougherty remarked, 'these fellows will come and listen to you and then go away to vote against their own interests from fear of the Pope'.[312]

But it was not only Ulster Liberalism which withered after the 1895 election, J. B. Armour's political career followed suit. The most significant feature of Armour's life from 1895 until the onset of the crisis over the third Home Rule bill after 1910 was his virtual political abdication. That is not to say that he did not make occasional forays into politics, but essentially we are now entering a twilight zone as far as he is concerned. This was not immediately apparent, since at the General Assembly of June 1896 he was once again in the thick of political controversy. Rev. J. S. Mairs, on behalf of the Route Presbytery, had presented a memorial to the Assembly expressing concern at the depressed state of agriculture, stressing the need for immediate relief and asking that the Assembly should submit an opinion to the government on the matter. Rev. H. B. Wilson, on behalf of the Committee on the State of the Country, then presented five resolutions, linking an expression of thanks for the deliverance of Ireland from Home Rule with that of a qualified welcome for the land bill being currently considered at Westminster. A much more radical amendment, urging the government to place the land bill first in its legislative programme, stressing the maladministration of the previous land acts, criticising the details of the current bill, particularly with regard to land purchase, and pressing for the reduction of judicial rents was proposed by Rev. J. B. Thompson of Castlereagh. His amendment warned the government that unless adequate changes were made, 'the farmers will be ruined, or tempted by the delay or the absence of justice, to attempt courses which this church would deprecate, but could not prevent'.

Armour supported Thompson's amendment in a speech which contained a few of his characteristic sallies. He was highly critical of the committee's report and resolutions:

> The tenants were asking for a little piece of bread and that committee had given them a stone, with a little sauce of Unionist butter with great grace, through Dr Wilson and Dr Lynd. Stones, however boiled in butter, were stones still.

He stressed that they must be sympathetic to the grievances of all farmers in Ireland, not just those in Ulster. He expressed his regret that John Morley's bill had been frustrated by the fall of the Liberal government. The amendment was subsequently passed by 111 votes to 69, but a specially appointed committee then toned down some of its more extravagant language and it

308. The full results were:
    N. Londonderry: John Atkinson (U.) 4,763, Arthur Houston (G.L.) 2.538: *S. Londonderry*: Thomas Lea (L.U.) 4,485, W. H. Dodd (G.L.) 4,068; *N. Tyrone*: Charles H. Hemphill (G.L.) 2,948, W. Wilson (U.) 2,857; *S. Tyrone*: T. W. Russell (L.U.) 3,239, T. Shillington (G.L.) 3,046.
309. The Nationalists did get something in return. It is generally agreed that the election of Vesey Knox for Londonderry City was due to the support of a handful of Protestant Liberals who held an effective balance of power. See McCann, *Protestant Home Rule movement*, pp 125-7.
310. *Ibid.*, pp 123-4.
311. Armour, *Armour of Ballymoney*, p. 137.
312. J. B. Dougherty to J. B. Armour, n.d. (D.1792/A1/1/9).

was reintroduced, receiving unanimous support.[313]

After 1896 Armour entered a political wasteland and becomes lost to view until 1910. It is hardly surprising that he took no part in the activities of the Presbyterian Unionist Voters Association, formed in 1898, a product of the frustration of Presbyterians at their continuing inability to secure government patronage and political representation. Even though he had long shared this sense of frustration, as a Liberal he could hardly associate himself with the new organisation. He achieved some local notoriety because of his lukewarm attitude towards Britain's role in the South African war, which he viewed as an irresponsible imperial adventure even though he criticised the Boers for commencing hostilities. The war having begun, he hoped for a British victory for the sake of the future of the empire, but only on the basis of equitable terms for the defeated Boers. His hostility towards 'the cormorants that have fattened on the empire' did not endear him to some.[314]

Armour did not take a very active part in the Russellite land purchase movement after 1900 or in local Liberal politics during the crucial North Antrim elections in 1906 and 1910. Why should this have been so? Was it perhaps due to poor health? Up to 1908 he was certainly very active, playing golf as a member of the Royal Portrush Club, continuing to take classes at Magee College, riding a bicycle and walking long distances. But in that year he was told that he had a serious heart condition.[315] As a result he had to curtail some of his activities, such as his thrice weekly journey to Londonderry. However, it would be a mistake to suppose that he now became a house-bound invalid.[316] Indeed he was to live for another twenty years. During those years he threw himself into new struggles and accepted new responsibilities. From 1906 onwards he was one of the personal chaplains to the viceroy, Lord Aberdeen, and in that capacity he made frequent trips to Dublin.[317] From 1910 to 1914 he was a member of the newly created Queen's University senate and, after the passage of Lloyd George's national insurance act in 1911, he became an insurance commissioner for Co. Antrim.[318] He also busied himself with the exercise of government patronage through his influence with his old friend, Sir James Dougherty, who succeeded Sir Antony MacDonnell as under-secretary for Ireland in 1908, and he was particularly anxious to secure the appointment of Liberals to the magistracy and as lieutenants of counties. There is a nice irony about Armour, who had for so long complained about the use of influence to secure appointments, becoming part of such a process himself. W. S. Armour was confident that Dougherty and his father were both believers in appointments on merit.[319] However, Armour's letters show his understandable desire to secure posts for Liberals after so many years of Unionist domination. In the autumn of 1910 the death of John Cooke necessitated the appointment of a new lieutenant for Co. Londonderry. Armour, writing to his son William, commented that the government would find it difficult to replace him 'as the gentry of Co. Derry are all violent Tories and there is no outstanding Liberal in the co[unty]'.[320] There were two possibilities—Sir William Baxter, who had unsuccessfully contested North Antrim for the Liberals in January 1910, and David Hogg, a Londonderry businessman.[321] Baxter proved unacceptable because, despite his knighthood, he was a mere Coleraine shop-keeper. Hogg therefore was appointed,[322] especially since his Liberal credentials were impeccable—'a courageous man who kept his Liberal legs under him amid all the gusts of Toryism and terrorism which have been sweeping through the gates of Derry for the last fifty

313. *Witness*, 9 June 1896; *General Assembly minutes*, ix, 97-9 (1896).
314. Armour, *Armour of Ballymoney*, pp 141-5.
315. See J. B. Armour to Jane MacMaster, 28 Nov. 1908 (D.1792/A3/13/9). Armour had been to Oxford to see a specialist and wrote to Miss MacMaster from London to tell her the bad news.
316. Dr W. H. Belford, who treated him during the last months of his life, is adamant that even then he was remarkably healthy, given his age and his heart condition. Interview with W. H. Belford, 26 June 1976.
317. For example he attended a viceregal *levee* in Dublin in 1910 and again in 1912. He was also in Dublin during Asquith's visit in July 1912. See J. B. Armour to Jane MacMaster, 25 April 1910 (D.1792/A3/13/12); J. B. Armour to Jennie Armour, 20 July 1912 (D.1792/A3/3/23)
318. Armour, *Armour of Ballymoney*, pp 245-6.
319. *Ibid.*, p. 182. Armour's friendship with Dougherty may also have enabled him to influence Liberal ministers' attitudes, especially those of Birrell. Certainly Armour shared Dougherty's view that the Ulster Unionists were bluffing, a view not shared by all of Birrell's advisers. On this point see Patricia Jalland, *The Liberals and Ireland* (Brighton, 1980), pp 74-5; 135.
320. J. B. Armour to W. S. Armour, 1 Sept. 1910 (D.1792/A3/1/17).
321. David Cleghorn Hogg of Deanfield, Londonderry, was in fact Cooke's brother-in-law. He had for a number of years managed the Londonderry shirt-making firm of McIntyre, Hogg, Marsh and Co. (in which his brother Adam Hogg was the senior partner), and then had founded his own firm, Hogg and Mitchell of Great James Street. He was an elder of the First Londonderry Presbyterian congregation.
322. See *N.C.*, 17 Dec. 1910.

years'.[323] Sir Francis Macnaghten's death in July 1911 created a similar problem in Co. Antrim. Armour worked hard on behalf of Lord Pirrie. He was somewhat taken aback when the government appointed Lord Shaftesbury, formerly lieutenant of Belfast, and then put Lord Pirrie in his place.[324]

The relationship with Lord and Lady Aberdeen was quite a close one. Certainly Armour greatly resented the hostility shown towards them in Ulster and the reluctance of Unionist supporters to accept them.[325] When the Aberdeens visited Ballymoney on 21 November 1906 to declare the new technical school officially open, they took tea with the Armours in Trinity manse.[326] Armour's greatest regret was the critical attitude displayed by his fellow Presbyterians towards the lord lieutenant, especially since 'his exc[ellency] has given more places of honour and emolument to Presbyterians during his reign than all the Tory l[ord] lieutenants for 100 years'. Armour concluded that 'the people of Ulster are fit for an asylum'.[327] From the evidence of this wide range of activities, it is clear that even after 1908 he himself was ready neither for asylumn nor grave. He often used his health as a reason for not taking a more active part in events from 1911 onwards, for example in February 1911 he refused an invitation to a dinner organised by the Irish parliamentary party in London.[328] His excuse was probably genuine enough, but it is hardly a convincing explanation for the fourteen preceding years of virtually non-existent political activity.

W. S. Armour accounted for the gap in his father's political career in a rather interesting way. Describing R. G. Glendinning's Liberal victory in North Antrim in 1906, he suggested that his father stayed in the background, 'lest his outspoken declarations of the past should tell against Mr Glendinning and identify him with Home Rule'.[329] In other words J. B. Armour was too radical to associate with Glendinning and his supporters. It is true that Glendinning stood as an independent in the election and was careful not to become too closely tainted with Home Rule. Once the election was safely over however, he openly took his seat on the Liberal benches in the house of commons.[330] A meeting held in Ballymoney Town Hall on 25 November 1907, addressed by the new chief secretary, Augustine Birrell, provides further valuable evidence on this important point. The meeting was organised by the North Antrim Reform Association, Glendinning's newly-founded constituency organisation, and Armour was not one of the official speakers. Birrell was on a tour of the North Antrim constituency, accompanied by Glendinning, Dr Thomas Taggart, a Ballymoney solicitor and Glendinning's electoral organiser, John Baxter, a member of Antrim County Council and T. W. Russell, M.P.[331] Birrell visited Ballycastle to inspect the inadequate harbour facilities there and then moved to Ballymoney to inspect the new technical school. The meeting was attended by between 500 to 700 people and was chaired by John Baxter. The advertised speakers were Birrell himself, T. W. Russell, R. G. Glendinning, J. Williamson and lastly, Sir William Baxter, who was to move the vote of thanks to the others. All had gone smoothly until Sir William rose to speak, then a carefully planned, but apparently spontaneous, explosion of shouts of 'Armour' interrupted him and left him 'non-plussed'. Armour duly intervened from the floor and there followed what he subsequently described as 'the best speech I ever delivered'. He welcomed the apparent Liberal revival in Ulster; praised the Liberal cabinet's intellectual calibre; paid tribute to the political and social work of Lord and Lady Pirrie in Belfast, the city ruled by 'Pharisees, Sadducees and Philistines'; welcomed T. W. Russell as a lost sheep returned to the Liberal fold; and warned Birrell that 'he had a rough road to travel, beset by jackals, screech owls and bores but, as he had the intellect of a giant and the humour of a Samson, he would carry off the gates of Gaza'. Most significantly of all, Armour publicly identified himself with Glendinning, who, 'though a silent member', had proved himself to be 'one of the honestest, most attentive ... to the wants of all Ulster constituents'.

323. J. B. Armour to W. S. Armour, 22 Sept. 1910 (D.1792/A3/1/20).
324. J. B. Armour to W. S. Armour, n.d. (D.1792/A3/2/32).
325. See for example his reaction to Unionist opposition in Coleraine to a visit by Lady Aberdeen to attend a meeting about public health in which she was very interested. J. B. Armour to W. S. Armour, 2 Feb. 1911 (D.1792/A3/2/5).
326. *B.F.P.*, 22 Nov. 1906.
327. J. B. Armour to W. S. Armour, 2 Feb. 1911 (D.1792/A3/2/5). See also Lord and Lady Aberdeen, *Wee Twa* (2 vols., London, 1925).
328. J. B. Armour to W. S. Armour, 23 Feb. 1911 (D.1792/A3/2/8).
329. Armour, *Armour of Ballymoney*, p. 181. J. B. Armour, in a letter written to R. G. Glendinning in 1923, advanced a similar argument, see J. B. Armour to R. G. Glendinning, 24 Jan. 1923 (P.R.O.N.I., Glendinning papers, D.3208/1).
330. *B.F.P.*, 22 Feb. 1906.
331. A full report of Birrell's tour is given in *ibid.*, 28 Nov. 1907.

He stressed that in the event of another election, he would be returned with a larger majority than before. 'His [Glendinning's] followers were perfectly wild with excitement and the poverty of his own speech was more than covered.' So pleased was Glendinning that he sat beside Armour at a lunch for Birrell and Russell in Londonderry the following day.[332] There may be something in W. S. Armour's argument that Armour had been omitted from the list of speakers because he had gone farther in the direction of Home Rule than the local committee organising the meeting was prepared to go,[333] especially since most of the leading figures in North Antrim Liberalism in these years were rather timid home rulers, as an examination of the elections of 1906 and 1910 reveals. However, Armour's own accounts of the meeting suggest considerable personal animosity between himself and the leaders of the North Antrim Reform Association, whom he dismissed as 'intriguers'. 'The pagans', he wrote, 'took it into their silly heads to ignore me entirely' and these 'pagans' were not very happy about his intervention. They were 'glum as they had caught a tartar, but they had to keep mum.' Sir William Baxter's seconder 'must have felt sore at not getting his innings.'[334]

In the general election of December 1910 Armour had even less reason for staying aloof from the Liberal candidate in North Antrim, a young lawyer from a well-known local family, William Macafee.[335] Whereas Glendinning in 1906 and Sir William Baxter in January 1910 had played down the Home Rule issue, Macafee made no secret of his support for it.[336] Armour again did not become involved. He may have felt that Macafee was a lost cause, indeed he wrote to his son that only Glendinning would have had any chance of success. However, personal feelings also influenced his attitude:

> McAfee [*sic*] has been chosen to fight N[orth] Antrim—which seems to me a poor choice. I have no objection to the youth, but in the first place he has not money to spend on a campaign and in the second place Taggart could win no election, as he has no head and will take no advice from anybody. If he had any *nous* he might have won the last, in spite of Kerr-Smiley's dollars.[337]

This dislike of those in control of the Liberal electoral machine in North Antrim in these years is perhaps a further reason, in addition to the state of his health, why Armour found it 'a sore trial to be in the background of life and only to view the fight from a canoe among the reeds and rushes'.[338]

The increasing prominence of the Irish issue in British politics after 1910, and with it the possibility that a Home Rule bill might become law in the not too distant future, pushed J. B. Armour, despite his advancing years, back to the edge of politics again. Newspaper interviews and the General Assembly provided him with platforms from which to attack Unionism. A very full record of his thoughts during these tense and crowded years is provided both by the regular weekly letters which he wrote to his son William (who in 1910 had taken up an appointment with the educational service of the Indian government at Benares) and those which he sent to Jane MacMaster, his 'daughter dear'. He supplied both of them with his personal analysis of the current political situation as well as local and family gossip.

He opened his new campaign as early as 13 January 1910, with an attack on Presbyterian support for Unionism in a letter to the nonconformist journal, *British Weekly*. He suggested that Presbyterians had gone mad, since they were now supporting a party whose members were opposed to the taxation introduced by the Liberal government—taxation which would powerfully aid the cause of temperance. 'A church which tramples on its own principles, applauds its hereditary foes and becomes the henchman of a crew of conspirators against freedom is doomed as a force either in social or religious life.'[339] It was this by now familiar argument which

332. J. B. Armour to an unknown correspondent, n.d. (D.1792/A2/32); *B.F.P.*, 28 Nov. 1907.
333. Armour, *Armour of Ballymoney*, pp 185-6.
334. J. B. Armour to an unknown correspondent, n.d. (D.1792/A2/32).
335. William Macafee was the son of Thomas Macafee of Currysiskin, Ballymoney. He had been educated at Coleraine Academical Institution and Trinity College, Dublin, from which he graduated in 1899. He was called to the bar in 1901 and practised on the north-eastern circuit. He was also a member of the land commission.
336. *B.F.P.*, 1 Dec. 1910.
337. J. B. Armour to W. S. Armour, 23 Nov. 1910 (D.1792/A3/1/28).
338. J. B. Armour to W. S. Armour, 30 Nov. 1910 (D.1792/A3/1/29). Armour's personal dislike of Thomas Taggart, the principle Liberal organiser in North Antrim, is further underlined in the surviving fragment of a letter dealing with the meeting to protest against Carsonism, held in Ballymoney in 1913, in which he said of Taggart that 'he is lamentably lacking in good management'. See J. B. Armour to W. S. Armour, 27 Oct. 1913 (D.1792/A3/4/31).
339. *British Weekly*, 13 Jan. 1910.

galvanised the London correspondent of the *Northern Whig* into attacking the *British Weekly* for giving insufficient coverage to the arguments of leading Presbyterians who were opposed to Home Rule, yet being able to find space for Armour's letter, 'purveying much grotesque misrepresentation of the Ulster Unionists'.[340]

Just as Unionist anger in Ulster was at its height over the McCann kidnapping case in January 1911, Armour gave an interview to the *Daily News* which was to draw down much criticism on his head. In the interview he dismissed Unionist threats regarding the use of force as bluff, the result of 'a bad attack of *delirium tremens*'. He argued that fears concerning the religious persecution of Protestants, if Home Rule became a reality, were groundless. Protestants would have one quarter of the representatives in any Dublin parliament to protect them and look after their interests. Presbyterians, in particular, had nothing to fear, 'for under no conceivable circumstances could they have less recognition then they had during all the days of Tory rule in Ireland'. That Presbyterians should oppose the Liberals who had done so much for them in the past, that they should support the party of the brewers, was proof that they 'still deserve to be called "God's silly people" '.[341] The *Northern Whig* replied by republishing the anti-Home Rule pamphlet of 1887 which had been attributed to Armour in the past.[342] After threatening the newspaper with legal action, he did eventually extract a promise that they would never use the pamphlet again.[343]

In the early months of 1912 he was greatly incensed by Unionist threats directed against Winston Churchill's proposed Ulster Hall meeting, which eventually had to be held in Celtic Park, Belfast. He strongly believed that even many Unionists disapproved of what was 'an attack on the right of free speech', which stood out in sharp contrast to the tolerance shown towards Sir Edward Carson in nationalist towns such as Omagh.[344] When he met Lady Pirrie at the viceregal lodge in Dublin, he assured her that her husband's employees at the Harland and Wolff shipyard would, despite their politics, ensure that no harm came to her husband at the Churchill meeting.[345] He was equally vehement in his condemnation of the Presbyterian Unionist convention held on 1 February 1912. Some non-Unionist Presbyterians suggested that a special General Assembly should be called to discuss Home Rule, in order to outflank the convention. However, Armour opposed this idea for a number of reasons. He believed that it would be difficult to persuade the necessary four presbyteries to request the meeting in the first place and, even if this could be done, such an Assembly would be a disaster for the anti-Unionist minority. They would be placed in the uncomfortable situation of having to lead off with an official resolution. 'We would be hopelessly beaten if we proposed any policy but we might get a respectable minority by criticising "the die-hards".'[346]

As for the Presbyterian Unionist convention itself, he saw it not simply as a meeting to protest against Home Rule, but also as an attempt 'to find out what ministers have ceased to believe in their shibboleths and bring to bear on them a little boycotting for the honour of God and the good of their souls'. He believed that the most honest thing that the convention could do, would be to pass a resolution that 'nobody who is an apologist for Home Rule ... can ever enter the kingdom of heaven'.[347] In such an atmosphere of political hysteria he recognised that his son, Max, had no hope of securing a congregation in Ireland.[348] The hysteria was, he thought, all the more remarkable since he was personally convinced that the Unionists would accept Home Rule in some form, if they returned to office.[349] However, he was encouraged by the fact that some two hundred Presbyterian ministers stayed away from the convention. A number of them had in fact met together in advance and unanimously decided not to take part. Armour had been invited to this advance meeting but had declined, 'not from want of sympathy for the object but because my presence might do more harm than good'.[350]

In 1912 Armour contributed a chapter to a volume of essays, edited by J. H. Morgan,

340. *N.W.*, 14 Jan. 1910.
341. *Daily News*, 5 Jan. 1911.
342. *N.W.*, 6 Jan. 1911.
343. Armour, *Armour of Ballymoney*, p. 86. See also J. B. Armour to W. S. Armour, 26 Jan. 1911 (D.1792/A3/2/4).
344. J. B. Armour to W. S. Armour, n.d. (D.1792/A3/3/5).
345. J. B. Armour to W. S. Armour, n.d. (D.1792/A3/3/6).
346. J. B. Armour to W. S. Armour, 11 Jan. 1912 (D.1792/A3/3/7).
347. J. B. Armour to W. S. Armour, n.d. (D.1792/A3/3/5).
348. In fact Max was forced to go to South Shields.
349. J. B. Armour to W. S. Armour, n.d. (D.1792/A3/3/9).
350. J. B. Armour to W. S. Armour, 11 Jan. 1912 (D.1792/A3/3/7).

entitled *The new Irish constitution*. An examination of his arguments shows that they had changed little from those he had advanced in his General Assembly speech of March 1893. Certainly he saw Home Rule as a force for reconciliation, undoing 'the evils of the paper union of 1800', certainly he agreed that Home Rule would increase rather than diminish the commerce and trade of Ireland, but he also justified it on the grounds that it was the principle of Presbyterian church government applied to secular affairs and because it would benefit Protestantism generally by ending the political monopoly of Anglicanism, thus allowing Protestantism to be judged on its merits as a spiritual force. As far as Presbyterians were concerned, the vital consideration was that they 'cannot possibly under Home Rule have a lesser share in the offices of emolument and dignity than they have had all down the years from 1800 to 1912'.[351]

Another platform for Armour's views was provided by the meeting of the General Assembly in June, though events there took a rather unexpected turn. The Committee on the State of the Country, as had been expected, submitted a report condemning the introduction of the third Home Rule bill and Armour tabled his predictable amendment. However, an unofficial midnight meeting, engineered by Dr McIlveen, persuaded the principal antagonists to agree to a compromise. As a result the controversial sentences in the report were dropped and a paragraph was substituted to the effect that since the views of the vast majority on the Home Rule issue had already received expression at the February convention, the committee did not feel that it was necessary to make any statement on the subject. Consequently, the Assembly passed the amended report unanimously, both Armour and a leading Unionist layman, Thomas Sinclair, speaking for it. Sinclair and Dr McIlveen stressed that the compromise was intended to prevent a serious division within the church, not over the issue of Home Rule itself which very few Presbyterians supported, but because a considerable minority believed that political questions ought not to be considered by a church court. They thus argued that a vote on the original report would be dangerously misleading. Armour's emphasis was rather different—he saw the compromise as a victory for the right of private judgement, as well as a victory for those who wished to keep politics out of the pulpit, and he pleaded for the spirit of charity to prevail. The debate ended with the singing of the doxology as a token of harmony.[352]

Inevitably, this outcome was variously interpreted. Nationalists, as represented by the *Irish News*, saw it as a victory for Home Rule by default.[353] Unionists equally interpreted it as a victory. *The Witness*, while welcoming the spirit of harmony, warned that the decision would be misunderstood, since almost all of those who had opposed the original report had done so only because they had been unhappy about church interference in politics.[354] Armour, too, seems to have fallen victim to misinterpretation—exaggerating the size of the minority opposed to the original report and suggesting that had a vote been taken on it, the report would have been either passed by a very small majority or even rejected.

> The deliverance without real doubt meant that the Presbyterian church as a church refused to allow a discussion on a political issue in the General Assembly, and that the General Assembly did not reiterate or re-affirm the resolutions of 1886 and 1893.[355]

It has been suggested that the Unionists were biding their time, waiting for the right moment to strike, and that perhaps Armour should have considered pushing his point of view when circumstances favoured victory.[356] However, this would have gone against his principles. In any case, as the General Assembly in 1913 was to show, his support was not very great.

'Ulster day', or 'Protestant fool's day' as Armour termed it,[357] filled him with revulsion. He refused to have anything to do with it, or even to announce it in his church.[358] He was contemptuous of the local organisers and of the few ministers in the area who took part.[359] He felt that the clause in the Covenant, binding the signatories to use 'every means necessary' in

351. J. B. Armour, 'A Presbyterian view', in J. H. Morgan (ed.), *The new Irish constitution* (London, 1912) The draft of this chapter can be found in D.1792/B.
352. *Witness*, 11 June 1912; *General Assembly minutes*, xii, 350 (1912).
353. *I.N.*, 8 June 1912.
354. *Witness*, 11 June 1912.
355. *Scotsman*, 7 Nov. 1912. Letter from J. B. Armour.
356. Armour, *Armour of Ballymoney*, pp 262-3.
357. J. B. Armour to W. S. Armour, n.d. (D.1792/A3/3/25).
358. J. B. Armour to W. S. Armour, 24 Sept. 1912 (D.1792/A3/3/31).
359. J. B. Armour to W. S. Armour, 12 Sept. 1912 (D.1792/A3/3/29).

their struggle, was such that any Christian could not accept it. He was pleased that the whole affair made relatively little impact in the Route, especially since his political opponents blamed this on the 'wickedness inspired from Trinity manse'. 'Carson has not set the Route on fire—a sheer mountebank, the greatest enemy of Protestantism in my opinion existing, inflaming men to violence whom he will probably leave and desert if any difficulty arises.'[360] Outside his own area he was aware that 'the day will produce mischief in congregations as many ministers will refuse to hold services'. But he took comfort from the fact that 'the orange tail' was 'wagging the Protestant dog' and that even the Unionists were beginning to realise that 'Home Rule in some form is coming'.[361]

The beginning of the new year saw a by-election for the Londonderry City seat. Armour sent a letter of support to the Liberal candidate, David Hogg, for whom he had earlier obtained the county lieutenancy.[362] The political temperature continued to rise and although Armour still regarded Unionist threats as 'a compound of bluff and bunkum',[363] he lamented the intolerance shown towards those who were not Unionists, especially within the Presbyterian church. 'If Home Rule, when it comes, manifests the same spirit towards the Protestants that the majority of the Protestants is doing towards those who differ from them, well the Protestants will have no rational ground of complaint.'[364] It was this same spirit of intolerance which led to the Ballymena Presbytery's refusal to allow him to speak in Ballymena about the sustentation fund, of which he was synodical convener.[365]

An even more violent storm raged at the General Assembly in 1913. The Unionists were not prepared to accept a continuation of the compromise of the previous year. A memorial, signed by 131,351 Presbyterians, was presented by a number of Presbyterian laymen led by Sir William Crawford, asking that the Assembly should declare against the Home Rule bill and that it should set aside a special day of prayer for divine guidance. The Unionists felt this to be necessary because of 'misrepresentation and misinterpretation of the resolution of the last Assembly'. They felt that the compromise agreed on at that Assembly had enabled home rulers to claim that a substantial section of the church agreed with them, and that it had been this which had forced the Unionist members of the Assembly to retreat. No doubt the memorialists had been partly motivated by the letters which had appeared in the columns of the *Glasgow Herald* and *The Scotsman* from the moderator, Dr Montgomery, and the replies these had elicited from Armour. Montgomery had claimed that the Presbyterians of Ireland were largely against Home Rule, whereas Armour had cited the General Assembly of 1912 as evidence that the church was deeply divided on the issue. He asserted that the compromise had been suggested to avoid the rejection of the anti-Home Rule report of the Committee on the State of the Country, or at best its passage by a margin of a few votes.[366]

After the memorial had been read, a resolution, declaring that the Assembly's opposition to Home Rule continued to be 'as determined and unyielding as in the years 1886 and 1893', was proposed by Rev. William Park and seconded by R. T. Martin. Armour, supported by George Henderson of Randalstown and his own elder, John McElderry, countered with an amendment reaffirming the unanimous compromise decision of 1912. His speech was constantly interrupted by booing, catcalls and points of order. Armour and his allies in consequence saw themselves as victims of an attempt to deny them the right of free speech. Unionists argued that he had provoked the hostile reception by his outspoken remarks, that he had seemed 'more inclined to burlesque his opponents than defend his amendment and any audience might be excused for manifesting some irritation and impatience at such proceedings in connection with a serious subject in a church court'. Certainly his speech was vigorous and some of his comments barbed. Describing himself as a man of peace, he warned that such a man was liable to be hissed by geese that had got into the wrong yard. He accused his opponents of adopting the tactics of the suffragettes. Rev. William Park, he claimed, had falsified the truth—which was that many Presbyterians were not Unionists. He pointed out that the seemingly impressive figure of 131,000 signatures to the memorial was rather less so, when one recalled that a considerable

360. J. B. Armour to W. S. Armour, 3 Oct. 1912 (D.1792/A3/3/33).
361. J. B. Armour to W. S. Armour, 5 Sept. 1912 (D.1792/A3/3/28).
362. J. B. Armour to W. S. Armour, 15 Jan. 1913 (D.1792/A3/4/4).
363. J. B. Armour to W. S. Armour, n.d. (D.1792/A3/4/24).
364. J. B. Armour to W. S. Armour, 12 Feb. 1913 (D.1792/A3/4/7).
365. Armour, *Armour of Ballymoney*, pp 266-7.
366. *Scotsman*, 7 Nov. 1912; Armour, *Armour of Ballymoney*, pp 260-1.

number of episcopalians had signed it and that there were altogether 482,000 Presbyterians in Ireland. He reminded the Assembly that the vast majority of English-speaking people throughout the world was in favour of Home Rule, including leading American statesmen such as Theodore Roosevelt, W. H. Taft and Woodrow Wilson. He argued that seventy per cent of Presbyterians and other nonconformists outside Ireland were in favour of Home Rule because Unionist members of parliament had in the past been hostile to everything in which they were interested. The Unionists had opposed the Scottish temperance bill and the Welsh disestablishment bill and had supported Balfour's education act of 1902 and his licensing act of 1904. Yet they in that Assembly, he said, were ready to send back to parliament, 'the very same squad to tighten the chains of slavery on them and their children'.

Opposition to Home Rule, he believed, was merely a futile attempt by the landlord class to preserve their waning power. But Home Rule was bound to come, especially since the Unionists would be willing to introduce a bill of their own. He dismissed the fear of religious persecution by a parliament in Dublin as an illusion and pointed to the fact that the duke of Norfolk and other Roman Catholic peers had voted against the principle of Home Rule—clearly they were not expecting its introduction to lead to the 'enthronement of Roman Catholicism'. In response to an objector requesting that he keep to the point, Armour quipped: 'Well, Solomon, I'll try'. He concluded by defending the compromise of 1912 and warning against a political witch-hunt in the church. He suggested that the official resolution should be altered to read: 'No man who confesses to be a home ruler can ever enter the kingdom of heaven'.

At the end of the six hour debate, amidst scenes of great confusion, the amendment was declared lost on a show of hands and the official resolution decisively passed by 921 votes to 43. There were the usual claims that some who were in favour of the amendment did not vote, either through fear of intimidation, or as a protest against the stifling of discussion. The precise number of abstentions can never be known, though various estimates have been made. W. S. Armour asserted that 165 abstained, however there is no evidence to support this figure. Undoubtedly there were some who abstained but, as *The Witness* remarked, it is incorrect to assume that such men were all in favour of Home Rule. Some may have been unable to make up their minds; some were old-fashioned radicals who, although they were anti-Unionist, were equally hostile to Home Rule; some took the view that the Assembly should not involve itself in politics; and perhaps some were indeed intimidated. An attempt to have the names of those who voted, along with how they voted, published was defeated. The fact that it was suggested at all indicates the strong feelings and the tension engendered by the debate.[367]

The last major political event with which Armour was to be associated before the outbreak of the war was the meeting of Protestants in Ballymoney Town Hall on 24 October 1913 to protest against 'the lawless policy of Carsonism'. The meeting seems to have been originally the brainchild of Captain Jack White, D.S.O.[368] His autobiography certainly suggests this[369] and J. B. Armour's correspondence to his son William confirms it. However, almost simultaneously, Sir Roger Casement appears to have had much the same idea.[370] In their different ways both men were incurable romantics and they seem to have chosen Ballymoney as the venue for such a meeting largely because of its traditional reputation as a centre of radical, anti-Unionist politics. White's excursion into Irish affairs had begun on Saturday 4 May 1912, when a letter written by him as a protest against Unionist efforts to prevent Winston Churchill speaking in the Ulster Hall was printed in the *Ulster Guardian*.[371] He conceived of his role, as he always did, in grandiose terms. Although knowing little of Irish politics or Irish history, he confidently expected

367. *Witness*, 10 June 1913; *General Assembly minutes*, xii, 635-6; Armour, *Armour of Ballymoney*, pp 270-80.
368. White was the son of Field Marshal Sir George White, V.C., the 'hero of Ladysmith', whose family owned the Whitehall estate near Ballymena. As a boy he had always been a sore trial to his father and he attended a succession of schools, including Winchester, and was a success at none of them. A natural rebel and non-conformist, he nevertheless obtained a cadetship at Sandhurst where more adventures followed. He served with 1st Gordon Highlanders and 6th Mounted Infantry and won a D.S.O. under hilarious circumstances in South Africa in 1899. In 1902 he joined his father, now governor of Gibraltar, as his a.d.c., and here he met his future wife, Mercedes (Dollie) Mosley, a half-Spanish Roman Catholic. Following army service in Peshawar and Aberdeen, he abandoned his military career and adopted an unconventional life-style. Working at a variety of unusual, unskilled jobs and a course of intensive reading of Bergson and Marx in the British Library persuaded him to join a Tolystoyan anarchist community in Gloucestershire. It was from 'Whiteway colony' that he made his first excursion into Irish politics in 1912.
369. J. R. White, *Misfit, an autobiography* (London, 1930), p. 182.
370. J. B. Armour to W. S. Armour, n.a. (D.1792/A3/4/27).
371. *Ulster Guardian*, 4 May 1912. The *B.N.L.* had refused to publish it.

'parties and personalities to respond to the predestined something I felt in myself ... . With my bible and my shillelagh, I went to the Route to chase the most elusive of all hares, the spirit of "98".' This republican spirit, he had been assured, still existed in North Antrim, 'waiting for discovery'.[372] So the ex-soldier, ex-tramp, ex-lumberjack, a devotee of Bergson and Marx, fresh from a Tolystoyan community in Gloucestershire, accompanied by his half-Spanish wife, Dollie, descended on Ballymoney in his new two-seater Ford car. He found what he sought, or at least he thought he had. He obtained the support of Dr Thomas Taggart and of J. B. Armour. Both were far from enthusiastic however, especially about White himself, whom Armour subsequently described as 'peculiar'.[373] A committee was set up to organise a meeting which would demonstrate to the world that Carson did not enjoy the unanimous support of Protestant Ulster.

According to Armour's account, Casement had written to him about a week after White's visit suggesting a similar kind of meeting.[374] Brian Inglis plays down Casement's organisational role, simply referring to his having received an invitation to speak in Ballymoney, thereby implying that he had no hand in instigating the meeting.[375] It is clear from Casement's correspondence with Alice Green, who at his suggestion was invited to speak, that he played a more active part than Inglis allows, and also that his original conception of the meeting's function and purpose was rather different from that of the other organisers. He hoped, with the assistance of every drop of fenian blood 'in my soul', to 'light a fire' which would 'set the Antrim hills ablaze', and would 'unite (for I think it is possible) Presbyterian and Catholic farmers and townsmen at Ballymoney in a clear message to Ireland'.[376]

Armour and Captain White had to make it clear to Casement that an 'Irish Ireland' meeting was out of the question, and that his suggestion of either Lord Ashbourne or F. J. Biggar as speakers would not be appropriate, since the former was a 'papish' and the latter 'a crank—a banner and pipe maniac', as Casement put it to Mrs Green.[377] They counselled instead that it would be better to limit the attendance to Protestants, since this would ensure that the meeting's essential message was underlined—namely that not all Protestants supported Carson. Having visited Ballymoney, lunched with Armour at Trinity manse and talked to some fifteen local Liberals, Casement was convinced that a successful meeting was possible and that it would be the forerunner of similar meetings elsewhere in the province. These discussions settled the speakers and the resolutions but not who was to chair the meeting.[378]

White had not been present and characteristically objected violently to all the decisions taken and to Casement's role in particular. He believed that Casement was a wily, wrangling diplomat as well as a 'knight-errant'.[379] A stormy interview between the two men followed in Belfast, White accusing Casement of dishonesty and Casement feeling insulted. Casement had at first been well disposed towards him. 'Captain White is not a "lunatic"—but I am not very sure of his ability ... I don't think there is very much in him—save good will and a desire to knock Carsonism out, which is a good fighting instinct.'[380] However, after their disagreement Casement became convinced that White had, as Armour put it, 'a slate off'. Armour intervened and calmed White down by stressing that he would be the first major speaker. Casement refused to take the chair, as did John Baxter, who feared damage to his local business interests and felt that White was using the meeting as a stepping stone to contesting the North Antrim seat. Ultimately, the veteran Ballymoney Liberal, John McElderry, agreed to take on this task.[381]

It fell to Armour, through his friendship with Sir James Dougherty, to thwart an alleged Unionist plot to disrupt the meeting by importing 'a band of Orange rowdies with drums to drown the speakers'.[382] Armour, because of his influence with the Dublin Castle authorities was able to secure the assistance of some seventy extra police to restrict entry to ticket holders only and to prevent drumming parties ensconcing themselves in the Protestant Hall, which lay

372. White, *Misfit*, p. 182.
373. J. B. Armour to W. S. Armour, n.d. (D.1792/A3/4/27).
374. *Ibid*.
375. Brian Inglis, *Roger Casement* (London, 1973), p. 235.
376. Roger Casement to Alice Stopford Green, 21 Sept. 1913 (N.L.I., A.S. Green papers, M.S. 10464).
377. *Ibid*.
378. J. B. Armour to W. S. Armour, n.d. (D.1792/A3/4/27).
379. White, *Misfit*, pp 183-4.
380. Roger Casement to Alice Stopford Green, 29 Sept. 1913 (N.L.I., A. S. Green papers, M.S. 10464).
381. J. B. Armour to W. S. Armour, n.d. (D.1792/A3/4/28).
382. J. B. Armour to W. S. Armour, 16 Oct. 1913 (D.1792/A3/4/29).

just across the street from the Town Hall.[383] In the event the town was 'as quiet as on a Sabbath day',[384] and the only threat which the police had to deal with was that posed by two surveyors, whose car halted in the Diamond while the meeting was in progress. In the darkness the police mistook their theodolite and levelling staff for a dismantled Maxim Nordenfeldt gun, and were about to arrest both men when the mistake was realised.[385]

The Town Hall was bedecked with Union Jacks and a banner, hung above the platform, bore the legend: 'No provisional or provincial government for us'. Estimates of the attendance varied between 400 and 500, many of those present being farmers or businessmen.[386] Some in the audience had come from as far away as Co. Londonderry to attend. The meeting passed two resolutions proposed by John McMaster and seconded by Robert Carson. The first rejected the claim of Sir Edward Carson's provisional government to speak for the Protestants of north-east Ulster and pledged lawful resistance to any decrees issued by this illegal and non-representative body. The second was Casement's work.[387] It was basically a call for the rejection of sectarianism as a divisive force amongst Irishmen and an invitation to the government to help bring all Irishmen together 'in one common field of national effort'. In addition to the resolutions, Captain White launched 'the new covenant', which was an anti-Home Rule pledge closely modelled on the Unionist Covenant of 1912.[388]

The three principal speakers—White, Casement and Alice Green—all delivered stirring, if somewhat idealistic, appeals for love rather than hate amongst Irishmen.[389] They all made references to the 'spirit of '98' and the need to revive it. Indeed, one of the supporting speakers, William Macafee, was so carried away by this spirit that he attributed the Dungannon convention of 1782 to the United Irishmen rather than to the Volunteers. Since White, Casement and Mrs Green were all romantics, essentially out of touch with the realities of Ireland past or present, their emphasis was hardly surprising. It is also significant that they were not resident in Ulster and they had little experience of public speaking. This was Casement's very first speech,[390] and both he and Mrs Green had declined Mrs Armour's invitation to have a meal at the manse before the meeting, because 'both of us wish to be quite to ourselves before the meeting—with no one to talk to, or talk to us'.[391]

It was left to Alec Wilson of Belfast and John Dinsmore of Ballymena to inject a note of realism into what Armour termed a 'high toned' meeting.[392] Wilson stressed that he was anxious not just to protest against Carsonism, but to suggest a peaceful alternative. Many anti-Unionist Ulster Protestants had reservations about Home Rule, he argued, but they would in the end do their best to make the new proposals work. Carsonism, he claimed, certainly did not reflect 'decent Ulster opinion' and it had led Ulster into a *cul-de-sac*, since Home Rule was inevitable. The proposed provisional government, he said, was unrepresentative and 'could not so much as collect the taxes', and at the end of the day Carson knew he would have to surrender since the U.V.F. was designed only to be a useful bargaining counter. He deplored the vicious anti-Catholic propaganda put about by the Unionists, born as it was out of unreasonable fears. 'If you cut the Pope out of Irish Unionism there is nothing left but a handful of rubbish.' He stressed that these fears of 'Rome rule' were irrelevant since nationalism tended to reduce, not increase, clerical influence. Many Protestants, he suggested, had been coerced into signing the Covenant, but in a new Ireland Irishmen would be able to work together for the welfare of all, and a new and more normal party political system would emerge once the constitutional issue was taken out of politics. He concluded by asking that the meeting should be seen as the starting point of a movement for a peaceful settlement, which had to begin somewhere, sometime.

---

383.   J. B. Armour to W. S. Armour, 22 Oct. 1913 (D.1792/A3/4/30). The town commissioners had to meet the cost of the extra police.
384.   J. B. Armour to J. B. M. Armour, n.d. (D.1792/A3/4/33).
385.   *B.F.P.*, 30 Oct. 1913.
386.   *Ibid.; The Times*, 25 Oct. 1913.
387.   J. B. Armour to W. S. Armour, n.d. (D.1792/A3/4/28). Casement also seems to have considerably influenced the first resolution. White had originally wanted this resolution to register opposition to the 'lovelessness' rather than the 'lawlessness' of Carsonism and in his speech he dwelt on this theme at some length. See White, *Misfit*, pp 184-5.
388.   The full text of the 'new covenant' is to be found in appendix G.
389.   All the speeches delivered at the meeting were subsequently printed in pamphlet form. See *A Protestant protest* (Ballymoney, 1913); copy in P.R.O.N.I., T.2362/2.
390.   Inglis, *Roger Casement*, p. 238. Mrs Green also found it difficult to prepare her speech. See R. B. McDowell, *Alice Stopford Green: a passionate historian* (Dublin, 1967), p. 94.
391.   Roger Casement to J. B. Armour, 23 Oct. 1913 (D.1792/A1/3/57).
392.   J. B. Armour to J. B. M. Armour, n.d. (D.1792/A3/4/33).

> Let Ballymoney have the great honour of starting a campaign which will show the world that Ulster Protestants are out for the welfare of all Ireland, no matter what the form of Irish government may be, and still more, that Ulster Protestants are Ulster Christians working for peace on earth and goodwill to men.[393]

It is interesting to contrast the arguments of Wilson, an Anglican, with those of the Presbyterian Dinsmore. It was really left to him to state the Presbyterian case, since Armour did not speak at all. The familiar arguments about the evil influence of Belfast upon Ulster politics and upon the attitude of most Presbyterian clergy were once again deployed. The failure of Belfast to support the land campaign was put down to a desire on the part of Belfast mill-owners for a continuing rural depression which would provide them with cheap labour. Once in the towns, the working class, Dinsmore argued, were distracted from their poverty through careful sectarian manipulation. 'When they asked for bread they were given "The Boyne water".' The Pope, he suggested, was worth 'at least half a million per annum to the linen lords of Ulster. It is not loyalty these men are out for, it is loot; and the true protagonists in the struggle are not the puppet Carsons and Londonderrys, but the great linen magnates of Belfast.'[394]

The impact of the meeting was not as considerable as its organisers had hoped, indeed Armour complained of the poor press coverage even in the *Irish News*.[395] At Casement's suggestion the speeches were printed in pamphlet form for local distribution.[396] Captain White's hopes of an Ulster Hall meeting came to nothing. Casement was at first delighted and wrote to Gertrude Bannister next day of 'a grand success'. 'Hall packed—smiling, good-faced farmers of the Route in hundreds and a magnificent table of reporters! I never saw so many in a small hall.'[397] But his attempt to organise a similar meeting in Coleraine foundered on local opposition,[398] and White and he soon found more exciting employment elsewhere—White in Dublin as the founder of the Irish Citizen Army and Casement as a gun-runner. The meeting did not even seem so numerically impressive to some observers, especially when the Ballymoney Unionists were able to attract much greater numbers to a meeting which they held on 21 November. Both the Town Hall and the Protestant Hall had to be used to accommodate it.[399] Unionist reaction was hostile but on the whole realistic. The *Ballymoney Free Press*, by now a thoroughly Unionist organ, argued that the organisers had failed to demonstrate that the majority of Protestants in the district were in favour of Home Rule,[400] and even had they been able to do so, as *The Witness* put it—'the hum of a corner is not the buzz of a province'. *The Witness* also pointed out that some of those on the platform were individuals who had either been the recipients of posts from the Liberals, or were hopeful of such posts.[401] Very similar comments appeared in the *Northern Constitution*, which pointed out that the existence of a small body of Protestant home rulers had never been denied by Unionists—they were 'merely the exception which proves the rule that at least ninety out of every hundred Ulster Protestants are Unionists'.[402] But perhaps the most eloquent and objective assessment of all was that of the special correspondent of *The Times*. He drew attention to the fact that Ballymoney was the most favourable venue in the whole province for this kind of meeting:

> There is drilling here among the covenanters, but you see little sign of political enthusiasm in either camp. Every one seems to agree that all parties cultivate tolerance and an excessive aimiability ... . The promoters of the meeting could say—what indeed elections had already made known—that there are a good number of radicals, substantial people too,[403] about Ballymoney and district. Probably these men dislike the methods of the covenanters more than they like Home Rule, but that is another matter.[404]

393. *A Protestant protest* (P.R.O.N.I., T.2362/2).
394. *Ibid.*
395. J. B. Armour to J. B. M. Armour, n.d. (D.1792/A3/4/33).
396. Roger Casement to J. B. Armour, n.d. (D.1792/A1/3/58).
397. B. L. Reid, *The lives of Roger Casement* (New York and London, 1976), p. 179.
398. *Ibid.*, p. 180. Despite the Coleraine set-back, the Ballymoney meeting was a significant landmark in Casement's career. As Reid points out, it drew him into the mainstream of Irish politics and was a link in a chain of events which led ultimately to his execution.
399. *B.F.P.*, 30 Nov. 1913.
400. *Ibid.*, 30 Oct. 1913.
401. *Witness*, 31 Oct. 1913.
402. *N.C.*, 1 Nov. 1913.
403. As regards the 'substantial' character of those at the meeting, it is interesting to note that the platform party contained ten magistrates, one county councillor, one rural district councillor and three urban district councillors.
404. *The Times*, 25 Oct. 1913.

The editor of *The Times* was rather more scathing when he dismissed the meeting as representing 'a small and isolated "pocket" of dissident Protestants, the last few survivors of the Ulster Liberals of the old types. Ulster Liberalism is very like the Cheshire cat in "Alice in Wonderland". It has vanished till only its grin lingers furtively in a corner of Co. Antrim.'[405] This view was to be echoed by the 'official' historian of Ulster Unionism, Ronald McNeill, when he asserted that the 'little handful of cranks' who had met in the 'village' [sic] of Ballymoney had simply emphasised the unanimity of Ulster behind Carson.[406]

From Armour's point of view, there was to be a rather unhappy postscript to the Ballymoney meeting in 1916. Following Casement's arrest and the failure of the Easter Rising, R. D. Megaw, the son of Armour's former friend and political enemy, John Megaw, wrote to the *Northern Whig*, reminding its readers of Armour's connection with the 'traitor' Casement in 1913. But as Armour wrote to his son:

> There was nothing said by Casement or anybody else at the meeting for which there is any need of apology. If Sir Roger has gone wrong in the mind, we cannot help that any more than we can help R. D. M.'s stupidities.[407]

Throughout the remainder of 1913 and 1914 Armour was simply a spectator of events both in Ulster and Europe. He was contemptuous of the Ballymoney Unionist meeting of 21 November 1913, which was organised as a reply to the meeting of 24 October, attributing its success to the importation of large numbers of Orangemen from Ballycastle and Portrush by train and to the influence of 'John Barleycorn'. He alleged that the sitting member, Peter Kerr-Smiley, had, whilst drunk, delivered a speech written for him by W. J. Lynn, editor of the *Northern Whig*.[408] He was also concerned about the impact of Carson's tactics on dissident groups elsewhere in the world. 'Carsonism has something to answer for in regard to Larkinism, suffragettism and Hindoo [sic] unrest.'[409]

He still remained optimistic that a compromise settlement would be arrived at for Ireland, and he reacted sceptically to increasing discussion about the possible exclusion of Ulster from the Home Rule bill. He saw this suggestion simply as a Unionist ruse to wreck the bill—'an idiotic proposal'[410] to which he was violently opposed:

> The Ulster counties are dependent commercially on their neighbours ... Derry would be in a nice position as a deal of its trade is with Donegal ... . 'The Tories' want Ulster to commit suicide. But they are not sincere ... their whole design is to upset the parliament act. From a Protestant point of view, it would be calamitous as the Tories ... would give Catholics and Protestant home rulers no quarter and therefore ... would stir up the Catholics in the south and west to harass ... the scattered Protestants.[411]

He continued to believe that a last minute compromise was still possible and that if a plebiscite was to be held, the majority of the people of Ulster would vote against exclusion. He suggested that greater Protestant representation in the proposed Irish parliament could be the basis for such a compromise.[412] He stuck to his point of view right up to the outbreak of war. As late as 30 July, he was still convinced that 'if the bill was on the statute book, the excitement in Ulster would die down in a few weeks, as no sane person wants exclusion in any shape'.[413]

The war and its effects on the Irish situation merely confirmed Armour's political retirement. As an ardent imperialist, he followed the line taken by John Redmond, whom he greatly admired, and supported the war wholeheartedly.[414] The events of Easter week 1916 and the growing power of Sinn Féin were abhorrent to him.[415] He was increasingly critical of government policy which he felt was betraying Redmond and playing into the hands of the more extreme

405. *Ibid.*
406. Ronald McNeill, *Ulster's stand for union* (London, 1922), p. 138.
407. J. B. Armour to W. S. Armour, 17 May 1916 (D.1792/A3/7/14).
408. J. B. Armour to W. S. Armour, 27 Nov. 1913 (D.1792/A3/4/38).
409. J. B. Armour to W. S. Armour, n.d. (D.1792/A3/4/39).
410. J. B. Armour to W. S. Armour, 19 Feb. 1914 (D.1792/A3/5/9).
411. J. B. Armour to Jane MacMaster, 17 Mar. 1914 (D.1792/A3/13/14).
412. J. B. Armour to W. S. Armour, 11 Mar. 1914 (D.1792/A3/5/12).
413. J. B. Armour to W. S. Armour, 30 July 1914 (D.1792/A3/5/20).
414. J. B. Armour to W. S. Armour, 19 Nov. 1914 (D.1792/A3/5/31).
415. J. B. Armour to W. S. Armour, 17 May 1916 (D.1792/A3/7/14).

nationalists.[416] The failure to extend the same recruiting privileges to southern Irish as to Ulster regiments, the reprisals after the abortive rising of 1916 and the policy of coercion and threatened conscription which developed in 1918 were all, he believed, blunders. He had a blind spot as regards the increasing influence of Sinn Féin and failed to appreciate its latent strength and powerful emotional appeal.[417]

After 1918, because of his extreme age, his political involvement was restricted to his annual General Assembly speeches in which he invariably condemned partition. In 1920 he argued that the separation of the six counties from the rest would be a commercial disaster and a betrayal of the Protestants of the other twenty-six counties. He reminded his colleagues that Unionist tactics between 1912 and 1914 had established a model which Sinn Féin had simply followed. In this and other speeches he stressed that it was he who was now the genuine unionist, opposed as he was to the division of Ireland.[418] In 1921, while dismissing the new Northern Ireland legislature as a 'kind of bastard parliament', he returned to a familiar theme when he bewailed the fact that only a small number of Presbyterians had been elected to it. 'When you look at the result of the elections you find that you have practically handed over your destinies to what I call the landlord and Church of Ireland party.'[419] Perhaps his best known condemnation of partition came in 1923 when, during the debate on the report of the Committee on the State of the Country, he pitied the plight of the northern Unionists who, after yelling 'no Home Rule' for a generation, had been compelled to accept a form of Home Rule 'that the devil himself could never have imagined'.[420]

Armour's final speech at a General Assembly was not, however, on the theme of partition, but it was an appropriate farewell appearance for one who had championed the rights of Presbyterians throughout his life. On Wednesday 4 June 1924 Armour, as the senior synodical convener, moved the adoption of the Sustentation Fund Committee report. He took the opportunity to remind his audience of the discrimination which had existed in the past against Presbyterians, particularly in the matter of judicial appointments, and of how he had helped to secure the appointment of seven or eight magistrates in Co. Londonderry. He then sounded a warning:

> At the present time the government of Northern Ireland, through some of its servants, hardly allowed a Presbyterian magistrate to be made, and it was for that Assembly not to allow their church and themselves to be trampled upon ... . He would like to leave with them this idea, so that they might rouse themselves and announce that they would not be trampled upon by any church or party in the state, and do their best to have their people represented everywhere.[421]

Thus, he ended his career as he had begun it.

Ill-health now really began to take its toll. On 2 September 1925 Armour's letter of resignation was read to the Route Presbytery.[422] His retirement was somewhat marred by a dispute amongst his congregation as to his successor. One of the serious contenders was his son, Rev. Max Armour, but many were determined not to have another Armour in Trinity manse and in the end Rev. H. C. Waddell was chosen.[423] Despite his retirement, Armour remained fairly active, preaching on most Sundays. It is a tragic irony that it was as a result of accepting an invitation to a luncheon held by the Ballymoney Chamber of Commerce to honour the architect of partition, Sir James Craig, that he caught a chill which subsequently developed into pneumonia.[424] He died on 25 January 1928.

416.   J. B. Armour to W. S. Armour, 2 Aug. 1916 (D.1792/A3/7/23).
417.   J. B. Armour to W. S. Armour, 15 Aug. 1917 (D.1792/A3/8/28).
418.   *Witness*, 11 June 1920.
419.   Armour, *Armour of Ballymoney*, pp 328-31.
420.   *Witness*, 29 June 1923. A similar argument is developed in J. B. Armour to R. G. Glendinning, 24 Jan. 1923 (P.R.O.N.I., Glendinning papers, D.3208/1).
421.   *Ibid.*, 6 June 1924.
422.   *Session minute book, Trinity Church, Ballymoney, 1924-54.*
423.   The elders seem to have been anxious to secure a more pliable pastor than J. B. Armour had been, hence their unwillingness to support Rev. J. B. M. Armour. The congregational membership was artificially expanded in order to influence the outcome. All of this greatly angered J. B. Armour and he made his feelings known. In the end, J. B. M. Armour was called, but only by the barest two-thirds majority necessary and he declined to accept. See *The war in the Roddenfoot*, an anonymous poem, possibly written by W. S. Armour, recounting these events, which took place between 1 Sept. and 3 Nov. 1925 (copy of the poem in the possession of the author).
424.   Armour, *Armour of Ballymoney*, p. 372.

J. B. Armour then did not play the major role in north Antrim and Ulster politics that many contemporaries, and some historians since, believed he did. Nor were his motives and beliefs quite what they seemed to some. He was a complex character in a complex situation. His political career needs to be interpreted in the light of his aggressive Presbyterianism and his hostility towards the Anglican church, the landed classes and the Conservative political establishment, the triform devil incarnate which he spent his life fighting. In that struggle the violent and unyielding nature of his language indicated the intensity of his feelings. Nowhere in his life is there any evidence of a positive enthusiasm for the concept of Irish nationalism. Indeed Armour conceived of Home Rule as a means of strengthening rather than weakening the bonds between Ireland and Britain, hence his attitude to the outbreak of war in 1914 and to the rise of Sinn Féin. He also conceived of Home Rule as a means of emancipating Irish Presbyterianism from the Anglican thrall in which he at least was convinced that it was still held fast. How else can one account for his gradual disenchantment with Liberal Unionism between 1886 and 1892?

As we have seen, his attitude towards his Roman Catholic fellow countrymen was a somewhat ambiguous one. Certainly he shared the hostility of his idol, Gladstone, towards the doctrinal tenets of their faith, although he was prepared, arguably for sound Presbyterian reasons, to support the Roman Catholic university scheme, just as he was prepared to encourage (tacitly) the growth of the Independent Orange Order. His views on the land issue were unexceptional and mirrored those of the society in which he lived and laboured. Undoubtedly, his attitude towards the property rights of the landlord class was conservative and his role in the north Antrim land reform movement was always a secondary one.

He dropped out of both the land agitation and local political activity in the late 1890s, staying aloof from the Russellite land purchase movement and from the briefly successful Liberal electoral challenge in his own constituency in 1906. In part, this may have been because of his close identification with Home Rule at a time when Ulster Liberals were attempting to play this issue down, but it seems certain that personal disagreements with the local Liberal leadership were also to blame. Instead, he contented himself with his annual appearances at the General Assembly, where he obviously delighted in living up to the reputation which his clerical colleagues, his political opponents and the press had created. One must presume that being a legend in one's own lifetime has its attractions. It is of course entirely appropriate that this most Presbyterian of Presbyterian politicians should have preferred the cut and thrust of the Assembly to the crudities of the hustings. It is even more appropriate that his conduct in connection with the three most significant events of his political career—the 1893 General Assembly, the Presbyterian Home Rule memorial to Gladstone and the anti-Carson rally in Ballymoney in 1913—should reflect his Presbyterian exclusiveness.

There is, however, an alternative interpretation which could be put forward to account for the colourful twists and turns of Armour's career. It is hard to resist the feeling, and it can be no more than a feeling, that he was motivated not only by deeply held principles, but by his natural nonconformism. One is also led to speculate as to what extent he had been disappointed in his life. He had been forced into a career which he perhaps may not have really wanted and had been forced to live in a small town far removed from the centre of the political and religious stage. Only in the Aberdeen years did he bask in the warmth of official favour, and even here what is most significant is the partisan enthusiasm with which he indirectly dispensed government patronage. But generally he was at his bitter and brilliant best in opposition—to landlordism, to Anglicanism, to Home Rule, to Unionism and to the General Assembly, often against the tide.[425]

---

425. For a more detailed discussion of County Antrim politics during Armour's lifetime, readers should consult J. R. B. McMinn, 'The social and political structure of north Antrim in 1869' in *The Glynns*, 10 (1982), pp 11-22; J. R. B. McMinn, 'The myth of "Route" Liberalism in County Antrim, 1869-1900' in *Eire-Ireland*, xvii, no. 1 (1982), pp 137-49; J. R. B. McMinn, 'Liberalism in north Antrim, 1900-14' in *I.H.S.*, xxiii, no. 89 (May 1982), pp 17-29; J. R. B. McMinn, 'The Land League in north Antrim, 1880-82' in *The Glynns*, 11 (1983), pp 35-40; J. R. B. McMinn, 'The Ballymoney meeting of 1913—a nationalist mirage?' in *The Glynns*, 12 (1984), pp 34-9; J. R. B. McMinn, 'John Pinkerton: an Ulster Unitarian at the court of "King Charles", 1886-1900' in *Eire-Ireland*, forthcoming. A general discussion of Ulster Presbyterian political attitudes in the late nineteenth century can be found in J. R. B. McMinn, 'Presbyterianism and politics in Ulster, 1871-1906' in *Studia Hib.*, xxi (1981), pp 127-46. F. Thompson, 'Land and politics in Ulster, 1868-86' (Ph.D. thesis, Queen's University, Belfast, 1982) is a very useful treatment of the land question and its impact on Ulster political life during the earlier years of Armour's political career.

CLASSIFICATION SCHEME (D.1792)

A	Correspondence	
A1/1-3	Letters *to* Rev. J. B. Armour, as follows:	
A1/1	1878-1928	26 letters to Rev. J. B. Armour from Sir James B. Dougherty, including letters to Mrs Armour and W. S. Armour on the deaths of J. B. Armour and Mrs Armour respectively.
A1/2	1893	31 letters to Rev. J. B. Armour from Ulster Home Rulers supporting a Presbyterian address in favour of Gladstone's second Home Rule bill.
A1/3	1876-1928	Letters to Armour from various correspondents.
A2-3	Letters *from* Rev. J. B. Armour, as follows:	
A2	1859-1928	Originals of letters from Armour to others, including 13 letters to his friend, John Megaw of Ballymoney, but excluding letters to members of his family or to his relative, Jane MacMaster (the sister of Professor James MacMaster, Armour's wife's brother-in-law).
A3/1-13	Originals of letters from J. B. Armour to members of his family and relatives, as follows:	
A3/1	1903-10	Letters from J. B. Armour to his wife and sons (principally to W. S. Armour).
A3/2	1911	,,
A3/3	1912	,,
A3/4	1913	,,
A3/5	1914	,,

A3/6	1915	Letters from Armour to his wife and sons, with the copy of an address to Lord Aberdeen.
A3/7	1916	Letters from Armour to his wife and sons.
A3/8	1917	"
A3/9	1918	"
A3/10	1919	"
A3/11	1920	"
A3/12	1921-7	"
A3/13	1892-1924	Letters from Armour to Jane Mac-Master.*
A4	1910-18:N.D.	Letters and fragments of letters from Mrs J. B. Armour.

— 0 — 0 — 0 —

B	N.D.	Drafts by Rev. J. B. Armour for sermons and political speeches.
C	N.D.	Printed and photographic material and other miscellaneous items relating to Rev. J. B. Armour's career.
D.	N.D.	'Notes on the life of J. B. Armour, M.A.', by his son, J. B. M. Armour, M.A., B.D.
E	1811-1902	Genealogical and miscellaneous papers about the Armour and Stavely families, including McLeod/Stavely emigrant letters.
F	1851 1954	File of miscellaneous papers, including W. S. Armour correspondence.

* This is the last section of the papers covered by the detailed calendar which follows.

D.1792/A1/1/1-23

1878-1928

Letters to Rev. J. B. Armour from Sir James B. Dougherty, under secretary for Ireland, including letters to Mrs Armour and W. S. Armour on the deaths of J. B. Armour and Mrs Armour respectively.

D.1792/A1/1/1

16 December 1878

Letter from J. B. Dougherty, 36 Cranmer Street, Nottingham, to Armour,

asking Armour's opinion of his chances of securing the chair of logic and English at Magee College, Londonderry, likely to become vacant as a consequence of an imminent reshuffle made necessary by the death of Professor Richard Smyth on 4 December 1878. Dougherty also refers to Armour's appointment as headmaster of Ballymoney's newly created intermediate school and asks him to do his best to support Sir Thomas McClure, who was contesting the Londonderry county seat which Smyth had held for the Liberals. McClure polled 2,479 votes as against the Conservative Samuel M. Alexander's 1,878.

'... You will see that, in the event of Cuskery being appointed to Smyth's chair, I shall become a candidate for the logic chair. It would suit me better than the one for which I ran last June and the reasons which induced me to stand then, exist in full force still. But I don't mean to be beaten a second time if I can help it, and I don't want to spend much money or do much *"Kotoing"*. What is your opinion of the situation? Do you think any strong opponent is likely to come into the field? If you think I ought to run, will you kindly stand to me as you did before.

I have read your obituary of [Professor Richard] Smyth today. It is the best of the lot by a good long way. Your Ballymoney brethren are rather weak.

What row have you had in Presbyterian circles in B[ally]money? I have had vague references made to it from time to time in recent letters but they assumed a knowledge which I don't possess. I hear you are at the head of the new school. How does it progress? I hope you will be able to make it pay.

Can you do anything for Tim McClure in Derry? It is the duty of every patriot to do his best to weaken and discredit the present government—the most shifty, mendacious, reckless and incapable administration of our time.

I have had an anxious time for some months over some business matters here and in America which took me to Ireland in a hurry in October. Things are pulling all right again I am glad to say but we must get the present government out to secure a return of commercial prosperity.'

D.1792/A1/1/2

[n.d. 1879?]

Letter from J. B. Dougherty, 37 Lonsdale Street, Belfast, to Armour,

possibly discussing Dougherty's campaign to become professor of logic and English at Magee College, Londonderry. Dougherty had entered the Presbyterian ministry in England, following his graduation from Queen's College, Belfast, and had resided in Nottingham for a number of years—indeed he had met and married his first wife Mary Donaldson there. The campaign which seems to be outlined below was successful and Dougherty held the Magee professorship until 1895.

'I am very sorry that I did not see you. Munro has sent me a good testimonial. Moffett has sent me to-day what Madill in his telegram calls an exceedingly good one.

*Trinity Presbyterian Church and manse, Ballymoney, County Antrim,
as it was in J. B. Armour's day.*

Shaw has declined to give Andrews of P[orta]down a testimonial on the ground that he would not interfere publicly in the election of his successor, and feels bound by this pledge. He says he is decidedly of opinion that I am the most eligible candidate and will say so to anybody who thinks his opinion worth having. He is writing to Orr of Portaferry, Beattie of Ballycopeland *etc.* and will write to any fellow-student or Magee College men whom I think he can influence. But he doesn't want to come into collision with Witherow. Can you suggest any names I could ask him to write to. If you think of any, send them on tomorrow afternoon to me care of Dr Macleod, 49 Shrewsbury Road, Birkenhead, so that I might get it on Monday morning. I am crossing tonight with Tom Dickson M.P. I think I shall try to fix him for a seconder. It would turn the tables on Charlie Morell which would be an advantage.

If anything strikes you, write. If I come over the Monday of the Assembly I think that must serve. I don't see that I could do anything by coming sooner. If Leslie doesn't send me testimonial in next day or two, shall run up to London and see him. I wrote to old Henry to post his testimonial to Nottingham. What am I to do with him? If he doesn't show up on Monday or Tuesday should I write or get somebody to call?

P.S. I think I shall try to get Hans to do something for me in the *Morning News*. Would it be fair and worthwhile to get him to run a-muck at Park with whom he's certain to be in a bad temper?'

D.1792/A1/1/3

25 May 1891

Letter from J. B. Dougherty, Liscarton, Shankhill, Co. Dublin, to Armour,

written on notepaper inscribed 'Educational Endowments (Ireland) Commission, 23 Nassau Street, Dublin' discussing the problems confronting the traditional Presbyterian policy of promoting united or mixed secular education (with separate provision for religious instruction) as opposed to the Anglican and Roman Catholic preference for denominational education. Dougherty was at this time a member of the Educational Endowments (Ireland) Commission (1885-92). He feels that frontal assaults on A. J. Balfour, chief secretary for Ireland, by Presbyterians are pointless and that private rational discussion with him might result in a compromise especially on the denominational training colleges issue. Dougherty also comments on the developing political crisis in the North Antrim constituency provoked by Charles Connor's selection as the Unionist candidate for the forthcoming general election. The constituency's Presbyterian Liberal Unionists, such as Armour, had been trying to promote J. J. Shaw, a Presbyterian lawyer, as a more acceptable alternative. Dougherty believes, rightly as it turned out, that in the final analysis Shaw will not run as an independent, but that the Liberal Unionists have the opportunity to use him to force Connor's retirement in favour of John Atkinson, solicitor-general for Ireland.

'I have no views on the education question, but a very distinct opinion that no amount of blethering about united education will get us much "forrarder" at the present moment. It is a pity that our friends in the North will not take the trouble of mastering the facts of the situation. They do not appear to be aware, even, that what they are protesting against has been actually in operation since September last and being acceptable alike to Roman Catholics and Episcopalians, is little likely to be abandoned at the demand of the Presbyterians. I should have thought that a wise course for us at this time would have been a private conference on the whole subject and afterwards an interview with Balfour to submit to him definite proposals as to what might be considered necessary to safeguard the interests of the church. But it appears the policy of the el[ementar]y ed[ucatio]n c[ommissione]r was to give Balfour another private lecture by Petticrew and Magill on "united secular and separate religious instruction". I understand that as Balfour had enjoyed a similar treat about a year ago he has respectfully declined its repetition on the present occasion. We are called upon therefore, to raise a public "howl" which is either fanatical folly or, as a game of bluff, a piece of weak dishonesty. If we approached Balfour in a practical spirit, I am quite sure he would discuss the difficulties which Lord Spencer's policy in recognising the denominational training colleges has created for us, in a friendly spirit, and some practical solution satisfactory to us as a church and no way hurtful to what remains of united education might be arrived at. But senseless heroics that have no relation to existing facts seems more in vogue than practical suggestions of any kind and I presume we are destined to make a laughing stock of ourselves on this as on every other public question.

I think you are mistaken in not using Shaw's candidature to effect a compromise. Of course he will not fight. Where is the man who will? If you do succeed in finding a candidate in the Irish condition of blue-moulding for want of a [?]. Will your position after defeat be better than if you now succeeded in compelling the withdrawal of Connor and the substitution of a candidate whom you might not altogether like but in whose choice you would have had some say. John Atkinson [solicitor-general for Ireland] would be a very good man and his selection would almost to a certainty leave a vacancy very soon for which you might, in altered circumstances, be able to make a better fight.

Peace with honour is your only policy now and the selection of the s[olicitor] g[eneral] would give you that. That is my opinion as an outsider. I have come up here till August 1, to escape railway travelling for a while. I may see you at the Assembly.'

D.1792/A1/1/4

[n.d. 25 May 1892 ?]

Letter from J. B. D[ougherty], Shelbourne Hotel, Dublin, to Armour,

discussing the possibility of persuading Rev. John D. Osborne, minister of Rutland Square Presbyterian Church, Dublin, to write a testimonial in support of W. H. Dodd's candidature in North Antrim. Although Osborne was not a home ruler, as this letter admits, he did in fact write in support of Dodd's personal character and the missive became something of a *cause celebre* in the election campaign. Dougherty also refers to the matter of the Erasmus Smith schools and in the process reveals a distinct anti-Anglican attitude which of course Armour shared. (*For the text of the Osborne letter see Appendix A.*)

'I have just got your letter as I am leaving town. John called yesterday and told me you had written him. I fancy he had been cautioned against writing pastorals as he told me he had had a letter from W. [?]. He also said that he was not a home ruler as he regarded Home Rule as great nonsense. I replied, I don't think you owe the other people much. That is perfectly true, said he, and if I could serve Dodd I should be very glad. I impressed upon him that what was wanted was not a political declaration but a testimony as to Dodd's personal merits and this I am pretty sure he will give. Don't press him and if he hasn't done anything at the Assembly we can get him to do what is right.

I shall be in Derry for a week anyway.

I have no doubt Munn (?) would have managed the Erasmus Smith business very much better than I have done. At the same time if we are only wise, things may come right. If however, there is the faintest indication of difference of opinion or of a readiness to march to the tap of the big drum, we shall be allowed to contend for Protestant interests, to our heart's content and our friends of the said church will sail off with the booty and with fingers outspread for more. I saw H. B. [Colvin ?] yesterday and warned him against any discussion in the Assembly. The committee should instruct counsel, keep its case to itself, let the other people imagine they are going in for the [Solicitor ?] and accept a fair compromise when it is proposed. Wilson agrees with me and I think will control Martin.'

D.1792/A1/1/5

[n.d. spring 1893 ?]

Part of a letter from J. B. Dougherty to Armour [date and address torn off],

making suggestions as to the mechanics of preparing, organising and presenting the proposed Presbyterian memorial to W. E. Gladstone in support of Home Rule.

'Will something like this do? It should be written out in foolscap by a practised hand and signed in alphabetical order. My idea is that you should retain the signatures, simply giving their number in the letter and enclosing [*page torn*] the letter. Can you get some practised penman, say an attorney's clerk, to do it?

Of course this is assuming that we should not think of the *deputation*. I am not quite clear whether some of us should not write to Gladstone's private secretary, explaining how the matter stands and asking him what course we should [*page torn*] are quite content [*page torn*] it by letter. What say you to this? If it strikes you as necessary—after what Bryce said—you might write at once addressing

> Private Secretary,
> Prime Minister,
> Downing Street.

I could write to Herbert Gladstone whom I know a little.

The time for presenting it [*page torn*] for a counter demonstration. Alter this letter as you like, for it has been written hastily.

I am sorry I could not send it sooner—why don't you come over next week to lunch; we can offer you a bed as we are moving into a larger house.'

D.1792/A1/1/6

[n.d. spring 1893 ?]

Letter from J. B. Dougherty, College Avenue, Londonderry, to Armour,

enclosing the draft of the covering letter to accompany the proposed Presbyterian Home Rule memorial to Gladstone and commenting on its content, in particular its emphasis on the need for a revision of judicial rents rather than compulsory sale. He suggests various ideas as to how and where signatures to the memorial might be obtained and feels that the collection of 1,000 signatures would be a considerable achievement.

'Will something like this do? Make any corrections and amendments you like and let me have result.

I should be satisfied with first paragraph alone but I suppose our agricultural friends would not. The second par[agraph] might be made shorter perhaps, but I think it desirable to rub in "revision of judicial rents" as compulsory sale is played out.

When you have settled this you can send copy to Stewart Hunter and set about getting it signed in your own district. I will see what can be done here. It is desirable signatures should be on separate sheets which can be afterwards pieced together. There should be a good many signatures to be got in Newtownards neighbourhood, and in other parts of Co. Down. If we could get 1,000 signatures, it would be a great success ... .'

D.1792/A1/1/6A

[n.d. spring 1893 ?]

Enclosed draft of the covering letter referred to in the previous letter,

explaining the nature of the Home Rule memorial and the reason why it has been decided not to seek a personal interview to present it. The letter also stresses the spontaneous and relatively unorganised manner in which the signatures have been collected and emphasises that these signatures indicate that Ulster Presbyterians are by no means unanimous in opposing Gladstone's Home Rule proposals.

'Sir, we have been requested to place in your hands a declaration expressive of gratitude to and confidence in you as well as of approval of the policy of the party of which you are the trusted and honoured leader, which has been signed by [*left blank*] members of the Presbyterian Church in Ireland in connexion with the General Assembly.

It was our intention to seek a personal interview in order to present it, but upon reflection we have been unwilling to make any unnecessary demand upon your time and strength which have been, of late, so severely taxed.

You will be interested to know that these signatures have been freely tendered without any public solicitation and without the intervention of any organisation which might have reached many districts in Ulster that are not represented on this list. We trust that the spontaneous character of the movement may enhance the value in your eyes of a declaration which we ask you to accept as an assurance that the great benefits which your statesmanship has already conferred upon our country are remembered with gratitude by our people, and that your present effort to secure the better government of Ireland has a large measure of sympathy even among those who are sometimes represented as entirely unanimous in offering a relentless opposition to the Irish policy of the Liberal party, we have the honour to be, sir, your obedient servants.'

D.1792/A1/1/7

[n.d. 9 July 1893 ?]

Letter from J. B. Dougherty, Buncrana, Co. Donegal, to Armour,

discussing the progress of collecting signatures to the memorial and arguing that it should be left up to Gladstone to decide whether or not it should be presented to him by a deputation.

'I send the names. Patterson has still some to forward. I dare say they may be forthcoming in a day or two but as he goes in for collecting all over the country you will need to see that they are not duplicates of signatures already obtained. I dare say there might be some trouble in organising a deputation and that our friends might be irritated by our taking this course. But they will be irritated in any case and we need not consult *their* feelings over much. I think from what Bryce said, Gladstone will not care to add to his labours at the present moment by receiving a deputation, but on the whole we are bound to ask him *how* he will receive the requisition and this should be done in such a way as to leave our friends no ground for saying that he had snubbed us by declining to receive us. It must be put to him as a matter for his own convenience in which he is to be supreme judge. Will you write to him when you have the signatures, in this sense and let us be guided by his reply? Have you a copy of your notice of Witherow in the [*Northern*] *Whig*? If so, can you lend it to me? I shall take care of it and return it.

I am going to Dublin on Wednesday but expect to return on Friday or Saturday.

Kind regards to the wife.'

D.1792/A1/1/8

[n.d. 24 April 1894 ?]

Letter from J. B. Dougherty, College Avenue, Londonderry, to Armour,

briefly commenting on Armour's address to a meeting of farmers at Ballynure, Co. Antrim, which had evoked violence—indeed Armour's hat had been struck by a stone—and contrasting this with his own more peaceful reception at a similar Liberal meeting in Portadown. Dougherty draws attention to the political capital to be made out of Unionist opposition to the land bill introduced by the Nationalist Dennis Kilbride and to the committee of inquiry into the land question set up by the Liberal chief secretary, John Morley. He also suggests that the Ulster Land Committee should choose its representatives to give evidence to the Morley committee with some care—Liberal leaders lacking in mental dexterity, such as Rev. Richard Lyttle of Moneyrea, should be avoided.

'I hope you will not refuse the proffered hand. Don't put any obstacle in the way of these people terminating their absurdities. One ought to be thankful for a gleam even of returning sanity.

I should have congratulated you upon your escape at Ballynure. I fared better at Portadown. All was serene within and without. There was a very fair report with bad occasional blunders in the *Irish News*.

Our friend Jeffrey was at Acheson's for tea when I called. I had advised him to keep out of the way. There was no need for him to get himself into hot water on my account.

The opposition to Morley's committee and Kilbride's bill ought to be well rubbed in to the farmers. Our Liberal Unionist friends won't like this tender subject to receive too much attention.

I am going to London next week. I shall have a look in at the Synod which I have not seen since I left it and I shall come in for a political reception at the National Liberal Club to Lord Rosebery and Co. on May 9. What do you think and come over for a holiday? I expect [Thomas] Dickson will be in London about that time.

Are you going to that committee in Belfast on Friday. They would be the better of a little guidance. I hope they will not nominate too many witnesses. They should send one or two men to speak to (?) principles and the rest of the witnesses should be farmers with a grievance. You may depend upon it, the witnesses will be severely heckled and only fellows with their heads screwed on the right way need be sent. [Rev. Richard] Lyttle, for example, would be made a holy show of.

Let me hear the result of the great hand-shake.

Kind regards to the wife.'

D.1792/A1/1/9

[n.d. 29 July 1894 ?]

Letter from J. B. Dougherty, College Avenue, Londonderry, to Armour,

referring to his efforts, at Armour's request, to use his influence to secure the commutation to life imprisonment of the death sentence passed on John Gilmour at the Belfast Assizes for the murder of Lyle Gardiner. The letter also obliquely hints at the basic sectarianism which underlies the thinking of the North Antrim farmers who attend Liberal land reform meetings.

'I have written the chancellor. The executive will be guided largely by the judge and I fear you will have uphill work with him. The insanity point seems to me the only one that can be pushed unless capital punishment is to be abolished altogether.

I have not written Fitzgibbon because I don't believe it would be of any use. He would not interfere in such a case and if he did would produce no effect. The Gibsons and he have no great love for one another, witness Bewley's production of his private letter at the Land Commission.

We go to Bushfoot on Wednesday. I suppose the 16th will do as well as any other day but what is the need for a meeting at all? These fellows will come and listen to you and then go away to vote against their own interests from fear of the Pope.

[T. W.] Russell is playing a funny game.

We shall see you during August, I hope. When are these Berwick people coming? Kind regards to the wife. Hope she enjoyed her London trip.'

D.1792/A1/1/10   **Letter from J. B. Dougherty, College Avenue, London-**
                                                   derry, to Armour,

[n.d.]

referring to a letter which he has sent to the *Northern Whig* praising S. C. McElroy and the Route Tenants Defence Association. He argues that the land issue is the only one which the Ulster Liberals can exploit to gain access to the readers of the *Northern Whig, Londonderry Standard* and *The Witness,* which after 1886 were all Unionist in their political sympathies.

'I have sent a brief note to the [*Northern*] *Whig* full of affection for Sam [McElroy] and his association and explaining, not apologizing or retracting. I hope he will like it. Our only chance of access to the readers of the [*Northern*] *Whig, The Witness* or [*Londonderry*] *Standard* is to take advantage of such opportunities.

May be I could take a day's golfing at Portrush when you are settled. Let me know what days would suit you best. The *Standard* is ferocious this morning. Did you ever see anything weaker than the *Echo*? These people are evidently beside themselves with fear.'

D.1792/A1/1/11   **Letter from J. B. Dougherty, Chief Secretary's Office,**
                                                   Dublin Castle, to Armour,

[n.d. 29 October]

responding to a request from Armour to use his influence to secure the appointment of an unnamed individual to an official position which may become vacant in the near future. The letter is an interesting example of Armour's fairly successful attempts to set himself up as an unofficial purveyor of government patronage via Dougherty, though in this instance the latter obviously has some doubts about the soundness of Armour's candidate. Dougherty was appointed assistant under secretary of state for Ireland by John Morley in 1895 before the fall of the Rosebery government and Armour then began to try to redress the balance of government appointments in Ulster in favour of the Liberals and Presbyterians. The date of the letter is uncertain, though Dougherty does make an oblique comment about a committee of inquiry into the land question and is rather scathing about the calibre of the tenants' representatives who had given evidence to it. This might possibly be a reference to the Morley Committee which reported in 1895.

'It is not certain that the vacancy for which Gibson wishes to name a candidate will occur. At all events the present holder of the office who is retiring voluntarily has asked the government to hold its hand for the present. I fear, however, it would take more witching horsemanship than [?] to land your man a winner. He is honest and capable, I agree, but he is occasionally wrongheaded and always obstinate. He has an unhappy knack of getting into rows, a thing abhorrent to the official mind, and I fear would be little likely to be thought of for an office which requires exceptional tact and temper. All the same he would have my best wishes though I greatly doubt whether I could give them any practical effect.

The Belfast enquiry was a sad fiasco. It is due to the fact that the people making the tenants' case are fit for little but the manufacture of gas of a very low illuminating power.

Todd among other elements of genius does not include the faculty of taking pains.

We are all well, with very kind regards to you all.'

D.1792/A1/1/12   **Letter from J. B. Dougherty, Chief Secretary's Office,**
                                                   Dublin Castle, to Armour,

9 November 1903

discussing the government plans to reform higher education in Ireland—an issue which had caused successive administrations heartburn ever since the failure of Gladstone's 1873 proposals. When the Unionists re-opened the issue after 1900 they encountered predictable difficulties, as Dougherty's letter indicates. Trinity College, the Catholic hierarchy and the Ulster Unionists all had axes to grind. The 'egregious representative' of the last-named group, whom Dougherty refers to, is presumably the member for North Antrim, William Moore. This opposition had delayed the reform and Dougherty fears that this delay may be fatal since the future of the Unionist government itself, torn by internal strife over Joseph Chamberlain's tariff reform scheme, is by no means assured and may indeed depend upon the Irish Nationalist party, though it too is threatening to become divided as a result of William O'Brien's activities. However, Dougherty and his colleague Sir Anthony MacDonnell are not totally downcast. In any reform scheme they favour generosity towards the Presbyterian Magee College, to be balanced by similar treatment of St Patrick's College, Maynooth. Dougherty presses Armour to persuade the Presbyterian lobby to take a realistic view—advice which Armour followed at successive General Assemblies from 1900 onwards. In supporting Catholic endowment, Armour was abandoning his own previous traditional Presbyterian preference for non-denominational 'mixed' education. It is interesting to speculate how far this was due to Dougherty's urgings.

'Many thanks for y[ou]r budget. The scene changes from day to day but things are at present less hopeful for the scheme than when I last wrote. In the first place T.C.D. is growling ominously. Next the bishops are not quite a happy family, and there is a large body of Catholic opinion more in favour of the Catholic college within the R[oyal] U[niversity] than of the broader and bigger proposal. Lastly it looks as if Ulster, including that egregious representative of yours, would fight. But beyond and above everything is the condition of the gov[ernmen]t. It seems hardly possible that they will be allowed to keep open for an indefinite length of time an issue so vital to the trade of this country as that which they have raised. Chamberlain, who does not expect to win the next election, and who is an old man in a hurry, will, I suspect, be anxious to see an early appeal to the country. Balfour, who seems anxious to postpone that evil day, could only carry on next session with the aid of the Irish vote. And now W. O'Brien threatens the destruction of that valuable asset. Altogether, it is a mad world. Taken at the best, and with the large assumption that the government will survive another session, it is hardly conceivable that they will take up a burning question which is certain to create another fissure in the party; in that case if their courage was equal to the heroic attempt, they have enough steam left in their boilers to fight through the enormous difficulties of the subject. The u[nder] s[ecretary] has not lost hope or heart, but that is about all that can be said.

He is inclined to treat Magee Coll[ege] fairly, though it is a difficult subject. However, it occupies a pretty strong position because its friends could make a strong opposition to any scheme that would propose to leave it out of account. Even the president of Q[ueen's] C[ollege] B[elfast] recognises, I think, the folly of the Commission in proposing to deprive it of privileges it has enjoyed for twenty years. However, there is a desire to get somehow for the students of Maynooth the benefits of a wider culture. All the more enlightened Catholic opinion favours this and lay opinion is very strong upon this point. But nothing can be done for Maynooth that is not done in a measure for Magee.

I think the great thing is to let our people know that there is a university question to be settled, quite apart from the Catholic demand; that the present state of affairs is thoroughly unsatisfactory and that a reasonable solution of the difficulty would be welcomed by Presbyterian opinion. To reaffirm your traditional position, to talk rot about "the nationalisation of Trinity College", a phrase which nobody understands, or to proclaim your undying opposition to Catholic endowment while a Jesuit college is working away with the goodwill apparently of everybody, on an endowment of £6,000 odd a year, would be a sorry contribution to the controversy. Take the broader view and claim that in any settlement the vested interests of Magee College shall be duly respected and you will have done a very good day's work that may bear fruit though I hardly think this harvest is at hand.'

D.1792/A1/1/13

12 January [19] 04

Letter from J. B. Dougherty, Chief Secretary's Office, Dublin Castle, to Armour,

appealing again to him to use his influence with the General Assembly's Higher Education Committee to persuade it to compromise on the government's university proposals. The southern Unionist landowner, Lord Dunraven, was at this time pursuing his 'conference plus business' approach in an attempt to break the educational deadlock just as he had broken the land reform deadlock. Dougherty again attacks the Presbyterian demand for the nationalisation' of Trinity College, Dublin, a demand which to some extent derived from anti-Anglicanism. Finally, he suggests that the chief secretary, George Wyndham, will be writing personally to the moderator to put the government's case.

'There is reason to believe that the R[oman] C[atholic] bishops will unanimously accept Dunraven's letter as the basis of a settlement of the university question. Do you think there is any chance of your H.E. Committee doing likewise? I think they should not miss an opportunity and if they disagree with any of the proposals or wish any safeguards that are not provided, let them say so. We have had enough of blethering resolutions about nationalizing Trinity College which the proposers could not tell the meaning of. Now let us have something definite.

I think the [chief ?] s[ecretary] will write to the moderator. You might let me know what you think and if you agree try to get a meeting of the committee.'

D.1792/A1/1/14

25 January [19] 05

Part of a letter from [J. B. Dougherty], Chief Secretary's Office, Dublin Castle, to Armour,

discussing the possible dates on which the sectarian faction fight at Garvagh (1813) had taken place. Garvagh was of course Dougherty's birthplace.

'My dear Armour, I had an idea that the "battle" of Garvagh—one of the decisive battles of history—was fought in *1812*. But I have got out the *Freeman's Journal* file. I find that those who had taken part in this affray were put upon their trial in April 1814 at the spring assizes. In the report it is stated that two bills had been found at the previous assizes which would be the summer assizes of 1813 and it is further stated that the fight took place "in July last" that is, July 1813. I hardly see how bills could be sent up at the summer assizes 1813 for a riot which took place on the 26th July 1813—the date of the fighting fair, but it may be that the summer assizes were held later in those days than now as the spring assizes certainly seem to have been. Unfortunately the papers for 1813 are missing from the file so that I have no account of what took place at the assizes of that year or of the fight itself which, however, would hardly be reported in a Dublin paper. On the evidence, as it stands, therefore, I accept the date 26 July 1813 as the date of this momentous battle.

I have spoken to [Sir David] Harrel about Carson. It appears ... .'

D.1792/A1/1/15

[n.d. 12 March]

Letter from J. B. Dougherty, Chief Secretary's Office, Dublin Castle, to Armour,

commenting on a request from the latter to secure the appointment of a friend to an official post--another example of Armour's role as a link in a Presbyterian/Liberal patronage chain, which was a rather ironic position in view of his past condemnations of similar Anglican/Conservative chains.

'I will take a note of what you say about your friend and if an opportunity occurs will use it for his benefit. I do not know what chance there is of any permanent appointment being made soon. These are not cases in which I can do very much and the man most likely to be successful given a fair record—is the man who has the most numerous and influential friends, parliamentary and other, outside official circles. I think you will see a land bill before the measures you anticipate are undertaken. But there is no saying what we may be driven to; you can't allow pandemonium to be set up at your back door. We are nearly through the festivities, I am happy to say, and I have got through them well. In spite of many indiscretions I am a great deal better than I have often been at the close of the season.

Give my kind regards to the wife.'

D.1792/A1/1/16	**Letter from J. B. Dougherty, Chief Secretary's Office, Dublin Castle, to Armour,**
27 August [19] 10	

dealing with further requests from the latter regarding patronage—in particular the reappointment of the young Ballymoney lawyer, William Macafee, to the Land Commission (Macafee subsequently fought the North Antrim seat as a Liberal in the general election of December 1910). Dougherty is able to reassure Armour that the Ballymoney Unionist lawyer, R. D. Megaw, will not be appointed. He also refers to the continuing controversy in the Queen's University, Belfast, senate over the position of the newly established university lectureship in scholastic philosophy. Armour was of course a member of the senate at this stage. Finally, Dougherty thanks Armour for his congratulations on being made a K.C.B.

'I will speak to the chancellor and the attorney about McAfee [*sic*]. They generally reappoint but owing to deaths and promotions they have this year at least four places at their disposal, but of course there is the usual clamourous crowd of hungry applicants. [R. D.] Megaw, I fear, will have to wait till his friends return to power which is not likely to be tomorrow.

I had a communication about King-Kerr from Lord Shaftesbury among others but it came too late for the recent batch.

I will see what can be done about the city magistracies.

I had a letter from [Sir Samuel] Dill the other day. He is heartily sick of the affairs of the university and I think contemplates washing his hands of the business. This would be a great pity. I hope you will get your compromise carried. [Rev. Thomas] Hamilton would be wise to fall in with it. I am surprised that John P[ark] is favourable. I understand that he has been at the bottom of most of the trouble. Hamilton must repent of not having retired him years ago under the '65 rule. He and I have saved his professional neck for the last four or five years and this is our reward!

My honour came altogether unexpectedly. I had no notice of it till I received the prime minister's letter on Wednesday last, and I do not yet know who set him in motion, though I have a strong suspicion it was A. B[irrell]. The additional "K" does not butter many parsnips, but it gives some members of my family infinite content that I am lifted out of the ruck of "ordinary" knights. Yours faithfully.'

D.1792/A1/1/17	**Letter from J. B. Dougherty, Under Secretary's Lodge, Phoenix Park, Dublin, to Armour,**
15 August ? [19] 13	

referring to Armour's defence of Home Rule at the General Assembly in June and lamenting that so many in the Presbyterian church, even amongst its young men, oppose self-government for Ireland. Dougherty expresses his intention of visiting Ulster in the near future but once again reiterates his view, which may have influenced both the chief secretary, Augustine Birrell, and Armour considerably, that the Ulster Unionists are engaged in a gigantic game of bluff. He is reassured by arms seizures in England which he feels have effectively prevented the Ulster Volunteer Force from replacing their wooden rifles with the real thing. It is certainly interesting that Armour in his public utterances and private letters expressed derisory views, similar to those expressed in this letter by Dougherty, about Unionist plans for resistance.

'I am glad your heroic struggle in the Assembly has produced no ill effects. You and I are not so young as we were and as you had been ["?"], I confess to having felt some misgivings as to the wisdom of your taking part in these stormy proceedings. It takes a good deal out of me to face a howling mob, and I know no worse mob than the Assembly when the fathers and brethren let themselves go as they seem to have done on this occasion. But you are well through the ordeal and you deserved, at least, the success which it was not in your power to command. Some day or other the unwisdom of the attitude of the Presbyterian church in this question will be known and read of all men. It's a pity the young men had not more backbone, but I suppose it would be unfair to expect too much from them. Their names would have been published and life would have been made unendurable for them. That creature McCullagh pestered us for years till he got a J.P. out of us. He could not get it from Shaftesbury or his Tory friends! Martin acted after his kind. Dill says he is a Co. Down Orangeman of a malignant type.

I want to go down to the North some time soon. Birrell is a bit anxious about things. He takes this Ulster *gasconade* more seriously than I am disposed to do. I don't know what the real secret of this importation of arms may be. I am sure it is not for purposes of warfare. They are weapons of an obsolete type discarded by the Italian army and bought at a cheap rate in a job lot from some German dealer in old metal. But they look like the real thing and I strongly suspect they were intended to replace the wooden guns which have furnished so much food for laughter. If they had been got through, the Ulster Volunteers would have appeared with them some fine morning—probably in July—and we should have been asked to behold a citizen army *under real arms*. If that was the game it has been spoiled. We have got 5,000 or 6,000 shipped via London, and we shall probably get hold this week of a small consignment which has been lying at Newcastle for six weeks watched carefully by the police who had no power to seize.

I saw that our friend [Rev. J. D.] Houston was the only man at the Assembly who had the courage to sound a warlike note. What a warrior he has become!

I am glad you have W[illiam] back again safe and sound. Please give him the enclosed note, with best regards to all.'

D.1792/A1/1/18   **Letter from J. B. Dougherty to Armour,**

[n.d. 15 December 1915 ?]   analysing the current political situation and in particular the fall of the Asquith coalition and its replacement with that headed by Lloyd George. He is rather pessimistic about the future of the new government and accurately diagnoses Lloyd George's now precarious political position. Dougherty was Liberal member of parliament for Londonderry City from 1914 to 1918.

'We have been passing through strange and exciting times. It seemed at one moment as if the pilot would weather the storm but the conspirators had laid their plans too well, and when the Uriah Heep of Tory politics, after all his professions of loyalty to the coalition, capitulated to Carson and with his colleagues sent an ultimatum to A[squith] there was nothing for it but resignation. Asquith to the chagrin of the Liberal [?] marched out with bag and baggage (including the Liberal funds!) and left Lloyd George at the head of this curiously composite administration. The Tories will press next for a general election. *They think* they could sweep the country, and if they succeed in their plans and the result is as they anticipate they will give short shrift to the little Welsh attorney whom they hate and never will fight. Meanwhile we sit till Christmas Eve and then parliament is to be prorogued. How long the recess will last I do not know.

I have been under the weather a little with a sort of influenza cold which in this vile climate one can't throw off but it is a common case.

My wife had to start for Bournemouth suddenly on Sunday evening week when an old and favourite cousin was dying of pneumonia. Before she got to her bedside her cousin had passed away. On Tuesday last she had a telegram from Dublin that her brother was dangerously ill with little or no hope of his recovery. She started that night and found things as bad as they had been reported. All this makes our arrangements for Christmas very uncertain. I am sorry for Mrs Dodd's death. The latest rumour is that William Moore is to be the new solicitor-general. This will be regarded on all sides as an atrocity. With all good Christmas wishes for the wife and yourself.'

D.1792/A1/1/19

[n.d. spring 1917 ?]

Letter from J. B. Dougherty, 15 Lancaster Gate, London W2, to Armour,

entirely devoted to personal news and gossip, apart from a few brief comments on Lloyd George's precarious political position at the head of his coalition government.

D.1792/A1/1/20

25 July 1917

Part of a letter from [J.B. Dougherty] to Armour, [written on house of commons notepaper],

describing his experience of German air raids and air raid scares in London and outlining his holiday plans and those of his family. He expresses pessimism about the likely outcome of the Irish Convention and comments on the manoeverings within the coalition government to shore up Lloyd George's position.

'... No bombs fell in our neighbourhood but we had a liberal supply of shell fragments from our own anti-air-craft guns which kept firing all the time without doing anything more than endangering the lives of any of the citizens adventurous enough to take their walks abroad while the battle lasted. We took refuge in the basement while a big ugly fragment of shell fell in our area. It was all over in ten minutes. The soldier says the Shoebury experts estimated the speed of the aircraft while flying out of range passed Shoebury at eighty miles an hour while when flying over London the speed was never less than seventy-five. To the uneducated eye they seemed to hover over the doomed city as if to pick and choose where to drop their bombs but this was an optical illusion. Last Sunday morning ... we had another alarm but it proved to be only the firing of blank bombs to give us notice that the raid which terminated at Harwich might reach London. People rushed to the tube stations and other places of refuge but we remained in bed till the "all clear" signal was given by policemen marching through our square with big placards on their broad backs. These experiences are getting on the nerves of the women folk and it is fortunate the holidays are no near. We will not be able to go to Ireland *en famille* this year; Elsie goes to Scotland to visit a school friend at Aberdeen. The Missus and Aileen make for Cornwall at the first of August. I shall join them a week or so later and perhaps in September I may run over to Ireland for a few days. We tried the Giant's Causeway Hotel but they could not take us in August.

What of the prospects of the convention? I take little stock in it, I don't see how anything can come of it while "Ulster" hankers after the clean cut. It may be, however, that Carson has [?] some wise successful. We must wait and see.

The great man [Carson] has been kicked upstairs into the war cabinet, where this great master of strategy will have full scope for the exercise of his abilities. But he made a poor show at the Admiralty, where to say the least he did not outshine his predecessors. L[loyd] G[eorge] has evidently begun to feel a little lonely in his present company and has taken Winston [Churchill] and Montague to his bosom. The Tories are furious. But they cannot help themselves. The time for dropping the great man overboard and leaving the Tory war in [?] procession has not yet arrived. What angers them is that L[loyd] G[eorge] has no doubt seen through their little game and quietly anticipated schism by strengthening the Liberal element in his company. He and his government have come badly out of recent events. They have lost ground greatly and there are many people who predict that they will not last beyond [?] if in the meantime they achieve no striking military or naval success. This prediction is likely enough to come true ... .'

D.1792/A1/1/21   **Part of a letter from J. B. Dougherty to Armour,**

[n.d. 1922 ?]   commenting on the death of Arthur Griffith and its likely reprecussions in Ireland and discussing the current state of the Ulster problem.

'... Last night the evening papers brought the news of Arthur Griffith's death. How does fortune favour poor old Ireland. I had no implicit faith in him but he was the best of the gang and the strongest (?) bulwark against the absurdities of that madman de Valera. Fortunately the people, who have been in the power of his irregulars, seem to be thoroughly disgusted with them and him. But who will step into Griffith's shoes? I absolutely distrust the postman.

Ulster seems to be a little question of late—there might be some faint hope of the future if their lordships of Down and Derry would withdraw their boys and allow Devlin and his merry men to take their seats in the Ulster parliament. They could soon assert themselves and teach their Orange friends to respect them and to shape their policy with a little more regard to the rights and interests of the minority. But their l[ord]ships are adamant, I am told, and I suppose the Ulster welter must go on till the contending factions learn more sense ... .'

D.1792/A1/1/22   **Letter from J. B. Dougherty, 25 Lytton Grove, Putney Hill, SW 15, to Armour,**

15 July 1924   commenting on the esteem in which Armour in his old age is now held by the General Assembly and analysing the increasingly rapid demise of their colleagues of 1860 at Queen's College, Belfast.

'... You failed to honour your self-denying ordinance to keep silent at the Assembly. One way and another you made considerable drafts upon the attention of "the fathers and brethren" which I was glad to see they fully honoured. After a stormy passage you seem to have reached in the Assembly that happy haven where all would desire to be—an abiding place in the goodwill and affection of your fellow-members. That is as it might be for as one door after another closes against us old fellows near the end of our pilgrimage, a hearty, friendly reception at those which are still open to us is very welcome ... .

The class of 1860, as the Americans say, has dwindled sadly and the wastage must inevitably proceed at an accelerated pace. We may be pardoned for thinking it was a great class well worthy of having a "Who's Who" all to itself. ...'

D.1792/A1/1/23   **Letter from J. B. Dougherty, 25 Lytton Grove, Putney Hill, SW 15, to Armour,**

19 December 1925   largely devoted to comments about the failure of Max Armour's attempt to become his father's assistant and successor at Trinity Church, Ballymoney. He also discusses the failure of the Boundary Commission.

'... I am sorry you have had to navigate troubled waters recently. Max was here some time ago and gave us a racy account of the transactions which seem to have stirred Ballymoney society to its depths. It must have been a trying time for you. But all's well that ends well, and in this affair the ending, I sincerely believe, has been for the best. Apart from the gratification which it would have been for you and his mother to have had Max as your assistant and successor, there was nothing to be said for his transfer to B[ally]money. I didn't wish to say anything harsh about the capital of the Route—in which you have spent your days, but recent occurrences compel me to declare that I could not wish my worst enemy a more unhappy fate than to be sentenced for life to dwell in that abode of envy, malice and all uncharitableness, however camouflaged (as Kennedy McKay said of Dr Morgan) by "assumed sanctity and pretended piety". Max has done and is doing good work in S[outh] Shields. He will be told to go up higher in due time ... . It is pleasant to hear that you like the prospect of having [Rev. H. C.] Waddell as coadjutor ... .

So there has been another "final" settlement of Irish affairs. The Boundary Commission has ended in the best possible way. They were set an impossible task and any readjustment of the boundary could only have made confusion more confounded. The bomb of the *Morning Post* was therefore a blessing in disguise. What a fool that man [Eoin] McNeill has made of himself. It is quite clear that Feetham captured him at an early stage by securing his adherence to a preliminary declaration of principle by which the commission were to be guided and it is fairly certain that he approved by appending initials to the boundary line as drawn. It was a dirty trick of McNeill to round on his colleagues when he found that Cosgrave and Co. disapproved of his action. But he is now put on the shelf for his natural life ... .'

D.1792/A1/2/1-31

1893

Letters to Rev. J. B. Armour from Ulster home rulers supporting a Presbyterian address in favour of Gladstone's second Home Rule bill.

D.1792/A1/2/1

3 June 1893

Letter from William Houston, Carnmoney, [Co. Antrim], to Armour,

agreeing to sign the address and pointing out that many of the Protestant home rulers in the area are Unitarians and 'of course are not eligible to sign'. He promises to supply Armour with the names of potential signatories in the Larne and Glenarm district and includes a list of likely individuals in the Ballyclare and Doagh areas.

D.1792/A1/2/2

6 June 1893

Letter from [T. ?] Irwin, Newry, [Co. Down], to Armour,

declining to sign the address and pointing out the social pressures which could be exerted upon those who do sign.

'I have gone to the friends in town whom I know to be in sympathy with your views; but none of them feel inclined to sign this address ... I am a partner in a business with three others, none of whom take any prominent part in politics. Were I to sign this without consulting them and that by any chance it should come out that I had done it and any injury to our business result ... I cannot face to take such a risk. Nothing else restrains me. I make no secret of my opinions and sympathies. ...'

D.1792/A1/2/3

9 June 1893

Letter from Rev. Richard Lyttle, Moneyrea, Comber, [Co. Down], to Armour,

sending names of possible signatories, 'Presbyterians who are sound in the Home Rule faith', and commenting on the June General Assembly debate on Home Rule in which Armour did not himself speak.

'I congratulate your party on the magnificent fight which you made this forenoon in the cause of Irish liberty ... . I fancy Mr Houston's [Rev. J. D. Craig Houston] speech will read well. As for Professor Dougherty's oration—it was a masterpiece. I was disappointed in not hearing the Rev. Champion from Ballymoney. ...'

D.1792/A1/2/4

10 June 1893

Letter from John Orr, Saintfield, [Co. Down], to Armour,

expressing his sympathy for Armour's views on the Home Rule question and his thanks for Armour's services to the cause of the tenant farmers.

'... I am in full sympathy with the matter ... which you have so nobly and ably advocated, believing that the only source of happiness and peace to this divided country of ours is in the people being allowed the management of their own affairs. Also in regard to the land question I believe that something definite must be done to meet the wants of the tenant farmers in these unfavourable times. That the judicial rents are much too high and as Mr Gladstone in the past has always been the pioneer of justice and fair play to all classes, especially to the tenant farmers who so much needed it, I have every faith in him for the future.

I sign my name on the form forwarded ... . In conclusion allow me to thank you for the firm and honourable stand for rights of the tenant farmers which you with others have taken in the deliberations of the General Assembly, a body who seem to forget the source of their power and strength. ...'

D.1792/A1/2/5

13 June 1893

Letter from Thomas Dickson, Ballykelly, Banbridge, [Co. Down], to Armour,

returning a number of signatures from his area and expressing support for Armour's views.

'I with many others desire to give you our sincere thanks for the sympathy you have for the strugling [*sic*] tenant farmers, and for the courage you have shown at the meeting of the General Assembly, called together to assist Tory tyranny. ...'

D.1792/A1/2/6

13 June 1893

Letter from William D. Blair, Ballymena, [Co. Antrim], to Armour,

promising to sign the address and obtain other signatures and expressing his sympathy 'with yourself and Professor Dougherty in your struggle against the intolerance of the Presbyterian majority of this province'.

D.1792/A1/2/7

16 June 1893

Letter from Thomas Robertson, Athy, [Co. Kildare], to Armour,

agreeing to sign the address and outlining the attitudes of the southern Presbyterian community in Athy towards Home Rule.

'... I am isolated here as a Presbyterian and can therefore only send you my own name. ... Every Scotchman and Irish member [of Athy Presbyterian Church] is, I believe, against Mr Gladstone's policy ... . It is inconceivable to me why any Presbyterian ... should be opposed to the furtherance of those democratic principles of which the Home Rule bill is one ... . In the church courts ... the Home Rule party ... should refuse to be silenced. ...'

D.1792/A1/2/8

19 June 1893

Letter from William Craig, Newtownards, [Co. Down], to Armour,

explaining the impossibility of his signing the Home Rule address because of his position as principal of Newtownards Model School.

'... Referring to your enclosures you judge aright I dare not touch it. Even soliciting signatures would be quite as dangerous as signing myself. Party feeling runs very high in this district. ... The fire eaters in the Assembly seem to be cooled down ... Professor Dougherty's speech was quite enough and the men who were not convinced by it could not be convinced by anything. ... '

D.1792/A1/2/9

19 June 1893

Letter from John McClure, Carrowdore, [Co. Down], to Armour,

indicating a considerable degree of Presbyterian support for Home Rule in the Ards peninsula.

'... I have now about 125 signatures, nearly all in the congregation of Carrowdore ... I am very glad that an effort is being made to put the Presbyterian church in its proper light before the prime minister ... I think our church would have occupied a more dignified position if they had ... accepted the government measure and tried to make the best of it ... . There is not a congregation in this presbytery that names could not be had.'

D.1792/A1/2/10   **Letter from Samuel McKee, Ballywalter, [Co. Down], to Armour,**

19 June 1893

explaining his ineligibility to sign the address because of his Anglicanism and expressing his support for Armour's views on the land question as outlined at the General Assembly.

'... Your speech ... was a bold assertion of what ... the agriculturalists know to be the truth but from pusillanimity ... fostered by the poverty and oppression of generations, they lack the courage to acknowledge and support the cause of truth and justice ... . There are many farmers who have been and are still being maintained in the possession of their holdings solely through the generosity of merchants who are strong nationalists, although these same farmers would tomorrow reject Mr Gladstone and his party who have brought about any relief we have ever received (I speak from knowledge) ... . Our working men who are not R. C. are to a man loyalists ... .'

D.1792/A1/2/11   **Letter from William C. McCullough, Belfast, to Armour,**

21 June 1893

concerning the circulation of the Home Rule address in the Banbridge district and McCullough's efforts to persuade Presbyterians to sign it. He criticises the conservatism of the General Assembly in both worship and politics, hence his decision to emigrate to California in September. He also discusses dissensions in the ranks of the Irish and Unionist parties and in particular the continuing desire of the Anglicans to dominate Unionism and also the persecution of Presbyterian Gladstonians.

'... Although the document in question is one of the most skilfully worded of its type that I have ever seen, I found men who would not identify themselves in the slightest degree with Unionism very diffident about signing ... . One older elder, who resides in a Roman Catholic district and who one month ago believed the bill was going to pass, I flattered myself I had succeeded in converting. With this fond belief I called upon him in order to obtain his signature to the petition. I had scarcely mentioned the subject when he got into a towering rage, said that the whole thing was a concoction of popery and that the bill would never pass. I came sadly away, thinking that for stiff-neckedness and general crookedness the Ulster country elder stands peerless. At the same time the cause is growing and growing with wonderful rapidity when we take into account the desperate conservatism of the Ulster character. In my peregrinations up and down the country I have again and again come upon instances where the good seed dropped by you and Professor Dougherty at the special Assembly had fallen upon good ground ... .

Dougherty's speech at the last Assembly was another splendid contribution and Tories with any pretence to fairness are constrained to admit that our side somehow or other have for so far had far the best of it. ... It is a most melancholy thing that at such a crisis in the history of the country the conduct of those Irish members at Westminster should be constantly undermining any little bit of confidence we might persuade a few individuals to have in them. I think that little puppy [T. M.] Healy is the centre of all the irritation in the party. We can however solace ourselves with the thought that there is also very considerable friction between the two wings of the Unionist party ... . The Episcopalians still mean to be the dominant party and this fact, coupled with the persecution that home rulers have been subjected to, are the causes of constant additions to the Gladstonian party in the country. It was the bigotry of these Belfast Tories that forced me to take a prominent stand but I do not take any credit for my courage as I purpose sailing for California ... I am completely sick of the conservatism of our church in both worship and politics ... . I am sorry that I am not staying in this country to watch the progress of the contest in our Assembly, but no one with the least political foresight can doubt that if the signs of the time indicate anything, they point to the ultimate victory of the party of progress. But if the [Home Rule] bill have been law tomorrow, I am fully persuaded that [Rev.] Petticrew would continue to move resolutions for its repeal and the Assembly to endorse them for at least the next fifty years. For tenacity in clinging to and worshipping ideals a century old, our Presbyterian church never will have a superior, excepting of course the great and important body of Reformed Presbyterians in this country. Weren't their Assembly resolutions on Home Rule a sight for gods and men in this 19th century? Judged by that solitary landmark at any rate, we have made some little progress ... . If the advocates of civil and religious liberty talked about it less and practised it more, it would be better for their own cause. ...'

D.1792/A1/2/12	**Letter from George Nelson, Culcavey, to Armour,**
21 June 1893	enclosing a list of signatures and indicating that there are few Gladstonian supporters in his immediate area

but 'there are some who recognise the necessity for a departure from the system of government which has been in operation in this country with such unsatisfactory results'.

D.1792/A1/2/13	**Part of a letter from [?], Ballynahinch, [Co. Down], to Armour,**
21 June 1893	explaining his hesitation about whether to sign the

address despite his approval of its contents, his reasons for finally deciding to do so and also his reservations concerning Gladstone's bill.

'I entirely approve of every statement in the document ... but I have hesitated to sign it for two reasons. Ist I had committed myself when my opinion was unformed upon the subject of Home Rule to the Unionist party ... and in the second place I would prefer, if I dared, to come out publicly on the side I now believe to be the right one for a Presbyterian to take. However, I have signed it as I believe there ought to be some speedy and radical change in the civil government of Ireland and in the land laws. I am not so much of a home ruler as to believe that the present bill is the safest and best and I therefore hesitate to commit myself to it, if I believed that it would pass as it is. I go so far, however, as not to be afraid if it did pass and also to believe that some measure similar to it will eventually become the law of the land. ...'

D.1792/A1/2/14	**Letter from John Morrison, Killinchy, [Co. Down], to Armour,**
22 June 1893	claiming that a considerable number of farmers in the

Killinchy area are home rulers, including many Unitarians who of course are not eligible to sign the Presbyterian address, but that these farmers have to contend with the power of the Orange Order whose supporters are the agricultural labourers.

'... Like all other Protestant districts in Co. Down an organisation exists almost in my farm with the members of which I endeavour ... to live at peace with: the so-called defenders of our free and religious liberties. On their roll book there does not appear a rated occupier and yet they are powerful enough to deter some who would be on our side from exercising a liberty of conscience. ...'

D.1792/A1/2/15	**Letter from T. Irwin, Newry, [Co. Down], to Armour,**
22 June 1893	referring to his decision to vote with Dougherty and

Armour at the General Assembly and the difficulties which this has placed him in locally.

'I do not ... regret my action in voting at the Assembly ... the calling of the roll was so evidently resorted to for the purpose of frightening ... the minority. ... I have an evening class of adults in an Orange district ... and some of them stayed away last Sabbath but ... I hope the trouble will soon be over. ... Would it do to allow Covenanters to sign?'

D.1792/A1/2/16

22 June 1893

Letter from Alexander McDowell, Craigavad, Co. Down, to Armour,

congratulating him on his speech in favour of Home Rule at the General Assembly and regretting his inability, as a Unitarian, to sign the Presbyterian Home Rule memorial to Gladstone. He indicates that he has been involved in helping to organise a similar Unitarian memorial.

'I have yours of 19th with enclosures—as a Unitarian I was debarred from signing the address myself but I did the next best thing—I got some friends to sign and take it up, one of whom Mr Sam Bailie, Helen's Bay, Co. Down, will probably forward it to you (I failed to see him yesterday ev[enin]g). I "lent a hand" with our Unitarian protest and was very pleased to see yours. I think it a great pity such ingratitude should be shown to W. E. Gladstone by farmers and I think Presbyterian ministers are largely the cause. There is not one in this district, with the exception of Dr Forbes, Newtownards, friendly, but I am glad to say that many of the laity are more advanced; most of the signatures forwarded to you will be from the congregation of the Rev[eren]d John [?] and from the estate of Lord Dufferin. I was glad to see the stand that you sir, and some others, made in the Assembly and trusting your movement may have great success. ...'

D.1792/A1/2/17

28 June 1893

Letter from Joseph Maxwell of Lurgan, [Co. Armagh], to Armour,

outlining the difficulties involved in obtaining signatures for the Presbyterian address because of Unionist pressure and enclosing a further signature on the understanding that it will not be published.

'... It is very hard on account of the strength of the "Unionists" to get very many to sign. Quite a large number of my friends sympathise with the object and are in the main willing to let Home Rule have a fair trial. Ah! If they would only open their eyes and look around them. ... The passport to public honour here is rank Toryism and Orangeism. ... These are the men who are to save for us our civil and religious liberty. ...'

D.1792/A1/2/18

[n.d. 1893 ?]

Letter from L. Millar, Rathfriland, [Co. Down], to Armour,

referring to his brother and himself having signed the address and having tried to whip up additional support and commenting favourably on Armour's speech on Home Rule to the special General Assembly.

'... This is my first letter to you on paper, but there was one written mentally ... after that memorable day in Belfast.

O, it is good to know that there is a remnant even in the General Assembly. ...'

D.1792/A1/2/19

Letter from Edward W. Lockhart, Jerrettspass, [Co. Down], to Armour,

29 June [1893 ?]
enclosing a number of signatures to the address, 'willingly signed'.

'... There are others which I could have got through persuasion but thought it better not to touch them at present as there is a great fear of "Rome rule" which I attribute largely to the reading of *The Witness* ... right will win in the end, but it is a pity we have not more men who are not afraid to speak out. ...'

D.1792/A1/2/20
Letter from J. Kirk, Antrim, [Co. Antrim] , to Armour,

30 June 1893
discussing the mechanics of collecting further signatures for the Presbyterian Home Rule address and in particular offering to collect some on an impending trip to the south and west of Ireland.

D.1792/A1/2/21
Letter from L. Millar, Rathfriland, Co. Down, [writing from London] , to Armour,

30 June 1893
responding to a request from Armour to obtain a few more signatures and discussing a trip to London, including a visit to a Roman Catholic service.

'... I've written home to my brother begging him to try for a few more names—even two—but greatly fear it will be in vain: however, I know he will do his best.

I was at the house of commons on Tuesday but there was nothing going on save army and navy estimates. It was through the kindness of Dr [Charles K. D.] Tanner [member for Mid-Cork] we were admitted. He is a warm friend and an admirer of yours. ... We ... look forward hopefully to seeing Mr Gladstone.

On Sunday evening at the Oratory for the first time. I had just a *little* sympathy with the Ulster people who fear the Catholic church getting the upper hand.

There were most wonderful prayers offered up for conversion of heretics and as a Protestant one was made to feel rather uncomfortable. It was the most bigoted and intolerant kind of thing I ever heard anywhere and I wish I hadn't heard it now. ...'

D.1792/A1/2/22
Letter from Francis Johnston, Broughshane, [Co. Antrim] , to Armour,

5 July 1893
explaining the delay in sending signatures to the address and expressing the hope that he will be able to gather more when he can find the time, given the distractions of his business where he is engaged in structural alterations.

'... We were all proud of the stand you took at the March meeting of Assembly ... I believe you have more sympathisers among the Presbyterian farmers than the *church* generally are aware of; aye even people who would scarcely admit it are sympathetic.

If the Presbyterian ministers generally had taken a more independent position on this question, they would not *be* in the position of humiliation they are now come to. ...'

D.1792/A1/2/23
Letter from Stewart [Hunter ?], Coleraine, [Co. Londonderry] , to Armour,

14 July 1893
asking that he be allowed to withdraw his promise to

sign the address to Gladstone on account of his father's opposition and to avoid exposing family differences in public.

'... He [the father] is awfully mortified and is eating his heart out about the fact that we all differ from him, and that it is publicly known we differ. I feel that in the rabid mood these feelings induce, he would regard my signing this letter as a deliberate attempt on my part to mortify him publicly ... .

I hope you will pardon this seeming desertion, but when I promised, this aspect of the question never occurred to me.'

D.1792/A1/2/24

14 July 1893

Letter from A. [McCaldin ?], Banbridge, [Co. Down], to Armour,

enclosing a number of signatures to the Home Rule address and commenting on the degree of support in the area amongst Presbyterians for Home Rule.

'... I may truly inform you that your statements delivered before the members of the General Assembly in March are the feelings and convictions of the great mass of Presbyterians throughout this part of our country. The name *Home Rule* is not relished by all, but the principles which underlie it are the principles of the entire Presbyterian farmers of the county. ...'

D.1792/A1/2/25

17 July 1893

Letter from R. Cooper, Balloo, [Co. Down], to Armour,

expressing his support for Gladstone and the Presbyterian address.

'... Wishing every success to Mr Gladstone, he done me a great benifit [*sic*].'

D.1792/A1/2/26

21 July 1893

Letter from J. Scott, Greenisland, [Co. Antrim], to Armour,

enclosing some signatures for the address but explaining that 'plenty of people have sympathy with it, but would be afraid to sign'.

D.1792/A1/2/27

25 July 1893

Letter from Stewart [Hunter ?], Coleraine, [Co. Londonderry], to Armour,

referring to his previous letter [D.1792/A1/2/23] which indicated his unwillingness to sign the Home Rule address and commenting on the amount of support in his area for Irish self-government.

'... Your solution, if difficult, is an exceedingly wise one, by adopting this definite basis no offence can be given or taken ... .

There is a good deal of change for the better with many people I meet, regarding their attitude toward Home Rule. It's wonderful how many people reconcile themselves to the inevitable, and while I don't think many are converted to an active position of help, still the intensely bitter feeling against it is going, save amongst the fanatics and fools. ...'

D.1792/A1/2/28

Letter from Robert Macauley, Mullaghduff, [Co. Antrim], to Armour,

explaining that he is unable to sign the Home Rule address or collect other signatures because of the opposition of his wife and family.

'I am sorry for not having filled up your list ... my wife and family has said against me interfering as long as I did not sign for the one the [?] would not consent to sign for the other. ...'

D.1792/A1/2/29

12 August 1893

Letter from W. E. Gladstone, 10 Downing Street, Whitehall, [London], to Armour and others, acknowledging with pleasure the receipt of the Presbyterian Home Rule memorial and commenting on its significance.

'I have received with pleasure the address from 3500 Presbyterians, favourable to Home Rule for Irish purposes in Ireland, which you have been good enough to send me.

I attach to it a great value, and I consider it as indicating a large section of favourable opinion, being well aware of the impediments which might deter many who entertain similar opinions from a gratuitous manifestation of them at the present time. I also observe what you have been good enough to state as to the spontaneous character of the address.

I look forward with confidence to a very large and early return of Presbyterians in particular, to the sentiments in favour of union with their fellow countrymen which governed them as a body one century ago; but this will in all likelihood be delayed until the parliamentary controversy has been closed.

It is constantly assumed by our opponents that what they term the loyal minority is homogeneous on all important questions. The sentiment now placed before me as to the land laws reminds me how likely it is that on this subject in particular they will ere long be largely undeceived.

P.S. You are at liberty to make any use you please of this letter.'

D.1792/A1/2/30

15 September 1893

Letter from Thomas A. Dickson, Dublin, to Armour, commenting on the progress made in collecting signatures for the Presbyterian Home Rule address to Gladstone and voicing concern that Gladstonian Liberals in Ireland lack an effective organisational base. He is also anxious that further propaganda work be undertaken in Britain. Dickson was a leading Ulster Liberal, formerly member of parliament for Dungannon and Co. Tyrone, who was returned as a nationalist/Liberal representative for the St Stephen's Green constituency in Dublin (1888-92) and for South Tyrone in 1892. Although he had acted as the Irish party's electoral organiser in Ulster from 1886 onwards, his connections with the party were always loose and he never took the parliamentary pledge. His description of his own political position in this letter is therefore of particular interest.

'... I watched ... the progress of the declaration to Mr Gladstone and was much pleased with your last letter. I am finding out daily how many would sign only in fear that their names would be disclosed. It is pleasing to think that there are yet 7,000 men and women in Ulster that have not yet bowed the knee to the Baal of Toryism. You have had your own share and more of abuse—but don't think that I am out of the fire, far from it, but I feel that in Ireland we Gladstonian Liberals have no platform.

Your services and Professor Dougherty's at the Assembly were *invaluable*. Dublin ministers tell me that *his* speech was a turning point in the situation and scores of ministers who can say nothing feel the position to be intolerable. I wish you and Dougherty later on could appear on some English and Scottish platforms. We are only at the beginning of the crisis and the weakness lies in dissensions in Ireland. ...'

D.1792/A1/2/31   Letter from Robert Lynd, [the journalist and essayist],
                                                   written from Carnlough, [Co. Down], to Armour,
25 July 1893
                                                   discussing the timetable for the publication of the
Presbyterian Home Rule address and thanking Armour and his wife for their help and sympathy on the occasion of a recent family bereavement.

'Thanks, warmly, for your address. We think it better to delay the publication for Friday, so that the [*Belfast*] *News-Letter*, [*Northern*] *Whig*, and *Witness* may have it simultaneously. ... At a time like this the hearts of mourners are specially susceptible to tokens of personal friendship and sympathy ... . The address could not be better if you had devoted three months to its preparation. ...'

LETTERS FROM VARIOUS CORRESPONDENTS

D.1792/A1/3/1-59

1876-1928

Letters to Rev. J. B. Armour from various correspondents.

D.1792/A1/3/1

9 February 1876

Letter from Maria B. Meierl, Kensington, [London], to Armour,

refers to a letter from 'Mr R.' of Ballymena, telling of 'a "spill" from an Irish jaunting car', but she doubts his story. She goes on to request a photograph of Armour.

D.1792/A1/3/2

4 April 1876

Incomplete letter from Maria B. Meierl, Kensington, [London], to Armour,

encloses a copy of her letter to 'J.R.', whom she thinks is 'drinking or drugging'. Armour is obviously connected in some way with him.

D.1792/A1/3/3

27 September 1882

Letter from Rev. John McErlain, [parish priest], Ballymoney, [Co. Antrim], to Armour,

promising a testimonial to be written on Armour's behalf.

'... I do not see any reason why I—a priest— should not take an interest in the welfare of you— a respectable clergyman of this town. From the fame you have acquired as a teacher of classics, I believe you to be eminently qualified for the office of examiner in connection with the intermediate system of education. ...'

D.1792/A1/3/4

18 January 1884

Letter from Rev. R. Jeffrey, Bombay, [India], to Armour,

outlining his plans to retire from the Indian mission field.

'... I hope to see you ... about Assembly time ... I'm at last decided to give up and make a permanent home ... somewhere in Ireland ... I have not formally announced my determination to my congregation ... . My seniors would advise 'furlough' but I would find my work of five years scattered under the hands of the missionaries ... so I simply hand in my gun ... . My turn in India has been more ... of a brilliant outing than anything else ... I dislike the thought of having my family scattered over the earth ... . Cholera has broken out ... and quarantine has ... upset my homegoing plans. I intended to go home by Egypt, Jerusalem. We hope to sail ... about the 1st of April.'

D.1792/A1/3/5

16 February 1884

Letter from John Browne, Drumart, [near Ballymoney, Co. Antrim], to Rev. J. D. Osborne, Ballymoney, [Co. Antrim],

refers to the activities of what would appear to be a church organisation in the Drumart area.

'... There is 80 members connected with our society ... our time of meeting is once a fortnight, the place is the Garry N[ational] schoolhouse ... . Our society has been in existence now about five years ... the cause is becoming more popular in the district.'

D.1792/A1/3/6A

4 November 1889

Letter from Jackson Smythe, Armagh, [Co. Armagh], to Armour,

refers to a proposed application to the lord lieutenant of County Antrim, Sir Edward Cowan, to have John Wood of Bushmills appointed as a magistrate. Wood was Smythe's brother-in-law.

D.1792/A1/3/6B

4 November 1889

Letter from 'J.S.' [Jackson Smythe], Armagh, [Co. Armagh], to Armour,

a further letter relating to the campaign to have John Wood appointed as a magistrate. He suggests that Armour send an enclosed letter, along with one of Smythe's own, to Sir Edward Cowan, the lord lieutenant of Co. Antrim.

D.1792/A1/3/7

7 April 1890

Letter from Rev. Alexander Cuskery, Coagh, [Co. Tyrone], to Armour,

promising to consider supporting Armour's attempt to secure the chair of church history at Magee College, Londonderry; attacking the *Northern Whig* and *The Witness* for their attitude on the land question; and expressing support for free, secular, compulsory education.

'... About the land question—I purpose to keep at it as well as the [*Northern*] *Whig* will allow me. The [*Northern*] *Whig* is not even "half with us on the question"—it is getting to be very conservative, and afraid to do or say anything that might possibly embarass the Unionist government. You perhaps noticed how the editor slashed at me after I reviewed [T.W.] Russell's new year's speech—I wrote him a reply that he never allowed to see the light. I read it at a meeting in Cookstown—Mr Gray of Lisburn and others present, said they never knew of the [*Northern*] *Whig* being so well answered—that our position was completely vindicated, and the [*Northern*] *Whig's* shown to be utterly inconsistent *etc. etc.* Though I had tried hard through a mutual friend of [Thomas] MacKnight's [editor of the *Northern Whig*] and my own, I failed to get it inserted; and I hesitated at the last whether I should not go to *The Witness*. Preferring to get my views ventilated through the [*Northern*] *Whig*, I sent my last letter there, but I had to write MacKnight a second time urging him to insert it; and then you saw the petty nibbling he tried on in his leader at my name and letter.

Through some bungling Friday's [*Northern*] *Whig* did not reach me till Saturday; as soon as I get this and some other letters off my hand, I purpose to turn my attention to it again. From what you say I am glad I did not ask *The Witness* for space on the subject; and I must handle MacKnight as delicately as possible and try to keep on the good side of him ... .

I ought to have said, before passing away from the land question, that I read some articles on it in *The Witness* with great relish; and I read others in it that I thought very insipid. The fact, explained by you, that they were not all from the same writer, accounts for this. I would like to see the present bill, even as it stands, become law. Suppose the sales were to go on as rapidly as the scheme would permit, it would take *150* years to work out the problem—leaving every farmer in the country the owner of his farm. Does anybody suppose the country will wait all that time? The government and country are committed to the principle of occupying ownership; they cannot stop where this bill leaves the question; they must hurry it through by another grant. ...'

D.1792/A1/3/8   **Letter from James J. Shaw, Dublin, to Armour,**

21 September 1890   the first of a series of letters relating to the possible
                                                 selection of Shaw as the Unionist candidate for the
North Antrim parliamentary seat at the next general election. At this stage Armour was still a
Liberal Unionist and the North Antrim Liberal Unionists were unhappy about their lack of
influence in the process of selecting the Unionist candidate. Shaw as a barrister and a Presbyterian was attractive to them, but in the end his ambition to become a judge made him
unwilling to upset the Unionist hierarchy.

'... I have been waiting patiently for the last three days to hear the result of your meeting on
Thursday, and I have been very much surprised that I have not heard. Was the meeting held?
Was anything done or settled? Please let me know. I start tomorrow for revision sessions. ...'

D.1792/A1/3/9   **Letter from James J. Shaw [in Enniksillen, Co.
                                                 Fermanagh] , to Armour,**

14 October 1890
                                                 refers to Shaw's desire to obtain a government appoint-
ment of some sort, though in this instance he is prepared to waive his claims in favour of a
Liberal Unionist, [William?] Hamilton, from Ballymoney. A post-script refers to the possibility
of Shaw's nomination to the Education Board, though he is not too keen on the idea.

'... I will either see or write to the att[orney]-general and try to get the matter of the commissionership arranged. I will gladly waive my claim in favour of Mr Hamilton who is, I know,
eminently suited for the position both by taste and experience. ...'

D.1792/A1/3/10   **Part of a letter from James J. Shaw, Dublin, to
                                                 Armour,**

3 November 1890
                                                 relates to the struggle between Conservatives and
Liberal Unionists to secure the North Antrim nomination.

'... With reference to your conference ... if the Conservatives proposed to lay two names before
Lords Salisbury and Hartington [the Conservative and Liberal Unionist leaders] , you ought at
once to accept the proposition. I don't think from what I hear they will be in a humour to
concede so much: but if they are, I don't see how you could with any grace refuse such an
offer and you will have much more influence at headquarters than you can have among the local
leaders. I am sure our claims could be regarded far more favourably in the larger circle of
political life than in the narrower. If the Conservatives do not make the proposal *I think you
ought.* ...'

D.1792/A1/3/11   **Letter from James J. Shaw, Dublin, to Armour,**

27 November 1890   further evidence of Shaw's ambitions; refers to the
                                                 impending death of 'the head of the Land Commission'
and requests advice and assistance towards securing the appointment.

'... The government will be anxious to have a man who is not regarded as a landlord's man
They will be particularly anxious ... to conciliate the Ulster farmers ... especially the central
association [presumably the Antrim Central Tenant Right Association or the Ulster Land
Committee] .

There is at present ... no Presbyterian on either the supreme or county court bench ... . Who are
the leading members of the Ulster Liberal Association who would be likely to take such a
matter in hand?'

D.1792/A1/3/12

[n.d. 1891?]

Part of a letter from James J. Shaw, Dublin, to Armour,

refers to the unhappiness of North Antrim Liberal Unionists at the selection of Charles Connor, a Belfast businessman, as the Unionist candidate for the constituency. Connor was a director of the Bushmills distillery and a former mayor of Belfast.

'... danger that the cause of the union should be identified before the English and Scotch people with Toryism and Orangeism. You should also state that this is not a time when Ulster can afford to send mere moneyed men to the house of commons to amuse themselves ... and that you would not consent to have your constituency jobbed for the convenience of any special clique ... . I think if you ... let it be known that if your views are disregarded in the choice of a Unionist candidate ... you will make a considerable impression ... have influence brought from above to bring the local Tories to reason ... . I think it is a scandal that [H.L.] Mulholland [Unionist] should be allowed to retain the seat in North Derry ... . You might let the committee know that if the Liberal Unionists are driven to fight in N[or]th Antrim, the split will not end there ... . You should insist ... on the necessity of the interference of the party leader. That is our only chance of any sort of favourable settlement.'

D.1792/A1/3/13

13 March 1891

Letter from James J. Shaw [in Downpatrick, Co. Down], to Armour,

reveals Shaw's continuing interest in the North Antrim seat.

'... I think the statement that I have withdrawn should be contradicted. My advice is that our friends should carefully consider the whole situation in conference. If they come to the conclusion that there is no fair chance of their putting in a Liberal Unionist, they should drop the matter for the present. If on the other hand they think they have a fair chance, let them say whether they still think I am their strongest candidate and I will let them know at a very early period whether I can undertake the contest under the altered circumstances.

Have you any information or can you obtain any as to whether the Nationalists will have a candidate? That of course would be an essential matter in the consideration of your own course. ...'

D.1792/A1/3/14

13 April 1891

Letter from James J. Shaw, Dublin, to Armour,

indicates that Shaw is beginning to back away from the prospect of a split Unionist vote in North Antrim, lest his future career be damaged.

'I have thought over the matter of the North Antrim election very carefully, and I cannot give an undertaking to fight in any event. In fact, I do not see my way clear to fight at all, if there is to be a contest between two Unionists. But I do not think we should assume just yet that there is to be such a contest. I think that Liberal Unionists should devote themselves at present to bringing pressure to bear upon the Tories from the leaders of the two wings of the party to compel them to give way. As far as I know nothing has been done in this way. No representation of the case has been made either to the Liberal Unionist leader or to the Conservative leader. I am quite willing that my name should be put forward as the adopted candidate of the liberal section of the constituency, and I will as far as I can in making the circumstances of the case known to the leaders and in pressing upon them the danger to the Unionist cause created by the arrogance and discourtesy of the local Tories. I do not see why your meeting on Thursday next should not adopt me as their candidate and agree to urge my acceptance as the Unionist candidate without asking from me any pledge that I will contest the constituency even though I should not be accepted by the Conservatives. That can very well stand over for future consideration; if the Liberal candidate be not accepted ultimately we may never be called on to fight. I think it is quite enough ... that I should stand before the world as the accepted candidate of the Liberal Unionist party and that we have shown that we have no intention of withdrawing our claim to the seat. If Connor withdraws, as I believe he will, we must be prepared to make the best terms we can in a new arrangement. I hardly expect the Conservatives would consent to take me straight off. Let me know what you and our other friends would think of a compromise by which the soli[citor] gen[eral] would be returned, with a distinct pledge that the Liberal Unionists should have the nomination on his retirement. I believe the soli[citor] gen[eral] wants a seat, but his tenure would be very short—probably not a year. If we could secure the reversion it would do you nearly as well, and it would suit me a great deal better. I have never suggested this to anyone but yourself: but I wish you would think over it. I believe it is practicable, if it would be acceptable.

You can easily see that for me as a Unionist to be the instrument of a Unionist split would be almost equally fatal whether I succeeded or failed. On the other hand if I could secure a safe seat as the representative of a united party it would be the making of me. ...

Let me know if you think our friends would come into this arrangement. If they would I believe the other side could be squeezed into it. But be absolutely silent for the present.'

D.1792/A1/3/15	**Part of a letter from James J. Shaw, Upper Pembroke Street, Dublin, to Armour,**
[n.d. March/April 1891?]	

discussing the selection of Charles Connor to fight the North Antrim seat for the Unionists in the impending general election and the claims of the local Liberal Unionists to the seat. He indicates that he may be willing, under certain circumstances, to oppose Connor.

'... I will be free to say whether or not I will fight the Tory and I will be free, in case I refuse, to get somebody else who will. I am of opinion that your meeting on Thursday should not declare war at once—it should re-assert the claim of the Liberal Unionists to the seat, select a candidate, and agree to appeal to the leaders of both wings of the party against the decision of the local Tories. I think you might fairly say to the meeting on Thursday that I am willing to accept their nomination of me as their candidate, but that I am of opinion much may still be done by bringing pressure from outside to compel the Tories to moderation, and that no open declaration of war should be made till all means of influence have been exhausted. If in the end we fail to induce the Tories to give way, I think that both the Liberals of the constituency and myself should then be free to consider our position and determine on all the circumstances of the case whether we should fight the Tories or not. It may be that under the circumstances the Liberals might find some stronger candidate but at any rate I will hold myself free to determine whether under those circumstances it would suit me to fight. ...'

D.1792/A1/3/16	**Letter from James J. Shaw, Dublin, to Armour,**
21 April 1891	expresses some hope that pressure from the Liberal Unionist leadership in London may yet secure him the North Antrim seat.

'I think you did wisely to postpone your meeting, and let the matter rest as it is for the present.

I had a visit yesterday from Mr [F. E.] Ball (son of the ex-chancellor) who represents the

Unionist registration association in this county [Dublin]. His chiefs in London are greatly alarmed about the state of matters in North Antrim and sent him to me to see how matters stood and what ought to be done. They see that if dissension breaks out in N[or]th Antrim it is sure to spread. I told Ball the whole facts of the case, and he said it was clearly a cause for some man of influence and rank to come over and try to compose matters. I told him in my opinion Connor must be withdrawn ... and then the two parties might start afresh and try to come to some understanding about a candidate. He says the people on the other side don't care about Connor as he is a bad speaker and they have enough of that sort ... they would be much better pleased if I were chosen. ... I told him that even if I did not stand the Liberal Unionists were sure to have a candidate and to make a fight unless some arrangement was come to.

I do not at all despair even yet of our being able to carry our point in N[or]th Antrim. Even if we cannot secure my acceptance as the Unionist candidate ... I believe we can secure the next best thing—a temporary Conservative member, and the right to the nomination on the next occasion. We ought to keep our forces in the field, and on the part of the Presby[teria]ns generally, a good deal might be done. I really think this matter has been allowed to be mismanaged ... as to Presby[teria]n claims to representation. If instead of putting paragraphs in the paper that irritated and alarmed all the local Tory cliques ... quiet action had been taken in the proper quarter ... a very different result might have ensued. ...'

D.1792/A1/3/17

19 May 1891

Letter from Rev. H. B. Wilson, Cookstown, [Co. Tyrone], to Armour,

'Would you kindly second the adoption of the report of the Elementary Education Committee at the Assembly? ... It is important that the Assembly speaks out strongly against Mr Balfour's [chief secretary for Ireland] proposal to endow ... the denominational training colleges ..'

D.1792/A1/3/18

29 July 1891

Part of a letter from an unidentified correspondent, Strandtown, Belfast, to Armour,

invites Armour to consider the possibility of moving from Trinity Church, Ballymoney, to a Belfast congregation.

'... I entertain the hope that you yourself would not be indisposed to face city work ... I ... ask you ... whether you would be disposed to undertake Great George's St[reet Church] *as a starting point.* ...'

D.1792/A1/3/19

Christmas 1891

Part of a letter from an unidentified correspondent, Randalstown, [Co. Antrim], to Armour,

comments on Armour's published sermon, *Life's new ideal.*

'... I enjoyed your sermon very much ... But ... It was like Arnold and I opened it looking for Carlyle. ...'

D.1792/A1/3/20

3 August 1892

Letter from Rev. J. D. Craig Houston, Hydepark, Belfast, to Armour,

discusses the difficulties faced by ministers who disagree politically with their congregations, as with Armour and the North Antrim election of 1892 and with Craig Houston's declaration of support for Home Rule.

'I am glad to hear that you have weathered the storm and that the damage done is not very great. I cannot say that my case is exactly parallel. I have only one elder left out of four and a good number of my committee have gone. I am thankful to say, however, that matters are not nearly so bad as they have been represented in town by those whose "wish was father to the thought". It was currently reported last week all through Belfast that I had preached the Sunday before last to just three people. But the fact is that the reduction in the Sunday attendance for the past four or five weeks is represented by a falling off of about 2/6 or 3/- in the halfpenny collection ... I suppose I have about thirty people fewer in the church on Sundays than I used to have ... . Of course some of them are beginning already to slip back, and all of them would only be too glad to appear in their places on next Sunday, if I would call and ask them to do so. That, however, I shall never do. As I took care to point out to the committee when it met last week, I have done nothing for which I feel sorry and consequently nothing for which I can honestly express regret. That, however, is a chief grievance with the dissentients. Their cry is "if he would only say he was sorry for what has happened, but he won't give way an inch"—about what or wherefore do I express sorrow—I have not been found drunk in the way side. I have kissed nobody's wife and I have forged nobody's hand, and yet if I had done any or all of these things the indignation of some people against me could not have been greater and would probably not have been half so great. My proximity to Belfast and the fact that Connor your member [of parliament] is a large employer of labour in these parts makes my fight a pretty stiff one. ...'

D.1792/A1/3/21

3 August 1892

Letter from W. H. Dodd, Belfast, to Armour,

refers to allegations by the Unionist press during the 1892 North Antrim election campaign directed against Armour and Dodd. See also D.1792/A1/3/22.

'I saw the [*Northern*] "*Whig*" people today, and I settled the form of apology. They are willing to insert it, but they pressed me so strongly ... that I finally consented they should write to you before doing so. ... I disclosed all the documents to them. But I could not prevail upon them to promise that this apology would be final. ...'

D.1792/A1/3/22

17 August 1892

Letter from W. H. Dodd, [writing from Port Salon, Co. Donegal], to Armour,

'... I am glad you think the [*Northern*] *Whig* sufficient. They have been very decent with me, and will for the future be with you ... McDowell [co-owner of the *Northern Whig*] undertook to make it right with the [*Belfast*] *News-Letter* to save us trouble. But I hear he has gone off to Switzerland for his holiday, and I do not see well how to manage the [*Belfast*] *News-Letter* from here. If I were in Belfast, I could do it in a couple of hours. I think we will let it alone. The [*Northern*] *Whig* is really the paper to vouch for us and it has done it. We need not mind the Tories. I have reason to think the [*Northern*] *Whig* has been using influence about the s[olicitor]-generalship. [Thomas] Dickson says [Rt Hon. C. H.] Hemphill was arranged for on Monday week last.'

D.1792/A1/3/23

22 March 1893

Letter from Thomas Macafee, Ardglass, [Co. Down], to Armour,

analysing the special meeting of the Presbyterian General Assembly held to discuss Gladstone's second Home Rule bill and Armour's stand in favour of the bill during the debate.

'... I consider your speech splendid and that in one thing if in little else the Assembly or the shouting majority of it showed wisdom in not attempting to reply to it. If our church had not wholly parted from its traditions and given up its proper position, it would have passed your amendment unanimously.

D

31

Any one can understand why landlordism and episcopacy should struggle earnestly to retain the remnants of their ascendancy, but why the Presbyterian church should unite with them in the struggle is more than I can understand.

Still I feel that I have no right to say anything on the subject whilst *we*, that is myself and so many who sympathise with your views, are such arrant cowards that we do not come out and support you. ... I suspect that [those who voted for the resolution were] not such an over-whelming majority of the whole as the [*Northern*] *Whig etc.* represent. I wonder that no notice has been taken of the somewhat suggestive fact that after the tremendous efforts made to get elders to attend in support of the resolutions the clerk announced 169 commissions of elders, not a very large proportion out of nearly 600.

I sincerely sympathise with you in what I am certain you are called upon to endure, but you are no doubt supported by the consciousness of having the courage to speak and act according to your convictions. Perhaps the time will come when we must all speak out. In the meantime I take no part in the meetings or doings of Unionists and I am generally credited with being a home ruler.'

D.1792/A1/3/24

6 May 1893

Part of a letter from [Robert C. Martin ?], Ballymoney, [Co. Antrim], to J. A. Rentoul,

thanking Rentoul on behalf of those members of Armour's congregation opposed to Home Rule for presenting their petition to the Assembly.

'... I fully concur in your friendly references to Mr Armour: all round he is one of the very best men. ...'

D.1792/A1/3/25

22 May 1893

Letter from Joseph Lupton, Chapel Allerton, Leeds, [Yorkshire], to Armour,

thanking Armour for a copy of his speech of 15 March 1893 at the special General Assembly held to discuss Gladstone's second Home Rule bill.

'... One of the grandest measures our great Liberal leader has ever produced, and when it becomes law will be the great means of satisfying your country and raising it again to the position she should take as a valuable part of the great United Kingdom. I wish your co-religionists could have seen the question in your light. ...'

D.1792/A1/3/26

24 May 1893

Part of a letter from [William Gibson ?] of Bally-walter, [Co. Down], to Armour,

thanking Armour for a copy of his speech of 15 March 1893 on Home Rule at the special General Assembly and giving his views on the majority of Presbyterians who voted for the official resolutions condemning Home Rule.

'... Men who would sell their flocks and their country for less than that for which Judas betrayed their lord—for a smile or the shake of the hand of the Tory task masters and slave drivers of our poor Presbyterian people. ...'

D.1792/A1/3/27

22 June 1893

Letter from J. F. X. O'Brien, [Irish National League of Great Britain], London, to Armour,

thanking him for his offer to speak on behalf of the Home Rule cause in Britain at some stage in the future.

'I beg to thank you ... for your willingness to help the Home Rule cause later on.

I do not think we shall make any demand on your services very soon. But it is pretty certain that we must by and bye start a vigorous campaign on this side—when the help of Ulster friends will be much prized. ...'

D.1792/A1/3/28	**Part of a letter from William H. Hill to Armour,**
[n.d. c.1893]	urging improved Home Rule propaganda and organis-

ation in Ulster and in particular the mobilisation of the farmers through the distribution of pamphlets and the creation of an 'Ulster Land League'. Yet again the over-dependence of Gladstonian Liberals on attracting the support of the farmers and their provincial exclusivity are underlined.

'... however be followed up by other and more effectual means, as it is quite evident that there will be a general election when the [Home Rule] bill is thrown out by the [house of] lords. If the opposition is broken down in Ulster the case is won. But the question is how is this to be done. Well the following is my idea about the matter.

(a) I think there is great room for a good Protestant Home Rule journal in Belfast which would take the place which the [*Northern*] *Whig* used to have. Such a paper would be very widely read at the present time even by opponents and would certainly pay and be a success if it were strong in the farmers' interests.

(b) The dissemination of political pamphlets such as your own address which I see was in this form, the speeches of the Ulster Land Committee *etc*.

(c) The formation of an Ulster Land League (club, society, if "league" is unsavoury) manned and controlled by men of its *own* order. This is a most important consideration for as sure as other men would get into it they would spoil it. The ministerial wolf would appear as the good shepherd and lead it his way, the no-pope fanatic his way and so on. This is the case as it stands. The farmers' lands are the happy hunting ground for every political impostor.

Now this would no longer be possible if the farmers would unite, if they knew their strength, if they knew the dignity of their own order and kept themselves unspotted from the world. ...'

D.1792/A1/3/29	**Letter from Rev. Richard Lyttle, Moneyrea, [Co. Down], to Thomas A. Dickson, [subsequently for-**
26 May 1894	**warded to Armour],**

suggesting the setting up of a new Gladstonian Liberal organisation to organise Protestant Home Rule opinion in Ulster to take advantage of the foundations laid by the Presbyterian and Unitarian Home Rule addresses, to capitalise on increasing middle class support and to try to attract the working class.

'Mr Shillington, Mr Killen and I have had several earnest talks lately as to the necessity of organising the Protestant Home Rule opinion in N.E. Ulster in a new "Irish Liberal and Radical Union". In the event of a general election it would be very necessary to have established some such organisation, in which every genuine Liberal over 18 years of age could be enrolled. Such an organisation could speak authoritatively on behalf of all our scattered units, issue manifestos to the British electors and counteract the efforts of our Unionist friends generally. We should be able to enrol at least 10,000 members. As you know the work done in connection with, in order of time, (1) the Unitarian Home Rule Resolution (2) the Presbyterian Home Rule Memorial (3) the Liberal Conference and Land Committee should furnish the bones of an organisation in the majority of districts in N.E. Ulster.

Messrs Killen and Shillington wished me to write to you and say that we think the time has come for the appointment of a salaried man to act as secretary and organiser.

The three of us are busy and hard worked men, and although we would continue under any circumstances to serve the cause in every way possible, the routine office work which is daily accumulating is now too much for us to cope with. Home Rule sentiment has certainly spread and increased considerably during the past twelve or eighteen months amongst farmers and in some cases among business people in the Protestant districts of N.E. Ulster. In my opinion it is not an hour too soon to make an effort to capture the labourers.

As to how to raise the necessary funds, we think that a private circular letter should be sent to a leading man in some of the more important districts, asking him if he could guarantee £5 or £10 annually for three years from his district. Then if you had a promise of at least £100 from such sources, we would be in a position to ask for a guarantee of another £150 annually for three years from some external source. We would be glad to hear your opinion on this proposition. We were thinking that perhaps the Liberal party might be able to help us in raising the other £150 annually for three years and we contemplated asking Professor [James] Bryce M.P. after we should have raised our local guarantee fund ... .

P.S. Might I trouble you to send on this letter to our friend Professor Dougherty and perhaps he would be good enough to forward it to the Rev. J. B. Armour. And if these gentlemen, as well as yourself, would kindly communicate their opinions on the suggestions made, we would have a valuable body of advice. ...'

D.1792/A1/3/30   **Letter from J. B. Killen, Dublin, to Armour,**

12 June 1894   asking for assistance in prevailing upon Professor
                                          James Bryce, president of board of Trade in the
Liberal government, to give him a job in view of his destitute state and his failure to make capital out of his imprisonment by successive Conservative and Liberal governments in 1879 and 1880. He had been at Queen's College, Cork, with Armour.

'I am sure you will for old time's sake if nothing else excuse me for asking your advice and possibly your assistance ... . You mentioned in a former letter that you had some acquaintance with Professor Bryce M.P. He has since been appointed president of the board of Trade. As such he has very extensive patronage, and my object in writing to you ... is with a view to the feasibility of getting a job from him—anything that will furnish the means of living. My ambition has become very limited ... . Perhaps Mr Bryce might not be unwilling to see that I have a kind of claim on the British government. ... In 1879 I was arrested and put in jail by the Beaconsfield government for having made a few trifling observations in favour of Home Rule and land reform, and little more than a year after, when I was just beginning to recover from the injurious effects of suffering in an unfashionable cause (at that time it was hardly even respectable), I was arrested by Mr Gladstone's government and kept in jail for nearly six months. Had I been as adroit as some other "patriots" of the period I might have made a fortune out of my "martyrdom", but I shrank from making capital out of sacred things, and all that concerned Ireland seemed then to me sacred. ...

If you can make up your mind to pardon me for having so far trespassed on your patience—perhaps you could do something for me with Bryce—I am I may say quite out of work here—for my legal connection was broken long ago and the position of parties (with neither of whom can I fully agree) since Parnell's fall and death has left me very much alone. If nothing comes out of the present move, I'll leave Ireland for the [United] States—where I am pretty well known—just as soon as I can raise the means of doing so. My extreme poverty, however, does not permit me the blessedness even of becoming an emigrant.'

D.1792/A1/3/31

Part of a letter from J. B. Killen, [written from Belfast], to Armour,

[n.d. 1894 ?]

again begging for assistance in securing a government appointment either in Ireland or in Britain, and drawing attention to the fact that his Christian names are 'James Bryce'.

'... I don't of course ask you to do anything against or beyond the capacity of your conscience. ... My scholastic *etc*. qualifications are good enough. T. P. O'Connor has promised me his aid. ... The chief secretary I believe practically has the giving of the thing away so that if I could hurry up so as to catch [John] Morley before he resigns, I might give him the satisfaction of knowing that in appointing me he had done at least one good deed during his administration. ...

I should very much like to meet you. ... A good many years have passed since the young days when we used to talk philosophy and twaddle by the hours in your room on the Western Road, Cork. Both of us can count a good many graves—graves of more than men and women—since then. At least I can.

P.S. I'll be in Belfast for another week at least. If I could reach Professor James Bryce M.P. it would be important. He is a sort of far away kinsman of mine and I bear his name. ... By accident we happen to agree on the great question of federalism on which he is an authority. A pamphlet of mine published in London (1880) ("The United States of Europe") anticipated some of his views and though I was called a "dreamer of dreams" at the time—the doctrine it advocated was taken up. ...'

D.1792/A1/3/32

Letter from William P. Blair, Ballymena, [Co. Antrim], to Armour,

5 September 1894

commenting on a meeting to be held in Ballymoney Town Hall to endorse the land reform proposals of the Morley Commission.

'I was glad to see from your circular that Ballymoney which has always been in the van of progress is again going to give the keynote to Ulster Liberalism in the present crisis. I should have liked above all things to have formed one of the audience in the new Town Hall on Thursday, but, unfortunately, the exigencies of the Irish Poor Law medical service [Blair was a doctor] demand my presence in the dispensary here until one o'clock on that day, and I shall, therefore, have to console myself with the account of your meeting on the *Irish News* of Friday.

Matters have long since resumed their normal quiet here, but the leaven of Liberalism introduced in April is, I am happy to say, still fermenting. Its action has been wonderfully assisted by the revelations of the Morley Commission and from information I can gather on all sides, I think we have every reason to congratulate ourselves on the advance that has been made throughout the parliamentary division of East Antrim. ...'

D.1792/A1/3/33

Letter from John Pinkerton, M.P., Seacon, Ballymoney, [Co. Antrim], to Armour,

20 October 1894

discussing the proposed Ballymoney meeting in support of the Morley Commission proposals and in particular the chances of John Morley himself attending it.

'I am glad you thought of inviting Mr Morley to attend our meeting in Ballymoney. He is almost certain to refuse but all the same it was right to ask him. By not accepting your invitation he misses a golden opportunity, inasmuch as the farmers are strongly sympathetic at the present moment, and the appearance of a change in northern opinion would carry consternation into the Tory ranks. One meeting in Antrim would count for more in changing the political current than twenty in the south.

If Mr Morley gave the northerners a chance of seeing and hearing him we could almost carry Ulster.'

D.1792/A1/3/34

30 April 1896

Letter from W. H. Dodd to Armour,

enclosing a copy of a pamphlet which he has written on the land question and discussing how it can be given publicity.

'I send you a paper, with my review of the land bill and the guarantee of [T. W.] Russell. It is perhaps too detailed and too legal. But I was anxious to make it convincing and overwhelming. I hope the farmers will be able to follow it. I asked the Freeman people [*Freeman's Journal*] to send a paper, as from them, to the editor of the *Coleraine Chronicle*. I have not liked to send a copy to [S. C.] McElroy [editor of *Ballymoney Free Press*]. He would think I wanted a notice. But I should be obliged if you would let him have it, without asking or suggesting any notice.'

D.1792/A1/3/35

9 June 1896

Letter from Rev. M. Meneely, Belfast, to Armour,

enclosing a contribution for 'the family of the late Mr Jeffrey of Portadown'.

D.1792/A1/3/36

20 November 1899

Letter from Rev. J. M. Hamilton, Donore, [Dublin], to Armour,

containing personal news and gossip about the impending selection of a new moderator for the Presbyterian church. The letter also discusses the desire of Presbyterian male trainee teachers in Dublin to be allowed to worship in Ormond Quay Presbyterian Church rather than Rutland Square, because of their conscientious objection to the organ in the latter.

'... Dougherty requested me to call and see him which I did last Monday and he then told me that he had seen D. Taylor the previous week. That A. Robinson had asked him to accept the moderatorship another year and that he had refused, also that an effort is being made to secure Prentis's nomination in the presbyteries. Of this last I can find no trace here and I think it is premature. But perhaps you could tell me if anything is being done in that direction in the north. ... The male teachers in training have memorialised the commissioners of Education to be allowed to worship in Ormond Quay because they have a conscientious objection to worship in R[utland] Sq[uare] where there is an organ. There is purity for you. ...'

D.1792/A1/3/37

16 April [1900 ?]

Letter from Rev. J. M. Hamilton, Donore, [Dublin], to Armour,

containing personal news and gossip and also references to the ending of a dispute between Armour and an unidentified 'William' and to an encounter with J. B. Dougherty at a meeting of the Education Board.

D.1792/A1/3/38   **Part of a letter from Rev. J. Robinson, to Armour,**

[n.d.]   concerning Robinson's unsuccessful attempt to obtain a government-sponsored Presbyterian chaplaincy.

'What wire-pulling, what hypocrisy, what chicanery I saw. "There's something rotten" in the church of our fathers!'

D.1792/A1/3/39   **Part of a letter from Dr Anthony Traill, Trinity College, Dublin, to Armour,**

13 June 1900   replying to a public attack by Armour on Trinity College, Dublin, Irish Anglicanism and Irish landlords at the Presbyterian General Assembly. A series of letters went back and forth and were published in the press. Traill, as provost of Trinity College, a prominent Anglican layman and the owner of a considerable estate near Bushmills, Co. Antrim, defended his church and his class against Armour's strictures.

'Your charge amounts shortly to this, that the "oppressors of their country" are (1) the landlords, (2) the clergymen of the Church of Ireland, (3) the judges of the land and the legal profession generally; and you state that Trinity College has educated 9/10ths of these three classes—this latter statement is true about no. 2, not nearly true about no. 3, and quite untrue about no. 1. With regard to no. 1, you mix up all landlords with those few who did charge rack-rents, and you imply that because reductions were voluntarily made without going into the land courts (as in my own case) there must have been exactions previously, forgetting the very prosperous years for agriculture which preceded those later years in which prices fell—you also assume that the reduction of rents by 40% is a proof of previous robbery by landlords. This is confounding "*post hoc*" with "*propter hoc*", and as long as tenant farmers are entrusted with the power to fix rents, as sub-commissioners, so long will there be a serious "swing of the pendulum" in the reduction of rents beyond what justice requires. It is rather hard, you know, to "knock a man down and then kick him for falling", which is what your 40% argument does. The fact that a Tory government has carried out land legislation more drastic than that of Mr Gladstone only proves that all governments are "opportunists", to whichever side of politics they belong. With regard to no. 2, your clerical *animus* crops up more distinctly. For the title "Church of Ireland", you have only to consult the Act of Union and the Act of Disestablishment for the rehearsal of what has always been a historical fact. It has always astonished me how such a title can act as a "red rag" to members of your church, seeing that it interferes with you in no way and seeing that our ministrations extend to every part of Ireland, which those of your church do not. One would have fancied "*a priori*" that all Protestant churches would have approved of the title, as a standing protest against the Church of Rome in this country. How you can visit on clergymen of the present day the short-comings or high-handedness of members of an established church in past centuries, I cannot imagine, but it must be clear to every fair-minded man that our clergy can scarcely be called now "oppressors of their country". As to no. 3, it is a still more astounding statement that judges and lawyers are "oppressors of their country", and that "the courts from the highest to the lowest are stuffed with men who strain the laws wherever possible in favour of the classes and against the masses".'

D.1792/A1/3/40   **Letter from Thomas W. Dougan, Holywood, [Co. Down], to Armour,**

8 January 1901   enclosing a number of leaflets and pro-Boer pamphlets relating to the war in South Africa, and discussing reform of the Irish universities, in particular the setting up of a separate Ulster university.

'... With regard to a northern university or a resident Queen's or Royal university, I don't think Cork should be included as they have very few students there. It might be wound up and its endowments used elsewhere. Galway also seems to be fed not from the spot but mainly from Ulster: I would therefore shut it up.

In enlarging Magee College would you propose to give it a complete set of faculties—medical, law and engineering as well as arts, or only to develop the arts faculty?

Many of the medical chairs must necessarily go to the local practitioners—would sufficiently able men be regularly forthcoming in a comparitively small place like Derry?

It appears to me that it could only properly be a question of two colleges in the university though power to all of the members might be provided. ...'

D.1792/A1/3/41   **Letter from James J. Shaw, Dublin, to Armour,**

7 May 1902   discussing the election of a new Presbyterian moder-
                                                   ator, commenting on the narrowness and intolerance
of Belfast Presbyterians and promising to try to assist Armour to obtain the post of superintendent at the Royal University of Ireland examinations.

'... I am glad you gave a vote to Thompson, and I hope many took the same view as you did. These Belfast men are no doubt a peculiar people, but are they Christian at all? If a man differs in opinion with them on any point he forthwith becomes an aetheist or an outlaw—with no claim to any consideration either in this world or the next. If the next world is constituted on the Belfast pattern, some of us will have a bad time.

I had a long walk with Dougherty last Sunday. It is like old times having him here. He mentioned twice your desire to be a superintendent at the R.U.I. examinations this year, and I will have another talk with Meredith on the subject.

I should not be deeply grieved if I were relieved of my duties as senator, but I would rather retire voluntarily. ...'

D.1792/A1/3/42   **Letter from C. J. Meredith, Dublin, to Armour,**

13 June [19?]   thanking him for a letter of congratulation on the
                                                   occasion of his civil service promotion.

D.1792/A1/3/43   **Letter from Rev. W. J. Jamison, Ballymaconnelly,**
                                                   Belfast, to Armour,
9 November 1903
                                                   discussing a dispute in Jamison's congregation which
had led to his being locked out of his church by one section of his flock.

'I found the gates locked yesterday and a number of the congregation standing on the road. I asked who had the keys and was informed Samuel Montgomery had received them "with an injunction from the people not to permit the church to be opened that day". I first asked and afterwards demanded admission as the representative of the General Assembly and the moder-ator of the Session. ... I then entered and held a service at which twenty members of the congregation were present. The opposing members did not enter the church at all. I called a meeting of the congregation at the close of the service and it was decided the keys should be retained by Mr McClarnon who is favourable to the continued connection with the General Assembly. ... I hear the disaffected party were in negotiation to get a minister from another body. ... I think the commission [of the General Assembly] should meet the congregation after an interval. ... I have been thinking if they had a service every other Sabbath then some would drop into other churches and those remaining would be more likely amenable to reason. ...'

D.1792/A1/3/44

Letter from Rev. S. R. Henry, Portglenone, [Co. Antrim], to Armour,

[n.d. 1903 ?]

concerning an attempt to exclude Rev. Henry from his church and inviting Armour to intervene on his behalf with the congregation.

D.1792/A1/3/45

Letter from J. Maconaghie, [Londonderry ?], to Armour,

26 January 1904

pressing the claims of a candidate for the vacant Dervock Presbyterian congregation and containing other church gossip.

'... We were well pleased with your sermon. ... You seem latterly to be the Route Presbytery, and not only to minister to our ministers in their trouble, but to see that their memory suffers not. If there is a special place in the beyond for utterly unselfish men who live only for others, one person should have the chief seat there. ...'

D.1792/A1/3/46

Letter from R. Pringle, Greystones, [Co. Wicklow], to Armour,

28 September 1905

responding to a suggestion from Armour that he put himself forward as a Liberal candidate, possibly in North Antrim, at the impending general election. It was certainly the case that the North Antrim supporters of T. W. Russell had been searching rather desperately for a candidate and in the end had to settle for the undynamic and taciturn Belfast linen merchant, R. G. Glendinning, who despite his shortcomings won the seat from the sitting Unionist member, W. Moore. Glendinning stood as an independent but subsequently sat with the Liberals at Westminster and identified himself with a revived Ulster Liberal Association.

'Your letter of the 25th has been forwarded to me and reached me last night and I fully appreciate your kindness in writing to me in this way—I quite agree with you in many things you say and especially that there is an excellent chance for a strong Liberal at the present time but up to the present I have taken no part in politics and indeed have had little inclination towards them for many reasons. Nor do I think I possess many of the requisites for a successful politician and it is of course out of the question to enter on such a contest in a half-hearted way and in the absence of special qualifications for the work, I am afraid you have more than given me the benefit of the doubt. When you assume that because I am my father's son I could fight the Liberal battle as he would have done some years ago and I regret greatly that I am not able to fall in with your suggestion, more especially as I know it would have been a pleasure to him to know that I was doing so. I quite agree with you that the money spent would be well invested and had I been thinking of entering political life your suggestion would have been most acceptable. ...'

D.1792/A1/3/47

Letter from Rev. J. L. Wilson, Belfast, to Armour,

2 February 1906

asking that Armour use his influence with Sir James B. Dougherty, under secretary of state for Ireland, to push the claims of a Catholic friend of Rev. Wilson to a deputy governorship in the prison service. The letter is an interesting example of Armour's role as a link in a patronage chain. The letter also comments favourably on the electoral progress made by the Russellites and Liberals in Ulster in the 1906 general election and refers specifically to R. G. Glendinning's victory in North Antrim.

'... You have been making havoc in the Route as we in Belfast at the election. What a wonderful change. Democracy is growing. ...'

D.1792/A1/3/48

Letter from J. W. Kirk, Antrim, [Co. Antrim], to Armour,

7 February 1906

asking Armour to use his influence with W. H. Dodd, the recently elected Liberal member for North Tyrone, to press the claims of two South Antrim Presbyterian Liberals to be appointed as justices of the peace. The letter also comments favourably on Glendinning's success in North Antrim.

'It is about twelve years since any of *our* friends have got the comm. of the peace. We have had no fight in South Antrim [the constituency was not contested by a Liberal or Russellite in 1906]. Consequently have no patron. There are two gent[lemen] whose names I would like put before the lord chancellor and their claims pressed. They are Mr John Boal, Antrim, and Mr Thomas K. Moore, Crookedstone, Muckamore. The former employs 3/400 hands in his factory and the Orange factions are so opposed to him politically that they would not elect him a town commissioner; I am the only magistrate *resident* in Antrim and being from home a good deal at certain seasons, the police are sometimes inconvenienced. Two appointments were made recently, the one a landlord, the other a land agent, the last named's sole interest in the county being a salary of £250 per annum from Lord Masserene. These were made in room of deaths.

Mr Moore lives half way between Antrim and Crumlin, is a large farmer, very intelligent and earned like a good many of us a large share of ill-will in the early nineties. He is hon. sec. of the Agricultural Association whose members number 600. He lives in a district in which (in fact in the same townland) there used to be two magistrates, his uncle Mr Wm. Morrison and a Mr [Samuel] Black. There have been no appointments since these ... now a good many years ago. Both Boal and Moore are Presbyterians and highly esteemed citizens.

I know Serjeant [W. H.] Dodd will have plenty to do with his own constituency but possibly he would also advance the claims of these two. I know he will do a good deal for you and if not trespassing too much on your good nature might I ask you to further the claims of these gentlemen.

North Antrim has done well. It is said [Colonel Edward] Saunderson [leader of the Ulster Unionists at Westminster] is for retiring in favour of [Wm.] Moore [the recently defeated Unionist member for North Antrim]. No matter, he and his party are discredited and the Liberals are into power for another twenty years.'

D.1792/A1/3/49

Letter from Thomas Shillington, Portadown, [Co. Armagh], to Armour,

7 December 1907

responding to a verbal suggestion from Armour that Shillington allow his name to go forward for a public appointment, possibly a magistracy or a knighthood. Shillington was a veteran Liberal and land reformer and clearly felt that the Liberals must avoid any suggestion of corruption in the making of public appointments, now that they were so firmly in power. Shillington was also concerned that the political independence which he had zealously protected over many years might be compromised. The letter recommends an alternative candidate for the position, Mr Hugh Mack of Lisburn. Mack did indeed receive a knighthood subsequently.

'... Now in what I have to say you must not misunderstand me as desiring to set up any super excellent standard of ethics or of conduct that could not be applied in this workaday world, I merely wish to state the aspect the question has for me, as accounting for my views stated hereafter.

As I mentioned, from my earliest attempts to influence public opinion, or to contribute towards the progress of what I considered affected the welfare of the community, I resolved that my action or speech should be determined only by public interests without regard to personal gain, society, or fear of personal loss—an extended experience of men and affairs has firmly confirmed me in this resolution, and I have often urged persons seeking place and honours, and their friends, to sink these questions and work disinterestedly for the public weal.

In this country, especially when for many generations the gifts of the government have been, in so many cases, corruptly bestowed, it is more incumbent on us to be circumspect if we wish our words or example to have influence.

Now, having said so much in explanation, I would ask you to use your influence to have the honour conferred upon Mr Hugh Mack of Lisburn instead, and you can represent in the proper quarter that this is with my entire concurrence.

It will make no difference whatsoever to my interest in affairs. ...'

D.1792/A1/3/50

20 March 1908

Letter from W. M. Clow, Portadown, [Co. Armagh], to Armour,

concerning the case of a Mr H. G. Patterson who had been evicted from his farm in 1887 and, the land having come into the hands of the estate commissioners, had been offered an opportunity of buying it back. This offer, having been made and agreed upon, had then been withdrawn. Clow is seeking Armour's help in trying to remedy the situation, in view of the latter's influence with the government.

D.1792/A1/3/51

11 August 1909

Letter from James J. Shaw, Killiney, [Co. Dublin], to Armour,

referring to Armour's public intervention in defence of the new Queen's University of Belfast against its critics, and his attack on proposals for an expansion of Magee College, Londonderry, in association with Trinity College, Dublin.

'I have just seen your "interview" in the [*Northern*] *Whig* and have read it with great interest and pleasure. It is uncommonly well done, and I am sure will do good. I hope it will appear in the *Witness* where that imposter [Rev.] Prenter has been writing the silliest and most disgusting stuff. I saw also the reply of a professor of the U.C.D. who judiciously refused to give his name. It is a very feeble performance. It passes over in silence all the critical points of the case. The fact is, there is no answer to your statement of the case.

I am quite sure the Belfast men like [Rev.] Todd-Martin, [Rev.] Heron *etc.* are beginning to realise their folly. It is quite evident this Magee movement is being made the basis of an attack upon the Assembly's College and we are threatened with a renewal of all the old controversies. ...'

D.1792/A1/3/52

26 August 1909

Letter from James J. Shaw, [writing from Edinburgh, Scotland], to Armour,

discussing criticisms of the Magee College proposals and of Chief Secretary Augustine Birrell's Irish universities act, in particular its provision for the teaching of scholastic philosophy in the new Irish university structure.

'Somebody has sent me last week's *Witness*. "Southern Presbyterian" exceeds himself in absurdity—he could not in dishonesty. He now contradicts all our anti-scholastic friends by asserting that scholastic philosophy is not only a legitimate, but a necessary, part of a philosophic course. But it must be taught by a Protestant who will expose its absurdities. As he elsewhere states that it is the basis of R.C. theology, this shows his notion of a non-sectarian university. It is one in which it will be a necessary part of the course to subvert the foundations of Roman

Catholic theology. Of course all these men in their hearts mean by a non-sectarian, a Protestant university, but I think it has never been so openly avowed.

I see that our friend [Rev.] MacDermott has petitioned against scholastic philosophy. I am very glad. It will give me the opportunity I have been longing for of exposing the falsities and mis-representations of our enemies and quieting the fears of our friends. I intend to take full advantage of it. ... The utter ignorance of the whole matter which lies at the root of all this alarm and excitement will be made apparent to everybody. [Rev.] Prenter, of course, is not only ignorant but dishonest and malignant. I give [Rev.] MacD[ermott] credit for honesty, but he knows nothing whatever about the matter he has taken in hand.

I don't think the Magee people will get much more money than appears in their list. What has become of Lady Smylie's £1,000 which we heard so much about? I suspect it disappeared with her son's withdrawal from West Belfast. The next thing will be the sale of the *Northern Whig* and the disappearance of Joe Fisher.

I hear, but I cannot believe, that the Magee people now put all the blame on me for their present position. If there is any truth in this, it only shows how desperate they must have become in their attempt to find an excuse for their own folly. They all know perfectly well that [Sir J. B.] Dougherty and I were the only friends they had when [Augustine] Birrell was framing his bill, and that it was to us they owe all the opportunities they threw away so recklessly.'

D.1792/A1/3/53

24 March 1910

Letter from M. A. Eagleson, Model School, Monaghan, [Co. Monaghan], to Armour,

asking for Armour's help in securing the vacant postmastership of Monaghan town for Thomas Dunwoody.

D.1792/A1/3/54

8 April [1910 ?]

Letter from Samuel Dill, Ulster Club, Belfast, to Armour,

setting out his views on the scholastic philosophy issue—views which were sympathetic to the Catholic point of view.

D.1792/A1/3/55

4 June 1910

Letter from Samuel Dill, Montpelier, Malone Road, Belfast, to Armour,

urging him not to revive the scholastic philosophy issue at the Queen's University senate, since he could not hope for much support there.

D.1792/A1/3/56

2 April 1912

Letter from J. H. Morgan, Professor of Constitutional Law at University College, London, 1 Mitre Court Buildings, Temple, [London], to Armour,

asking for a contribution from Armour to the forthcoming book on the Irish question which Morgan is editing for publication by the Eighty Club, in association with Hodder and Stoughton.

'I am editing a book on the Irish question on behalf of the Eighty Club and Sir William Robertson Nicoll has recommended your name to me as that of an eminent Presbyterian minister who might be willing to write as an Ulster Protestant in favour of Home Rule. Would you be prepared to do this? If so, I and my committee would be greatly obliged. What I have in mind is a short article of three to four thousand words which would tend to allay the fears of English Protestants as to possible oppression by the Catholic community under Home Rule. ...'

D.1792/A1/3/57

23 October 1913

Letter from Sir Roger Casement, 'Ardrigh', Antrim Road, Belfast, to Armour,

declining hospitality in Trinity Manse prior to the 1913 anti-Carson meeting in Ballymoney Town Hall. It clearly indicates Casement's nervousness about his first major public speaking engagement.

'It is very kind of you to want Mrs [Alice] Green and me to go to the Manse—but I fear it is not possible. Both of us wish to be quite to ourselves before the meeting—with no one to talk to or talk to us—and we are firmly fixed on this. Besides Mrs Green is not well. She bids me thank you very much for your kind thought of her and to say how much she appreciates it and that she feels sure you will understand. After the meeting we will probably motor away somewhere—that is our present thought and not sleep in Ballymoney at all. We shall, however, see you at the meeting I hope—and will then thank you for your kindness.'

D.1792/A1/3/58

[n.d. 1913]

Part of a letter from Sir Roger Casement, Marine Hotel, Ballycastle, Co. Antrim, to Armour,

thanking him for his hospitality on the previous evening following the anti-Carson meeting in Ballymoney Town Hall; suggesting that the speeches delivered at the meeting should be printed in pamphlet form (this was in fact done); indicating that like others including Armour himself, he regarded Alec Wilson's contribution as perhaps the best; and enclosing an article which he has written for the *Fortnightly Review*.

'I am up first and take the morning shine to drop you a line to say how very much Mrs [Alice] Green, Mr [Alec] Wilson and I felt your kindness and that of your wife last night. I really left you with great regret—but I wanted very much to spend today down here and see my friends in this part.

I think we should have the speeches of last night printed in a little pamphlet for local (Co. Antrim) use. The printed word remains on record—and there were things said last night especially Mr Wilson's—will last and perhaps go far. Here is the article I told you of that will appear in the Nov[ember] *Fortnightly Review*—I hope you will understand my reference to the "Rectory capturing the Manse"—that might give offence in some quarters, but I am sure you will see the justice of the criticism in view of the "reek of bigotry" that has gone up from both of late and hidden a far loftier head than that of the poor Irish Catholic. I am sorry there were so many references to the Catholic church. ...'

D.1792/A1/3/59

30 May 1914

Letter from Richardson Evans, The Keir, Wimbledon Common, [Middlesex], to Armour,

devoted entirely to personal and family news.

and that the Covenanter minister
McVicker is turned likewise.

No more at present
but remains yours
truly
James B Armour

Mr John Megaw

[D.]1792/A2/1   A2/1

Belfast September 14
1859

Mr John Megaw
Dear Sir
I am sure by
this time you will have thought that
the motto "out of sight out of mind"
is verified at last in your case.
But since I came up this time things
have gone on so smoothly and there
have been so many strange lecturers
in town that I scarcely ever knew
the time going round. I had the
pleasure of hearing Mr B Wrath
on five occasions & every time

Facsimile of a letter from J. B. Armour to J. Megaw, Ballyboyland,
County Antrim, 14 September 1859 (D.1792/A2/1).

LETTERS FROM REV. J. B. ARMOUR

D.1792/A2/1-38

1859-1928

Originals and copies of letters from Rev. J. B. Armour to others, including 13 letters to his friend, John Megaw of Ballyboyland, Ballymoney, Co. Antrim, but excluding letters to members of his family or to his relative, Jane MacMaster (the sister of Professor James MacMaster, Armour's wife's brother-in-law). All letters from Armour are written from Trinity Manse, Ballymoney, Co. Antrim, unless otherwise stated.

D.1792/A2/1

14 September 1859

Letter to J. Megaw, Ballyboyland, [Co. Antrim], from Armour, [written from Belfast],

the first of a series (D.1792/A2/1-13) written by Armour as a student at the Royal Belfast Academical Institution and the Queen's College, Belfast, to his childhood friend, John Megaw, who lived on the Megaw family farm at Ballyboyland, not far from Armour's own home. These letters record Armour's adolescent and student experiences in Belfast, his opinions on the religious and political issues of the day, church and educational gossip. This initial letter is mainly concerned with the religious revival of 1859, as seen through Armour's eyes in Belfast, and includes sceptical comments on some of its more lurid excesses.

'I am sure by this time you will have thought that the motto "out of sight, out of mind" is verified at least in your case. But since I came up this time things have gone on so smoothly and there have been so many strange lectures in town that I scarcely ever knew the time going round. I had the pleasure of hearing Mr B. North on five occasions and every time I heard him, I liked him better, every word he says is a thought and in explaining anything he could come to the point at once.

The revival is progressing in general very well but there are means used for its extension even by Presbyterian ministers which I think is very far from right, for example Mr Thomas Toye's. They have prayer meetings I think every night and they have a penitent's form where those that are burned with sin kneel and groan over their sins and then the Rev. Thomas prays with them. If ever you were in a Methodist chapel it is something of the same in Mr Toye's.

I cannot understand the sleeping cases at all, some say that they get a vision from the other world and that they see Christ and the place of woe, but I would be inclined to think that it is only imagination and I think that they should be advised not to look for any visions. Another dreadful imposture is a practising in this town, girls painting on their breast the words "Jesus Christ" and saying it came there when they were in their sleep.

I would be very glad to hear your opinion respecting these matters.

I believe the two young men that you had at Kilraughts from Connor are both turned to the Baptists and that the Covenanting minister McVicker is turned likewise.

No more at present.'

D.1792/A2/2

20 March 1860

Letter to J. Megaw from Armour, [written from Belfast],

largely containing gossip, with some comments on the progress of the 1859 revival and an indication of Armour's Liberal sympathies in his expression of support for the Liberal, Samuel Greer, in an impending Londonderry City by-election. Greer was defeated by William McCormick (Conservative).

'... Since I wrote before nothing of any importance has happened. The revival I am happy to say appears to be going on as much as ever. The meetings are very well attended and at the prayer meetings there are always a great many requests for prayer by sisters for brothers *etc*. I hear you are establishing an association at the Ganaby [school] but how it will be managed I did not hear. I hope you will get our William [Armour's brother] connected with it. Ichabod may be engraved on Ballymacwilliam ... since you are left it.

It appears that the Rev. Magill of Cork is to be the pastor of York St[reet]. However, there has been no poll taken yet but the most of the people are for him although they never heard him. He is a very clever, good man but he is getting old and has very poor health. I suppose you'll know him as he was in Coleraine long before he went to Cork. I see that [Samuel] Greer is putting in for the borough of Derry as the other [the sitting Liberal member, Sir R. A. Ferguson] is dead. I earnestly wish he may get it but I have some doubts.

Between deaths, one thing and another, the Presbyterian church has suffered greatly this year. ...'

D.1792/A2/3

Letter to J. Megaw from Armour, [written from Belfast],

8 May 1860

concerning alleged falling educational standards at the Queen's College and the decision no longer to insist upon knowledge of a classical language as a prerequisite for taking a degree. Foreign languages are seen by Armour as no substitute. The continuing revival is criticised, or at least those who are on its fringe.

'... I am very sorry that the degree of A.M. is lowered. If it ever be put into effect as it is every way likely it will, it will destroy all Queen's Colleges. I suppose you will have by the paper that a degree can be taken without any ancient language. If a fellow knows a little gibberish of French and some smatter of German he may have a degree any time. It is to give the merchants' sons who are too lazy to learn anything that requires work an A.B. and A.M. and I think it is to spoil these Q[ueen's] colleges for there are some fellows go from them that are able to get as high marks as any from Trinity College. The fact of the matter is no man that has any learning will go for a degree. The professors are all raging at it. Dr Steen is afraid that he will have to turn his hand to something else than teaching classics.

We had a fine address from Rev. Moran of Newry on "How to read the bible and how to teach it" on Thursday evening. The awakening I think is going on well but there are a very great many deceivers. I am beginning to think that the letting of young men speak that knew nothing before has done a very serious injury since all they can say is that they are born again and that is merely a fancy with the majority.'

D.1792/A2/4

Letter to J. Megaw from Armour, [written from Belfast],

24 August 1860

containing a *melange* of gossip and some further comments about the religious revival.

'... I have to be very busy in preparing for the examinations. I have the historics and the mathematics to make up at home. The weather here has been for the last week very wet, it has rained nearly all the time. There are rumours afloat that there will be a famine this winter in consequence of so much rain. I hear that hay and oats about the Co. Mayo are perfectly rotted. They say that the floods in that part were so high that a man was carried two or three miles in a hay rick. I am very sorry to say that Belfast College has lost this year three of its cleverest men. One of them was taken away by the hand of death. The other two are being removed to higher and more emolumentary positions. Dr McCosh has got a professorship in Aberdeen; he is about as clever a man as Belfast can produce. The professor of mathematics has got the chair of natural philosophy in Edinburgh which will be worth about £1,400. The fact of the matter is that the endowment of the Queen's Colleges is far too little. £250 a year is too little for a man that has spent all his lifetime learning, a banker has nearly as much more.

I see that our moderator has got an American D.D. to his name. Truly we live in a wonderful age. I think it will be possible to get degrees yet without going to college at all. It is about as odd a thing as ever I knew that Dill, a man that never was heard tell of before, by going to America a while and coming home and being appointed moderator should get D.D. and Mr Gibson, a man universally known, a professor in College, writer of a splendid book and who has travelled not only in America but nearly throughout Europe and who was also moderator of the Assembly should get none. In my humble opinion the one deserved it and the other did not. There will no place in Ireland there will be so many clergy as about Ballymoney, if all that are looking forward to that holy calling attain it but I am afraid that some of them will stick. The revival sent a great many to learn but a great many have turned. ... I see H. H. Finlay has got the Mrs without I think asking the congregation but your Kilraughts people will not allow [Rev.] Samuel [Finlay, minister of Kilraughts Presbyterian Church] to marry without asking you.'

D.1792/A2/5

Letter to J. Megaw from Armour, [written from Belfast],

1 November 1860

attempting to explain his failure to win a scholarship, recounting the usual gossip about clerics and laymen and giving his opinion on the worth of country towns.

'I have been defeated for the first time in my life. I have missed the scholarship. I can say however that I am not very heavily disappointed. I knew that I was not rightly prepared for standing an examination with a great number of those that were going in. You will have seen the names of the fellows in the *Banner* [*of Ulster*] so that I need not tell you them. The first scholar was prepared for a sizarship in Dublin but thinking he would not be successful in so difficult an examination he came to Belfast. The second is a little fellow that has been at classics for the last six years. He was in Dr Steen's highest class when I went to the [Royal Belfast Academical] Institution, so that it was no wonder that he was successful. The next two were very good at English and very nice writers which has a good deal of weight in an English exam[ination]. They were very good at Latin and Greek also. ...

I am not sure whether I will try for the second year's scholarship or not, it all depends on how I do at the end of the session.

[Rev.] Hanson, I believe, is doing well in York St[reet]. The house is always crowded as yet but I expect that will go away. He seems to be very attentive to visitation which is the chief thing in keeping up a congregation. He is by no means a clever man, at least in my judgement, but he is a plain, practical preacher. I am sure he will not be so much esteemed as his predecessor. I don't know whether we are going to loose [Rev.] Hugh Hanna or not. I see that three of the Scotch ministers are to be on a deputation to the Presbytery when it meets next. If he goes, Belfast will have lost a clever man. I am sure you will have seen in the *Banner* [*of Ulster*] his letter to the [*Northern*] *Whig*. I have never read so cutting a letter in my life, however, it is rather low for a minister to write. ...

Country towns are like country schools [of] very little worth. ...

I suppose the corn is all in about that quarter by this time but I am sure the potatoes will not be all raised at the 12th of Nov[ember] this year. ...

I intend to read pretty largely at English this winter as I have neglected that very important branch for some time. I have been giving my attention more particularly to classics.'

D.1792/A2/6

31 January 1861

Letter to J. Megaw from Armour, [written from Belfast],

discussing his courses at Queen's College, Belfast, and giving his views on the relative merits of psalms and hymns in Presbyterian worship.

'... The studies which we have to pursue in the first year are nearly all very uninteresting. However, I cannot say but that I like them all very well with the exception of mathematics which I consider to be the Slough of Despond. I can follow all the professors but the mathematical and I must confess that he soars too high for me to see him. I am kept pretty busy preparing for the classes, more so than the last term as I have taken a German class this time in addition to the others, and as I know nothing about it, not even the letters—it takes me a considerable time to prepare in order to keep up with the other chums. I expect I will be able to manage it anyhow. All things are going on very quietly in this town except that there is a great fuss about psalms and hymns. The question is being very ably debated on both sides, however I think the advocates of the psalms—as it is decidedly the right cause—have the best of it. The principal advocate for psalms is a divinity student. He is a brother of Martin who preaches in Eglington St[reet]. I will send you after a little some of the pamphlets that you may see. ...'

D.1792/A2/7

6 Feburary 1862

Letter to J. Megaw from Armour, [written from Belfast],

containing a variety of church gossip, criticising the passive orthodoxy of many Presbyterians and forecasting the total collapse of Arianism within the Presbyterian camp.

'... I have little news of any kind this time as I have read little or nothing at the papers since I came up. Matters are going on very quietly here. I am glad to be able to tell you that Mr Carson has filled his house almost already. The people seem to be well pleased with him. We have had two new churches opened within the last fortnight, one directly opposite the Queen's College and the other at Sydenham near Holywood. They have been both built by Belfast merchants, the former by Mr [J. P.] Corry and the latter by Mr [Thomas] McClure. It is reported and I believe very truly that Mr Moore of Connor is going to get the one opposite to College. It has been offered to him but I believe that he has not decided on taking it. I hear that the B'weany people have given a unanimous call to Mr Forsythe but I have never heard whether he has accepted it or not. I know that he was in doubts whether to take it or not. His principal objection to it was that there was no prospect of having any society in that part of the country. I saw him this day but I did not get asking him about it. He is attending the law classes at present. In my opinion the B'weany people have made a very judicious choice as he is a man of talent. These "essay and reviews" have occasioned a great stir in the religious world. Dr Williams is being tried before a law court at present respecting one of them. It is very humiliating I am sure for a man of his abilities to be tried by laymen but such is the state of things in the Church of England. McCosh has brought out a book in answer to one of these essays which is entitled the "relation of the natural to the supernatural". I have not seen it yet but I expect to see it in a few days. It has every chance of getting a scorching from some of the reviews as I am sure his views will be rather too pietistic for some of the London prints. The essays without question show great talent. ... I have seen one of them but I had only time to read about the third of it and I confess that I could not follow the train of the reasoning as it was treated in a very metaphysical style. If you have seen any of Mr Nelson's pamphlets entitled the "year of delusion", I will give you the reading of one of them. They are very well written and in my opinion he has the best of the argument. I go very frequently to hear him on the Sabbath days as I believe I can learn more from him than any other man. His sermons or rather his lectures are not very long but they always contain a great deal of thought and he always throws out something to occupy one's thoughts during the week. That I think is a great fault among Presbyterians that they do not think enough of themselves, they take everything as gospel that falls from their pastor's mouth without even inquiring into the reason of those things for themselves. It is a deplorable state of things but yet it is quite true. One of the oldest ministers of the Arian body in town has at last acknowledged the personality of the spirit which is a very important matter. This is a body which I believe will soon die out as they are beginning to disagree among themselves, some of them nearly turning to infidelity and others again leaning towards Presbyterianism. ...'

D.1792/A2/8

1 April 1862

Letter to J. Megaw from Armour, [written from Belfast],

containing church and college gossip and a sharp attack on the majority of Presbyterian ministers, especially on their vocational motivation.

'I must now issue my number of our "monthly periodical" although I am dreadfully at a loss for articles to fill it up. As I was anticipating in my last that McCosh's "natural and supernatural" would get a slashing from some of the London prints, so it has come to pass. *The Critic* I believe gave him an awful shaving. Persons who have read it tell me they never heard any man getting it so tremendously. It is also reported but I think without grounds that it is [Rev.] Isaac Nelson who is the author of it. There is however no man with the exception of Professor Gibson against whom Nelson has a greater antipathy than McCosh but he has given him enough in his "year of delusion" without having recourse to an infidel London print. Dr Cooke says McCosh's book is a very philosophical work and answers the "essay" remarkably well but I am inclined to think that the Dr would like to soap a little. He could have been as popular at any rate if he had never written it although an answer to such writings was much needed. He [McCosh] is a clever man but in no way a man of great originality of thought. I saw one time an American review of his works and I thought the critique on it was remarkably just. It said McCosh's mind was like a magnet ... that it brought out what was good and left the refuse and trash. I saw in the *Banner [of Ulster]* the other day that he had been nominated by a country presbytery to the chair vacant by the death of Cunningham but he has just as much chance of getting it as I have, which is precious little. As I have learned, that is not at all popular in Scotland. The government are thinking of doing away with metaphysics altogether and amalgamating the topic with the English. If this takes place Dr McCosh will have to look out for another situation. It would ruin the Q[ueen's] Colleges, if it would take place and it would establish the Magee College, as all the intending clergy would have to go there. You said in your last that Mr Forsythe's principles were far ahead of his practice. It is wonderful how an ill report spreads—had it been anything good it would not have been known so very soon. I suppose like all the rest of us he was a little rakish but I think he is greatly settled within the last year. ... I hope he will get on well where [he] is placed. The fact of the matter is anyway that there is no class of men more liable to be Christians in *theory* only as ministers and I am very much afraid that the majority of the Gen[eral] Ass[embly] are merely theoretical Christians. You will perhaps say this is a bold assertion but I will give you my reason for forming such an opinion. There is not more than one tenth of them who choose the ministry from sheer desire to do good. Many choose it from a desire of show and of having a respectable position in society; others for the sake of the £.s.d., others again for the sake of being called great, but the greater number from the ambition of their parents. I ask, going no farther than our own congregation, what is the reason of so many young chaps being sent to learning. ... Is it that people are becoming more zealous for a good cause? I should like to think so but yet I think it would be too much for a person who is weak in faith. Do you not think yourself that there are a good deal of selfish ambitions sometimes at the bottom? I am as able to give my son an education, says such a one, as ... so and so, or perhaps they expect that the Lord will do them good if they have a Levite for their priest. I rejoice to think that so many are giving their sons an education but I protest against the goal to which they wish to direct them to very often against their will. If this is true the reason of [*sic*] so many theoretic ministers is quite obvious. This may not be your vision of the matter but I give you mine confidentially.

We have lost our French professor which is a sore grievance to us, as he was very much liked by all the students. But he was like all the foreigners a little lax in his morals. His wife and he did not live together for some time past and as a substitute he kept a lady in the house with him whom he introduced to the professors as his niece, but in reality she was a concubine. She was very handsome and some medical student of Trinity College took a passion for her and was at church to get the words said but the vicar had heard that she had lived with our professor and was with child to him, so that he refused to marry her to the young fellow. This reached the senators' ears and they sent down word to the president to have the matter investigated. He, knowing that the matter would not stand investigation, advised him to resign. So he took his advice and we are left without a man. For my part I would have liked he had stayed on whatever his faults, as he was a remarkably good teacher and good linguist. The clergy are taking a wonderful mania for having a congregation in Belfast. Moore of Connor is placed lately in Queen's Elms—a man by the way who will never do Belfast as he is too plain and ready spoken for a Belfast audience. ...'

D.1792/A2/9

1 May 1863

Part of a letter to J. Megaw from Armour, [written from Cookstown],

commenting on the American Civil War and on disaffection against British rule in Ireland, as well as including the usual clercial gossip. Armour was at this time undertaking some teaching for financial reasons.

'No careful observer who takes pleasure in the peace and security of his country can behold without terror the events that are occuring daily to widen the breach between this country and America. The Yankees seem to have arrived at that stage of insanity that they intend picking a quarrel with whomsoever they may come in contact, without ever calculating how unequal they are at present for carrying on hostilities. It will take great tact combined with coolness and judgement on the part of British statesmen to steer clear of collision with the said infatuated people. The insanity of an individual is a woeful matter, but when a nation is resolved to adopt measures which have been carefully rejected by wise statesmen and elect as their chief officers those whom the world calls infamous merely because the world holds them as such, the evil is much worse. Now America has done so with Wilkes and Butler. However, I think there is little fear of her sending the latter with twenty thousand men with ropes to tear Ireland from England and add it as a province to the *disunited* States of Am[erica]. Though it is a country of "Haythens and Turks" who are beginning to look upon murder as the only effectual means of getting rid of a troublesome bailiff or tyrannising landlord, yet it is to be expected that Eng[land] would not just give up a sister isle without a struggle.

In all probability Rogers will be moderator as Killen who is rather of retiring habits has withdrawn his name. The former deserves it well both in consideration of his intrinsic merits and his hatred of all truckling humbug. ... Carson is "a gun of sma bore". ... His character is however unimpeachable but we want a little more for a minister of the 19th century than a good character. I see Finlay is leaving Moneydig for the gold diggings. Is it for the sake (do *you* think) of enlarging his sphere of usefulness as every minister who intends making a change ... asserts or merely for the sake of pelf. According to all accounts his congregation and he were mutually tired of each other. ...'

D.1792/A2/10

29 August 1863

Letter to J. Megaw from Armour, [written from Cookstown],

emphasising his desire not to enter the Presbyterian ministry, discussing the economic condition of the Galway area and drawing attention to the expansion of the linen industry as a result of the American Civil War.

'There are few things "in this vale of tears" more interesting, at least to me, than the undisguised interchange of ideas with a congenial spirit and yet there are few sub-lunary [*sic*] matters more rare than the finding of a person to whom you can freely unmask your mind and unbutton your brain and give as freely as the thoughts occur to you the results of your deliberations. He is no hermit, though placed in the wilds of Africa, who has a trusty friend to whom he can impart his thoughts and plans and projects: his chimerical fancies and perhaps noble aspirations. Willingly have I always shared with you my [?] projects and heartily shall I continue to do so, knowing that you would be the last to divulge or comment upon any of my plans even though they appeared the results of boyish impetuousity rather than those of mature judgement. You doubtless will have gathered from various hints thrown out that it is not my intention of entering the ministry. This was my resolution from the first, and as I grow older and know more of the world, there are matters occurring which render that altogether impossible. It remains for me now to choose some employment which shall keep me comfortable and enable me to repay, to some extent, the money already spent on my education—a matter I shall yet perform if health and strength be granted. After a good deal of anxiety, I have resolved to try my hand at an Indian Civil Service appointment, if my literary attainments enable me. The position is one of considerable emolument but the climate is bad so that it is not one European out of twenty can stand it. I may alter my mind considerably supposing as good an offer nearer home present[s] itself, but at any rate I shall for the future direct my energies to that as my ultimum. If the "I" bears a prominent place in this epistle you must not account it as a mark of self-importance but rather the shortest way of acquainting you with my ideas.

The opening of this Galway line of steamers will be of considerable importance to the west of Ireland, if the inhabitants have the sense to make it of use, but they seem to have a far greater relish in that quarter for talking about an English oppression and brandishing their scythes, though their greatest oppression seems to be popery and innate slothfulness. Galway might soon be made as flourishing as Belfast were any pains taken now to improve their trade which has gotten so good an assistance from the government.

It "is an ill wind that blows nobody good", saith the old proverb, and certainly if the American war has been almost the ruination of the cotton trade it has certainly opened a way for the extension of the flax trade which is (especially in these bad seasons) the one and only thing keeping the small Irish farmer from poverty and starvation.

The flax market has already opened in this town, which might be properly designated "Flaxopolis", with pretty high prices and a good quality of material. There is little chance of it falling much during the winter and in all likelihood it will be steady. ...'

D.1792/A2/11

4 November 1863

Letter to J. Megaw from Armour, [written from Cork],

the first of three letters written to Megaw whilst Armour was attending Queen's College, Cork, recounting his experiences and advancing his, as always scathing, opinions about his fellow students.

'Circumstances over which I had no control prevented me from writing at the appointed time. However, I am now able to announce to you that I am 2nd scholar in my third year, which is very well considering that I had never opened a book or made the slightest preparation. Preparation, however, was altogether out of my power in Cookstown and, though here a week previous to my examinations, I was laid up with quinsey, which not only stopped my reading but, what was more vital, also my sleeping and eating capabilities. It is now restored again through the application of a blister and other emollient plasters so that I have now fairly entered the arena against my opponents the Corkonians. They are much inferior in attainments to our Belfast men, not from any want of talent (for the majority are smart fellows) but rather from indolence and paying too much pains in decorating their exterior rather than storing their minds with useful information. What appeared strange to me was that the students here in general seem to belong to the respectable class of society; they are even more gentlemanly in their appearance than the Belfast men, and there seems to be none of that bigotry with regard to religious principles which, I blush to say it, is too evident in Belfast. This town is one of the most handsome in Ireland and the scenery of the surrounding country is magnificent. In fact you can have no conception how grand it is unless you have seen [it] for yourself. ...'

D.1792/A2/12

12 December 1863

Letter to J. Megaw from Armour, [written from Cork],

expressing Armour's condolences on learning of the death of Megaw's mother.

D.1792/A2/13

[n.d. 1863 ?]

Letter to J. Megaw from Armour, [written from Cork],

the last in the Megaw series conveying the news of Armour's success in gaining a scholarship.

'Though I was rather unfortunate in Dublin, I have not just been so unfortunate here. I have got a scholarship value £40. I had little hope of it for a few days after the examination as it was a very hard one and the professor is one of the hardest in the university. ... [He] is now in the place for seven years and this is the second scholarship he ever gave since he came here.'

D.1792/A2/14

[n.d. 1880 ?]

Part of a letter to Mrs Jennie Hamilton from Armour,

the first of a series of four love letters [D.1792/A2/14-17] written to Mrs Hamilton, a widow whom Armour was to marry. This letter indicates the obstacles which Armour had to overcome in order to woo the seemingly reluctant object of his affections.

'I am grieved to hear you felt miserable after the fine sermon on Sabbath. You did not look it. Nay you seemed as happy as somebody else who is bound to report that there was no particular sadness save that which accompanies such pleasure. All true joy seems to me to have a rim of sorrow round it. ... "To be or not to be" is a question which other people as well as the Dane have to discuss and feelings and circumstances take different sides. To have a feeling start up you know not whence or why and to find that instead of passing away in a month as a well regulated spasm of the kind should do or of decaying by the ordeal of personal contact which damps many illusions, it seems to be rather gaining in strength and volume is [?] perplexing to a simple-minded person especially when fate and the future appear to take a delight in whispering with no bated breath, "it is foolish for the subject and foolisher for the object of the feeling if it were to be embodied in a *fait accompli*". You have a guess about the reality of the feeling on the other side and you know the facts on both sides. You have put the question several times, can one be in love twice and you seem now and then to doubt its possibility. ... You speak of drawing in a certain direction and I can understand the figure keenly, but your friends' chaff about lowering a great clan might make "the drawing" unfortunate. I could not be expected to admit the lowering though perhaps the outward appearances might justify the inference in the eyes of those who judge life by the usual conventional standards. I should not like to pull anyone down in life and least of all one whose attractions to me are purely personal. Still as I have not the talents with which my friends credit me and as the present is not bright (at the same time it is not dark), the wisest course is to begin that difficult operation of cutting off the right hand. ... I was out seeing my mother tonight and when she asked me where I was going this year, I replied to the North Pole or Australia. "Talk" was her comment. I am going to America, I think.'

D.1792/A2/15

3 December 1881

Letter to Mrs Jennie Hamilton from Armour,

recounting some gossip about mutual friends in relation to appointments at Magee College, Londonderry, and elsewhere; the letter also attempts to justify Armour's lack of worldly success and claims that he is satisfied with his lot in life.

'Many thanks for your friendly interest. I had a letter last week from Dougherty and I learned from it that there would be strong opposition to Prof[essor] MacMaster's succession to Nesbitt's chair but he said in the letter that it is tolerably certain that he (MacM[aster]) would get the appointment. In regard to the other matter Dick will not be a candidate at all. He could not well stand for it and I think he would have little chance of getting it as it is a church appointment. As for myself I have not much ambition in that direction and it is as well, for my chances of obtaining it would be slim. The temptation is not very strong and therefore I shall not likely be disappointed. You say truly enough that the world usually takes a man at his own valuation. But at the same time if one really cares little for the world's valuation, what harm does he receive if it passes him by with indifference. I have not been, I would hope, morbidly careful about popular esteem and consequently I am in no way a disappointed man. I have been able to help my friends a little and have not been unduly [craving ?] for a return of favours though I have received as much kindness from all my friends as any man could wish. I cannot tax them with anything more and do not intend to do so. And when one has so many distinguished acquaintances, he ought to be satisfied with the lot in life arranged for him. As to the future which may be mine, I know nothing of it. I hope to be of some little use and to live and die an honest man. ...'

D.1792/A2/16

27 June 1882

Part of a letter to an unknown correspondent, [possibly Mrs Jennie Hamilton, later Mrs Armour], from Armour,

discussing the reasons for, and the consequences of, his giving up the principalship of Ballymoney intermediate school.

D.1792/A2/17

31 January 1883

Part of a letter to an unidentified correspondent, [probably Mrs Jennie Hamilton], from Armour,

discussing the entry of Professor James B. Dougherty into active politics and Armour's teaching at Magee College, Londonderry, and also making more observations about their mutual relationship.

'... Decidedly I'll go tomorrow as I feel quite well enough and the beds here are as harsh as the plank cribs in Portland prison. There is no possibility of sleeping comfortably on planks with a bare sufficiency of clothing. J.B.D. [James Dougherty] is very much better but I fancy he will keep the house tomorrow again to prepare physically for the great Co. Derry conference on Saturday at which Sir Thomas McClure [a leading Belfast Liberal] and the attorney-general [Hugh Law, Q.C.] are to be present. It is likely to be a little stormy at first especially as it is to be a private gathering and our friend must be in good form to take his part in the raging sea of politics. You seem to think his powers might be better employed but he does not think so at least and I have no manner of doubt that he will be M.P. for Derry before many years. He is one of the most long-headed men of my acquaintance and he is as decent as he is politically wise and mentally able. ... I suppose I will take his classes tomorrow again. ... There is no particular good in either of us subjecting ourselves to a moral scrutiny about things concerning which we might not grow wiser if we reasoned for years. Facts are enough for me and I find a goodly number of theories which seemed fine at the time upset by the course of events of the last twelve months at least. You found me and discovered me to myself and unconsciously drew out a deal of feeling of which I thought myself entirely wanting and for better I believe things have come to the present point and I trust you completely, like you passionately yet purely and, except God dies and the devil takes the reins of our life, I see no reason for looking forward with a wry face. Neither of us is doing this, I fancy, and if we try to learn the lesson you insist on in your letter this morning, if we trust in God and do the right, there will be no want in the future and no particular need for melancholy. I fear too that I may seem a different man from what many think but I have not assumed many airs and have not posed as anything and if people put an overestimate on me the fault is theirs not mine. And now let me say that the opinion of those who have touched your life is absolutely correct and your weaknesses whatever they are only bring out the virtues. It is paining to hear you calling yourself stupid. If any body else said so, you would be fierce and would have a right to be. Your reply would not show many signs of stupidity. I'll talk to you ... on this subject and face to face. ...'

D.1792/A2/18

Draft of a letter to an unidentified correspondent, [possibly Sir James Bryce] , from Armour,

9 August 1892

pressing the necessity for compulsory sale, rejoicing in the prospect of a Liberal government following the defeat of the Unionists in the 1892 general election and arguing that Bryce himself would be a more suitable Irish chief secretary than John Morley, the most likely candidate. He also presses the claims of William Houston Dodd to the Irish solicitor-generalship, especially in the light of his unsuccessful fight to secure the North Antrim seat in 1892 and also on the grounds of his Presbyterianism.

'According to promise I send you a statement of Mr [Samuel Craig] McElroy's [editor of the *Ballymoney Free Press*] views, along with my own, on the necessity for compulsory sale. I have had the statement printed for your convenience. No copy will be given to any other by me. You may use the documents in whatever way you think best.

I suppose that by the time you receive this the present government will be out of office, whereat I will rejoice. Certainly they have abused to a shameless extent the power of appointment to office during these dying days. I hope it will be a long time before they get a similar opportunity of serving their friends at the expense of the public service. I suppose that the new chief secretary will be Mr Morley, and on the ground of ability he will be an ideal chief, but I am half afraid on the score of prudence it will be a doubtful appointment. A dead set will be made on him by the Tories and their allies and damage will be done to the administration. If Mr Gladstone could see his way to appoint yourself to the perilous post, religious as well as political animosities would be less acute, and he would have a chief secretary who in literary distinction, proved capacity for administration and in sympathy with Irish wants, would be more than an equal to any one we have ever had in Ireland.

In regard to the new solicitor-general for Ireland, I hope you will, if you have the opportunity, press the claims of my friend Mr Dodd who is a very able man, clear-headed, perfect in temper, and who has been one of the warmest and most consistent supporters of Mr Gladstone's policy towards Ireland. His candidature for N. Antrim has done a world of good. I have had letters from all parts of our church approving of Mr Dodd's pluck in contesting N. Antrim and thanking me for the attitude I took in regard to Mr Gladstone's proposals.

I am convinced that Mr Dodd's candidature has broken the boom and that the passionate opposition to Mr Gladstone on the part of the wiser Presbyterians is on the turn. To conciliate the Presbyterians, the appointment of Mr Dodd, who is a thorough Presbyterian, would be a wise stroke of policy and I am sure that on the ground of ability and character none of the aspirants to that office can compare with Mr Dodd.'

D.1792/A2/19

Part of a draft letter to the *Northern Whig* from Armour,

9 August 1892

complaining about the decision to publish a report of a speech made by the Ballymoney Liberal Unionist, William Hamilton, accusing Armour of suppressing part of a letter written by Rev. J. D. Osborne in support of the candidature of W. H. Dodd in the 1892 general election in North Antrim. Armour of course vehemently denied Hamilton's charge.

'In regard to your letter of the 4th inst., I have to say that your proposed correction seems to me utterly inadequate. You published a report of a speech by Mr [William] Hamilton three days after it appeared in the [*Belfast*] *News-Letter* in which Mr Hamilton accused me practically of dishonourable conduct in suppressing part of a letter—a material part as he alleged. The [*Northern*] *Whig* makes it a rule not to publish what has already appeared in other journals and yet it violated its own rule and published what competent authority declares to be a libel on me. Two or three gentlemen have volunteered to go into the witness box to say that the impression left on their mind on reading the report was that I had been guilty of a dishonourable act. Before a word of reply was given by me, you admit a letter from Mr Hamilton quite as offensive in its innuendoes as the original speech. Do you think it fair to allow an attack on a man to appear and then before he has given a rejoinder to allow a second? Then you refused to allow Mr Osborne's letter which ...' [*page missing*]

'... you would not think it so very trivial as it appears to you sitting in your office. You seem to think that if you inserted what you propose you would be compelled to insert letters on the subject. In regard to that I have no objection to your publishing any letters you please if the names of the writers are appended and if you give me a similar right if I wish to exercise it. I object to anonymous attacks in the post. I have no desire to keep up a snarl with the [*Northern*] *Whig* nor indeed with Mr Hamilton but unless he changes his tune very much in the near future, I may be compelled to vindicate myself in a court of law and if that necessity is laid on me, I wish that this matter be direct between him and myself without the necessity of claiming damages from the [*Northern*] *Whig*. ...'

D.1792/A2/20

18 March 1893

Draft of a letter to J. W. Kirk, Antrim, [Co. Antrim], from Armour,

expressing thanks for Kirk's support for Armour's espousal of Home Rule at the special General Assembly of March 1893, attacking the attitudes of the majority of Presbyterians on the Home Rule issue and defending his right as a minister to involve himself in political activity while making sure that politics are kept out of his pulpit.

'Accept my warmest thanks for your telegram and letter. The telegram came but it was delivered as coming from John Kerr, and though I believed it was from you—as I knew no John Kerr in Antrim—I did not like to reply until I was sure of the source from which it came. However, both letter and telegram have, in a time when the bitterest things imaginable are being said against me, given me encouragement and have revealed the fact that there are men in our church who refuse to be carried away by prejudice and blind passion. It was very manly and very kindly and very considerate of you to write to me as you have done, and I thank you very heartily. I have received many other letters of a similar kind to yours, and though the outlook for our church whatever happens seems bad, you and I may comfort ourselves by the thought that in a time of political insanity on the part of the majority we hastened to do at least our duty. I said in the Assembly that the new doctrine was being enforced, with powerful pains, that no man can be saved, or be a loyal Presbyterian, unless he renounces Home Rule. I said it because during the elections, and within the last few weeks, nothing but sermons denouncing Home Rule are being preached and because I have found that any one who refused to denounce Home Rule is held up as a traitor to his church. I have never during all my life and during all this excitement ever mentioned the political situation, and never will. Christianity is independent of any form of government and I will never degrade mine office on the Sabbath by preaching any form of politics. I claim and exercise my right of taking part in politics and expressing my views on politics on week days and on platforms but no man on the Sabbath, whatever his political creed, will ever be insulted by me from the pulpit or in the church where he has not the right of reply.'

D.1792/A2/21

31 March 1893

Letter to T. A. Dickson, [the former Liberal member of parliament], from Armour,

discussing the special General Assembly debate on the

official resolutions condemning Home Rule, commenting on the social ostracism which Armour has suffered in consequence of his opinions and claiming that, despite his pro-Home Rule stand, he has lost very few members of his Ballymoney congregation. Dickson had been eliminated from active Irish politics by his defeat at the hands of T. W. Russell (Liberal Unionist) in the South Tyrone seat (1892).

'Many thanks for your kindly note. ... Things are moving in a very confused and excited state just now. The Assembly is over and the majority of the members seems far from being satisfied with the proceedings. The wilder spirits are, I hear, blaming Petticrew and Megaw, who, they aver, made a very poor fight on behalf of the imperilled interests—money and religion. The Union has fallen into the background of late and even Protestantism is getting a back seat in the Unionist chariot. It is only heard of in remote country districts where the Orangemen do congregate and the only recognition it gets in Belfast is under the very vague phrase civil and religious liberties. The Assembly was a mistake as even the Tory Presbyterians are admitting, and the mob ... got the worst of it as far as arguments go. If you ever see the *Witness*, that most enlightened journal, you will notice that it has changed its tune considerably in reference to Dougherty and those of us who go in with him, though in some of its innuendoes it is quite as nasty and malicious as ever. Of course we are coming in for a large share of abuse in almost all quarters but as far as I can judge there are more to take our side than during the election. The Assembly did good in this respect that I got a chance of putting the case from my point of view and the general impression in many quarters is that had it not been for the intimidation, our amendment would have carried. Dougherty spoke splendidly as usual. He bowled over in beautiful form the Clerk and Geo[rge] Magill and others and he was [drowned ?] only through fear of the effects of his speech. I fancy sometimes that you cannot be easy in your mind, being beyond the reach of the doses of abuse measured out to you during all the storms of the past quarter of a century. It is a good while since you were out of a political row before, and I fear that even the mild temperature of Italy and France will hardly make up for the absence of the invigorating breezes of an Irish political storm. I heartily hope you will come back in good trim after a holiday which you have fully earned. The community generally is hardly so bitter at me as during the election. I have little coming or going with the neighbouring parsons. Almost no minister in the Assembly would ask or allow me to preach for him, but that does not annoy me in the least. I kept politics out of the pulpit all these years and the people here—even the strong Conservatives—on that account have stood to me like bricks, so that the annoyance from the congregation has been almost nothing. I lost two or three but they did not count. ...'

D.1792/A2/22

23 June 1893

Part of a draft of a letter to an unidentified correspondent from Armour,

outlining his views on Home Rule; discussing the special General Assembly and the June General Assembly debates on the issue; describing the problems of social ostracism and intimidation encountered by the opponents of the Unionists; arguing that the minority of Presbyterians who support Gladstone is increasing, especially outside Belfast; and predicting that even the Unionist party will come round to introducing some form of Irish self-government in the end.

'In reply to your letter I would earnestly ask you to remain a thorough supporter of the policy of the present government as it seems to me sane, sound, statesmanlike and fitted to solve a very vexed question. I did not like the Bill of '86 and opposed it principally on the ground that the Irish members were to be excluded from Westminster which gave foundation for the cry, which did duty in Ireland as elsewhere, that the Irish were seeking separation from the United Kingdom. That cry has now had its day and we seldom hear it mentioned now. The retention of the Irish members at Westminster will prevent the other possible danger—namely religious persecution on the part of the majority. ... In regard to the proceedings of the General Assembly at its special meeting in March, I have sent you a copy of the speech I delivered there. The audience was hostile—free discussion was practically boycotted and under the circumstances the minority simply refused to take part in what was a mockery. The resolutions were under the circumstances said to be passed unanimously, but I may say that a very large number of members came to me afterwards and assured me that, if it had not been for the terrorisation going on and if vot[ing] had been by ballot, my amendment [would] have carried. I have very little doubt [on] that point. I have received hundreds [of] letters from all parts of the church [thank]ing me for the stand taken. You can have no conception of the bitterness of feeling existing, and of how everyone who even dares to be neutral is made to feel the anxieties of social ostracism. The Assembly at its regular meeting is this month brought up the subject again. It was sprung on us without warning. No one expected it would be brought up again. A new set of resolutions, hatched in secret, was launched on the house. Prof[essor] Dougherty and others spoke effectively against them [and] the roll was called—a most unusual thing—for the purpose of pillorying any [who] voted against the resolutions. Eleven [in] the face of terror recorded their votes on [the] side of sanity. However, the triumph [of the] majority is not great if you look [at] the facts. The General Assembly all told consists of over a thousand members and there were at least 750 present. Well in a matter which the majority is never tired of saying involves civil and religious liberty, it does not seem as if even the General Assembly was very unanimous when only some 320 in all recorded their votes. There were at least 250 present who walked out rather than vote for the resolutions. If you think of this which is an absolute fact, you will see that devotion to what is called the Union is not growing among Irish Presbyterians. It is true that only eleven voted against but you are to remember that every one of them did so at the greatest risk a man can run. I am thankful to be able to say that my congregation, though made up of stern Tories and enthusiastic radicals, has behaved well to me. I have lost only a very few, but unfortunately I know from experience what the social boycott is and I do not blame my brethren for keeping clear of "the railings of rash and rancorous tongues". That the majority of Irish Presbyterians is opposed to Mr Gladstone's policy is true— that there is a strong minority in favour of his policy and that it is growing is equally true. Belfast is the centre of the opposition. But understand this about Belfast, that during the last fifty years it has been the sworn and unwavering foe of all legislation for the good of the people. It is the necropolis of Liberalism, it is the temple of the rankest Toryism; in politics it has always been reactionary. Do not heed the rubbish which is published in the Unionist papers. Hatred of Mr Gladstone seems to be their ruling passion and I have lost all faith either in their fairness or in their so-called facts.

I earnestly hope for the sake of Ireland you will keep to your faith in Mr Gladstone's policy. To me it is clear as the sun that Home Rule in some shape is sure to come and the question is simply which party will grant it. If the Tories come back to power they will either grant it in a form which will mean that their friends—the landlord party and ascendancy party—will have the management as of old and the old sores will not be healed, or they will by bribery on the education question stave it off for a few years, and then it will come *too late* and in a form which will be revolutionary.'

D.1792/A2/23

4 July 1893

Letter to Rev. A. M. Stavely, [Armour's father-in-law], from Armour,

thanking him in a teasing and gently mocking way for the gift of a Gladstone bag and also commenting on the progress so far made in collecting signatures for the Presbyterian Home Rule address to Gladstone.

'It is verily a great blessing to have a kindly and thoughtful daddy and I have no ... words wherewith to thank you for your gift, so unexpected but so suitable to a man without travelling gear. There is only one thing about your valued gift which surprises me. That you a good Covenanter and Unionist should select in these times a bag bearing the name of Gladstone is surprising and lest you should get into trouble now about the 12th of July, I assure you I will not give the name of your gift to any body. I read in your gift a secret leaning towards the G.O.M. but that will be a secret. I can only say thank you with all my heart and long life to "your honour". ... Tell Gay that the signatures are getting on very well. We have—this is only for Gay— over 2,300 in up to this morning and we expect, or at least hope, to reach 3,000. I have got no returns of any kind from Ballyclare as yet. The Co. Down is doing well. I have over 700 from it already and fancy that Co. Down will reach 1,000. Of course you will not take any interest in this but Gay will. ... I hope to have the business wound up by Saturday as it has entailed a good deal of writing. ...'

D.1792/A2/24A-B

July 1893

Two printed copies of the Presbyterian Home Rule address to W. E. Gladstone, one signed by the family of W. H. Dodd, [Dublin], and various inhabitants of Coleraine, [Co. Londonderry], the other unsigned,

expressing support for self-government for Ireland and pressing for a revision of judicially fixed rents, both for its own sake and as a basis for future legislation to establish occupying ownership.

'To the Right Hon. William Ewart Gladstone, M.P., First Lord of the Treasury.

We, the undersigned members and adherents of the Presbyterian Church in Ireland, hereby express our heartfelt gratitude to the Right Hon. W. E. Gladstone for the great benefits which his splendid statesmanship, as leader of the Liberal party, has already conferred upon our country; our sympathy with him in his present efforts to secure the better government of Ireland; and our determination to co-operate heartily with our fellow-countrymen of every class and creed in order to make a measure for local self-government in Ireland a practical success.

We further record our conviction that an urgent necessity exists for an immediate revision of judicial rents, in accordance with the depressed state of agriculture, which, while saving many from a crushing burden, will also provide an equitable basis for a measure to abolish dual owner-ship in land, by which alone a final settlement of this Irish land question can be achieved.'

D.1792/A2/25

July 1893

Draft of a letter to W. E. Gladstone, to accompany the Home Rule address, from J. B. Dougherty, Londonderry; J. Craig Houston, Hydepark, Belfast; J. McElderry, Ballymoney; J. Steen, Portstewart; and Armour, [in Armour's hand],

stressing that the 3,535 Presbyterians who have signed the address are drawn from a wide cross-section of society and that the movement to promote this demonstration of support for Gladstone's policies in general and his commitment to Home Rule in particular has been spontaneous. Confidentiality with regard to the signatures is requested. Two of the authors of the letter, Steen and McElderry, were prominent Presbyterian elders, the others ministers.

'We have been requested to place in your hands the accompanying declaration signed by 3,535 members of the Presbyterian Church in Ireland in connexion with the General Assembly, expressive of gratitude to, and confidence in you, as the trusted and honoured leader of the Liberal party. The names on the list (which is not intended for publication) include ministers, magistrates, merchants, labourers, farmers, physicians and lawyers. You will be interested to know that these signatures have been freely tendered without any public solicitation and with-out the intervention of any organisation which might have reached many districts not represented in this list.

We trust the spontaneous character of the movement may enhance the value in your eyes of a declaration which we ask you to accept as an assurance that the great benefits which your statesmanship has already conferred on our country are remembered with gratitude by our people, and that your present effort to secure the better government of Ireland has a large measure of sympathy even among those who are sometimes represented as entirely unanimous in offering a relentless opposition to the Irish policy of the Liberal party.'

To the
Right Hon
W. E. Gladstone

Sir

We have been requested to place in your hands the accompanying declaration signed by 3535 members of the Presbyterian Church in Ireland in connexion with the General Assembly, expressive of gratitude to, and confidence in you as the trusted and honoured leader of the Liberal party. The names on the list (which is not intended for publication) include ministers, magistrates, merchants, labourers, farmers, bishops and lawyers. You will be interested to know that these signatures have been freely tendered without any public solicitation and without the intervention of any organisation which might have reached many districts not represented in this list.

We trust that the spontaneous character of the movement may enhance the value in your eyes, of a declaration which we ask you to accept as an assurance that the great benefits which your statesmanship has already conferred on our country are remembered with

Facsimile of the draft of a letter from J. B. Armour and others to
W. E. Gladstone, July 1893 (D.1792/A2/25).

D.1792/A2/26

25 August 1893

Incomplete draft of a letter to W. E. Gladstone's private secretary from Armour,

replying to a letter from Gladstone requesting further background information about the signatures to the Presbyterian Home Rule memorial.

'Your letter requesting information as to the signatures to the Presbyterian address forwarded to Mr Gladstone has just come in. I am starting for Scotland for a few days. I will write Mr Gladstone from Berwick on Monday. I think I am able to substantiate every statement made. ...'

D.1792/A2/27

25 July [1894 ?]

Part of a draft of a letter to W. H. Dodd, [Dublin], from Armour,

expressing the hope that Dodd will come north when his legal commitments permit and asking him to use his influence on behalf of one John Gilmour, so that the sentence of death passed on Gilmour at the recent Belfast Assizes for the murder of Lyle Gardiner may be commuted to life imprisonment. In particular, Armour was anxious that Dodd should persuade Judge Gibson to second the recommendation of the jury that Gilmour be treated mercifully on the grounds of his age and previous good character.

D.1792/A2/28

[n.d. July 1894 ?]

Letter to W. H. Dodd, [Dublin], from Armour,

again discussing the circumstances of the Gardiner murder case and defending the coroner, Dr Camac, against the accusation that he was drunk while investigating it.

D.1792/A2/29A

[n.d. 1894 ?]

Draft of a letter to J. Morley, chief secretary for Ireland, [Dublin], from Armour,

supporting a petition to the lord lieutenant which sought the commutation of John Gilmour's death sentence for the murder of Lyle Gardiner to one of life imprisonment.

D.1792/A2/29B

[n.d. June 1894 ?]

Draft of a letter to Professor J. Bryce, M.P., [London], from Armour,

seeking Bryce's help to secure a government appointment for James Bryce Killen, an indigent nationalist barrister and former friend of Armour in his student days at Queen's College, Cork. Killen had written supplicatory letters to Armour asking him to intercede on his behalf with his namesake and distant relation, Professor Bryce [*see D.1792/A1/3/30-1*]. The letter also comments on Bryce's elevation to the cabinet and the general situation of the Liberal government.

'I was glad to see that you got to more congenial work as a member of the cabinet. It is plain to most people that the present government is growing in strength from month to month, whereat as a Liberal and Irishman I rejoice greatly.'

D.1792/A2/30A-B

[September ?] 1894

Two printed copies of an address to J. Morley, [chief secretary for Ireland], signed by D. H. Burke, [parish priest], J. Connolly, J. Magill, H. Jamieson, J. McGaw, J. McClennan and an unidentified individual whose signature is illegible,

expressing the thanks of the signatories, all from the Ballymoney, Co. Antrim, area, to John Morley for his appointment of a parliamentary committee of inquiry into the land question and pressing for legislation to implement the committee's recommendations. The signatories, 'representing various shades of political opinion', invite the chief secretary to speak at a public meeting to be held in Ballymoney at some time in November.

'We, the undersigned residents in the neighbourhood of Ballymoney, representing various shades of political opinion, desire to acknowledge our deep sense of obligation to the Right Honourable John Morley, chief secretary for Ireland, for his services to the cause of land reform in connection with the appointment and the conduct of the proceedings of the Parliamentary Land Committee of last session.

We are anxious to see the important recommendations of that committee embodied at the earliest possible date in an act of parliament, and we are ready to co-operate, by every means in our power, to secure this most desirable result. We believe that a powerful impulse towards this end would be given by a public address from one who has borne so important a part in the recent investigation of the Irish land question, and we hereby cordially invite the right honourable, the chief secretary, to visit Ballymoney at any date during the month of November which may be convenient to him, for the purpose of addressing a public meeting on the present position of the Irish land question, and on any other political topic he may desire to touch upon.

We pledge ourselves to secure him a friendly reception and an impartial hearing.'

D.1792/A2/31

[n.d. June 1900]

Draft of a letter to the editor of the *Northern Whig* in response to a published letter from Dr Anthony Traill, provost of Trinity College, Dublin,

attempting to answer the arguments advanced in Traill's letter [*see D.1792/A1/3/39*], in particular objecting to Traill's publication of earlier correspondence without Armour's permission; attacking the landlord class and Traill's personal record as a landlord; repeating his familiar charges as to the reactionary character of the Church of Ireland; condemning Anglican domination of the Irish judicial bench; and significantly qualifying his earlier statements concerning the oppression of contemporary Ireland by the Anglican clergy.

'It is surely a breach of the ordinary courtesies of civilised life to publish, without permission, a correspondence which has not concluded. But perhaps Dr Traill's manners, like his opinions, are [?]. He says of my first statement—namely that "most of the landlords at least in this district were educated at Trinity·and that the landlords as a class have been regarded as oppressors."—that it is quite untrue. Might I ask what part of it is untrue? Is it that most of the landlords have been educated at Trinity? If he says they have not been educated in Trinity, then he is accusing them of a want of patriotism—a worse charge than I brought against them—in not supporting a college which has the inestimable advantage of Dr Traill's lectures on tangents. If he means that the landlords as a class have not been oppressors of their country, he is contradicting established facts and five or six acts of parliament. He speaks of good landlords—they have been too few to save the class from merited condemnation. I tell him that ninety per cent of them have been decidedly, as landlords, bad. The passably good have been few and, with very few exceptions, the passably good have been found to be possessed of large estates. The vast proportion have been of the rack-renting type—some worse than others—they could hardly help being so. They were beyond the pale of law; they were served by agents who, as a whole, had neither a sense of mercy nor justice with the result that Ireland, considering its circumstances, was more highly rented than England and Scotland by thirty to forty per cent. Dr Traill tells the public that he settled with his tenants. He did not tell the public it was when he could not help it. It was after the land act was passed—to use his own phrase "*post hoc* therefore *propter hoc.*" He deserves no credit for his act and no human being gives him any credit. However kindly he may be in speech, he has never been accused of over-generosity to his own tenantry. The class which he attempts to defend, two out of three of his own tenants regard as the bane of our country and fully eighty per cent of the Protestants of Ireland and ninety per cent of the Catholics will endorse my statement.

Then he admits that the majority of the clerics were educated in Trinity but he takes good care to pass by the instances cited in which acts of parliament had to be passed to restrain their tyranny. A member of his own church some years ago put forward a public challenge which never was taken up, "name any act which was ever proposed for the good of Ireland that was not opposed by the clerics of the established church". As a body, they opposed Catholic emancipation, the legalising of marriages performed by Presbyterian ministers, the repeal of duties on paper, all the land acts and many other useful measures which were passed in spite of their opposition. That a few clerics and many laymen were found in favour of all the great remedial measures for Ireland's welfare I gladly admit. Indeed, I have often said publicly that some of the clerics and many of the laity of the church to which Dr Traill belongs have, for generosity and liberality of sentiment, been unsurpassed by the members of any other church. Dr Traill, instead of facing the facts mentioned, lectures me and the Presbyterians generally for the [enormity ?] of refusing to call his church "The Church of Ireland". Personally I never felt any grievance about the name. I care not they call it "The Church of the Solar System" with Ballylough [the Traill estate] as the only telegraph station between it and the rest of this earth. Still for the sake of the church itself, I think it is unfortunate that a title should have been chosen which asserts that there is no other church in Ireland save itself—and that all outside it belong not to the Christian world. If this is not arrogant pretentiousness, pray what is? One of the ablest of episcopal bishops has said that "the church of any country consists of all the real Christians of that country by whatever name they may be called". That is the true definition of the real Church of Ireland and for Dr Traill to try to justify a sect in assuming that it is the only Church of Ireland—if it does not mean this what does the title mean—is very like the Dr Traill we know in the north of Ireland. [*A slightly different version of this paragraph is also included.*]

As to No. 3, as he calls it, my statement was "I presume most of those who administer the laws were educated in Trinity College and the universal impression over Ireland is that the courts from the highest to the lowest are stuffed with men who strain the laws whenever possible in favour of the classes and against the masses". This he calls an astounding statement—anything with which Dr Traill disagrees, I admit, astounds him. The fact is as I have stated it and the impression is undeniable. It will be news to the Presbyterians and Catholics of Ireland that many of their persuasion are administering the laws in the higher courts. Till within the last few years there was not a Presbyterian in any of the higher courts and precious few in the lower. I have not said many things with which Dr Traill credits me. I did not say that the clergy of his church are now the oppressors of our country—their power in that direction has been crippled.'

D.1792/A2/32   **Part of a letter to an unidentified correspondent from Armour,**

[n.d. November 1907]

describing a Liberal meeting in Ballymoney Town Hall, chaired by John Baxter and addressed by Augustine Birrell, chief secretary for Ireland. It is a vital piece of evidence concerning the rift which existed between Armour and the local Liberal leadership, the despair which had resulted in his virtual political abdication after the Liberal electoral defeat in 1895, the weaknesses of R. G. Glendinning, the recently elected Liberal member for North Antrim, and the reasons why Armour would continue to be excluded from the local Liberal inner circle.

'Then occurred a scene—I have to resort to other [*sic*] kind of paper—which will not be forgotten for some time and in which I was involved innocently. The pagans who had arranged the speakers took it into their silly heads to ignore me entirely—to give me no place in the show. I did not care a straw. Hill of Boveedy had come into town in the afternoon for the meeting—by some means he had come to knowledge of the game and when I was going down from the Technical [School] to the Manse, he ran after me to tell me what I knew, and to say that the audience would insist on my speaking. I said nothing other than that I was not expecting the honour and therefore had not straightened out my thoughts. He then got a number of people, specially young people, scattered through the hall, who at a given signal were to yell out "Armour, Armour". The mine was carefully laid and only required the match which started up when needed. When the speakers were exhausted John Baxter got up to call on Sir William Baxter to move a vote of thanks to the speakers. Then the explosion came and from men, women and boys a hurricane of shouts for "Armour" arose and continued for apparently several minutes. Baxter was non-plussed and Birrell looked amused and the Pirries were radiant, as Lady P. had said at the luncheon she would like to hear me. I jumped to my feet—the audience nearly beside itself with joy that its will was supreme—and poured forth a stream of phrases which I think constituted the best speech I ever delivered—I could not repeat a tithe of what I said as the [afflatus ?] was on me. I praised the meeting, saying that it reminded me of the old radical days—that fourteen years ago I had thought Liberalism was dead and buried but a new era was dawning as the meeting proved. Then I praised the cabinet, saying it was the best that had ever directed the government of the land since the days of the glorious Gladstone, paid a truthful tribute to C[ampbell] B[annerman], pointing out that the cabinet contained five or six men who for sheer intellectual ability could not be matched in the three kingdoms or indeed in any country in the world—Haldane, Asquith, Grey, Morley, Lloyd George and last but not least Birrell. Then I pointed out that he had a rough road to travel, beset by jackals, screech owls and bores but, as he had the intellect of a giant and the humour of a Samson, he would carry off the gates of Gaza and on the hill of success would grin at his opponents. Then I called for a cheer for B[irrell] such as they only could give.

Then I took up the Pirries, pointing out that they had shown the rare virtue of courage in organising two splendid meetings in Belfast, a city which was ruled by Pharisees, Sadducees and Philistines. The Pharisees standing and looking to the other parts of Ireland and saying "thank God we are not as these publicans", the Sadducees asserting that there was no resurrection for Ireland, the Philistines holding that the only thing for Ireland was to be ruled with the rod of coercion—that Lord P[irrie], as director of Harland and Wolff, had done more for the material prosperity of the city than all the sects referred to put together had done, that Lady P[irrie] had raised £150,000 for a splendid hospital—that both of them had received no thanks from the rulers of the city. ...

Then I took up [T. W.] Russell and pointed out that I had opposed him often but that I always believed there was some hidden fire of Liberalism burning in the depths of his soul, which all the waters of the Red Sea of Toryism could not extinguish—that I was glad he had come back to his true self and that I hoped he would devote his energies and talents not only to the work of his office but to the advancement of the cause of sanity and common sense. I called for cheers for him which were given in no hesitating manner.

Then I took up [R.G.] Glendinning and said some gutter sparrows were asking who was Glendinning, a leaflet was being circulated locally with that as one of the queries, and I said I would answer it ... saying that, though a silent member, he had proved himself as one of the honestest, most attentive to the wants not only of his own constituents but to the wants of all Ulster constituents, that had ever been sent to Westminster from Ulster and told the audience that if he cared to contest the seat again, he would be returned with a bigger majority than before. I called for three cheers for him also. His followers were perfectly wild with excitement and the poverty of his own speech was more than covered. Birrell seemed very interested and amused and said to me this morning—"I hope you were nothing the worse of your guest speech last night". The Pirries were overjoyed, some of the audience saying afterwards that P[irrie] would give a thousand pounds to have the words printed in the Belfast papers. Glendinning was much pleased and insisted on sitting beside me today at the Derry luncheon which was very good—120 guests—good speaking by Birrell and Russell and the others so so. I have not time to tell you more. Of course a few of the pagans were glum as they had caught a tartar but they had to keep mum and the poor sinner who was appointed to second Baxter must have felt sore at not getting his innings. I hear it was Millar which shows the wisdom of the runners of the show. ...'

D.1792/A2/33

Part of a letter to an unidentified correspondent from Armour,

[n.d. November 1907]

discussing an interview which he had had with a member of the chief secretary, Augustine Birrell's staff to discuss the government's impending legislation on the Irish university system, in which he had urged that Birrell should take advice from the under secretary of state for Ireland, Sir James Dougherty, Armour's old friend.

'... Sir J[ames] B[rown] D[ougherty] could be relied on to keep from all and sundry any confidences reposed in him. I further gave a hint that Sir Antony [MacDonnell] who might be regarded as the natural consultant, posed not so much as an adviser as a director—that he had already indicated in several ways lines of policy which could not and possibly should not be carried out and that while he had great abilities, yet had not a mind nimble enough to guide the motor car of state round a corner safely and I added that if Mr B[irrell] wants not only to keep from mistakes but to find a way through the labyrinth, he would consult Sir J.B.D. The youth listened earnestly and promised obedience. He said that B[irrell] had already a decided respect for Sir J.B.D. and that he would certainly not forget my message. That he will not I think is almost certain. I went to the station to see the distinguished guests off. The youth was in the smoking compartment of the saloon carriage and as the train was about to move off he beckoned me forward and said—"I will not forget what you said to me". This is of course strictly private and if you mention it to any one we part for ever. I wrote a note to Sir J.B.D. last night giving him an outline of what I had said but he is the only one I have breathed it to. The only axe I had to grind—apart from B[irrell]'s welfare—was that perhaps Magee College might not be entirely shunted, supposing Sir J.B.D. was taken into confidence before the scheme for higher education was launched. ...'

D.1792/A2/34

Draft or copy of a letter to an unidentified correspondent from Armour,

21 January 1910

replying to a letter which he had received and commenting on the major issues in the general election then in progress, in particular on tariff reform and the possible reform of the house of lords.

'It is perfectly true you do not quote my words correctly and as a matter of course you cannot interpret correctly. That would be a perfectly just reason why you deserve no answer at my hands. However, let that pass. I think you might admit that I have the right of private judgement as well as you. You might also admit that I am as likely to form a correct estimate of the situation as you could. You are not infallible and, even though a Presbyterian, you are not the keeper of my conscience. If you had read my note with any care you would have seen that I did not mention the question of the Union at all. The simple points were tariff reform and the house of lords—the only real issues in this contest according to Mr Balfour and Mr Chamberlain. As to tariff reform, the tariffites in my judgement are introducing a new arithmetic that two and two are *not* four but seven. You have only to increase the price of everything and you will live cheaper. It is a free country and you may believe that if you like, but I could not subscribe to anything so utterly absurd. Then as to the house of lords, the members are putting forth the same claims to control legislation which James II put forth on behalf of the crown. The majority of the house of lords took the side of James. Were they good Protestants think you? William III gained a victory for liberty and a great victory it was. The lords are anxious to assert for themselves the very same claims James II made and if they are successful then farewell to freedom and the right of democracy to rule in the land. The principle of Presbyterianism is upset. If they were not good Protestants who voted for James II, how could they be good Protestants who vote for the very identical thing William III delivered the nation from? If as a Presbyterian you had studied the question dispassionately and had read my note without prejudice, you would have modified your letter very considerably. It is always easy to refute statements an opponent never made, but is it strictly honest to try a thing like that on? I have no doubt but that you think yourself right but is it not possible that somebody who differs from you might have good and sufficient reasons for his opinion?'

D.1792/A2/35A

12 November 1910

Copy of a letter to Sir Otto Jaffe, [Belfast], from Armour,

appealing to Jaffe for his support, as a fellow member of the senate of the newly created Queen's University of Belfast, in protesting against the decision of the university examiners to reject some sixty per cent of the students at matriculation. 'Their action is an insult to the teachers and students of Ulster and has given a kick to the university from which it will not recover for years.' The letter argues that this action of the 'Rabbis at the wheel' should not be taken lying down by the senate.

D.1792/A2/35B

15 November 1910

Copy of a letter, [in Armour's hand], from Sir Otto Jaffe, Belfast, to Armour,

replying to D.1792/A2/35A in a conciliatory but non-commital fashion; assuring Armour that he has passed on his comments to those who matter and also that the senate has the ultimate authority under the university statutes to draw up regulations governing examinations; and expressing the view that a satisfactory solution will be found.

D.1792/A2/36

[n.d. December 1910]

Copy or draft of a letter to Lord Aberdeen, the lord lieutenant of Ireland, from Armour,

thanking him for a letter announcing the appointment of the Londonderry, Liberal, Presbyterian, businessman, David Hogg, as his majesty's lieutenant for Co. Londonderry, ridiculing those Unionists who have been critical of Lord Aberdeen's political views and assuring him of the affection in which he and Lady Aberdeen are held in Ulster by people with Liberal sympathies. Armour was one of Lord Aberdeen's personal chaplains.

'Accept my sincere thanks for your courteous letter announcing the appointment of Mr David Hogg as H.M.L[ieutenant] for Co. Derry. It was the pleasantest letter I ever received and "thanks, and more thanks" expresses my feelings. Mr Hogg fully deserves this high honour at the hands of your excellency as he has, in the city of Tory idolatry, stood up for the cause you so worthily uphold. He is a Scotchman who stands six feet four in his shoes, with all the grit of your countrymen and with a perennial fund of patient courage. He knows no fear, never sought honour for himself and never swerved from the path of Liberal policy. That a true, straight, fearless man has obtained one of the high honours of state at your hands is to me like manna to a hungry man and that the Tories in Derry and elsewhere will rage and gnash their teeth, now that what they thought their natural prey has escaped from their hands, affords me pleasurable amusement.

I see that your excellency has fallen on evil tongues but if you only sit tight and say nothing further, the spiteful malice of your conscienceless assailants cannot hurt your character—that is beyond their power or the dignity of your position. The pitiable band of Tory leaguers was claiming the right of buying weapons to fight against his majesty's government and of goading excitable mobs to deeds of blood on the grounds that a certain policy was sure to bring to them loss of citizenship from the empire and persecution for religious convictions and your excellency simply stated the real facts when you wrote that the fears of persecution for religion's sake were groundless and imaginary. That was your duty and is beyond rational criticism.

But the Tories of Ulster are a peculiar people, steeped to the lips in bigotry, the apostles of religious and racial hate, the apologists of lawlessness on the make. Their onset on you is the result of their reckless rage at defeat in a square, stand-up fight and need not disturb your slumbers. They would prefer Mr Asquith's resignation to yours but I am glad to know that his resignation will not be for long yet and I personally hope that his resignation and yours will be contemporaneous. These people and Mr Long forget that lord lieutenants of the Tory brand have invariably, with perhaps the exception of Lord Dudley, played the Tory fiddle on all public occasions, the harangues of Conservative lord lieutenants being hailed as part of the sermon on the Mount. But for the representative of his majesty under a Liberal administration to hint that the policy of the party in office cannot lead to persecution of religious opinions is a sin against their [Mecca ?] and is sure to [disrupt] the solar system.

It is hopeless to argue with Ulster Tories at present, as it would be to argue with the inmates of a lunatic asylum. Clerics and Orange lodges may rail at you but, if it answers them to hurl paper cartridges at you, you will not be hurt. Many even in Ulster pray that the reign of her exc[ellency] and yourself in Dublin Castle (which in the past has contributed very much to Ireland's health political and physical) may be long, and you may rest assured that when you lay down the wand of office, your departure will cause sincere regret to the 7,000 in Ulster who have not bowed the knee to Baal. May heaven's benison rest on your excellencies at these Xmas times.'

D.1792/A2/37   **Copy of a letter to J. L. Brown, K.C., [Belfast], from Armour,**

23 January 1911

asking for Brown's legal opinion on the publication by the *Northern Whig* of an anti-Home Rule broadsheet of 1887, allegedly signed by Armour, This broadsheet dated from Armour's pro-Union years and had been first used against him in 1894, following his Home Rule conversion, and was being used again in an attempt to discredit him in 1911. In this letter he gives his account of the origins of the broadsheet and his role in relation to it. [*For the details of the broadsheet see the introduction.*]

'Perhaps this letter may seem unusual and hardly in accordance with the etiquette of the Bar but the circumstances are unusual. I want an opinion unbiassed by any political leanings and I have heard you have never publicly declared yourself as either Unionist or Liberal. The *Northern Whig* published an article on me on the 6th of January and on page 12 prints a document issued in 1887 to which my name is attached in the publication. I wrote the editor to call his attention to the article founded largely on the document in 1887. I pointed out to him (1) that the document was not published by me; (2) that when published it did not bear my name; (3) that in 1894 it was republished unwarrantably with my name forged to it; and (4) that the forger had bungled the business as most people of that ilk do: for he had written my name in full—a form of signature I have never employed in any letter published by me. I send you the document of 1887 which you will see has no signature at all—then the document of 1894 with my name attached to it in full and then the *Northern Whig* of the 6 January 184 [*sic*—does he mean 1911 ?] with the article largely founded on the document found on page 12. The editor of the *Whig* rather tried to ride the high horse at first but in the second letter he dismounts and promises that said document will not be again used against me—which I think tacitly admits that the course pursued is without justification. The questions I wish to direct your attention to are: is it legal—not to speak of the morality of the matter—for a paper to publish and circulate a document with my name attached to it—which document was never published nor signed by me? Are there grounds for an action at law against the paper and what would be the possibilities for a successful action? Is such publication libellous and defamatory?

I may say there is no solicitor here who is not strongly on one side or other politically and I therefore take the course of writing you directly so as to avoid initial bias for me or against me.

I have nothing to conceal and therefore I tell you frankly my connection with the original document but it is simply for private edification. In 1887 some four or five gentlemen wished to publish a manifesto in view of a public meeting to be held and they asked me to sketch something for them which I did and sent it to them. They corrected and added sentences to it and held a meeting I believe at which I was not present and resolved to publish it—which was done. That was my connection with it. I did not regard it as mine as I have never published anything that I regarded as mine without putting my name to it. I have always avoided anonymous letters. One of the gentlemen had a quarrel with me and made a libellous speech on me which was published in the *Whig*. I called the attention of the *Whig* to his speech as published in the paper and a public apology to me was inserted. Then at a special meeting of the General Assembly in '94, I made a speech which did not please the powers that rule there—I seldom please the fathers and brethren—my misfortune perhaps not my fault. It is generally supposed— it may be only a suspicion—the gentlemen referred to sent the document to the *Whig* with my name appended. That is the whole thing as far as I know it.'

D.1792/A2/38

7 October 1912

Draft of a letter to the editor of *The Scotsman* **from Armour,**

replying to a letter from the moderator of the Presbyterian Church in Ireland, Dr Montgomery, which the newspaper had published. Dr Montgomery had objected to an interpretation of the 1912 General Assembly compromise on Home Rule offered by Dr Wells at a meeting of the Glasgow Presbytery. Armour, on the other hand, shares the views of Wells.

'In Friday's issue of your paper there is a letter from the moderator of the Irish Presbyterian General Assembly apparently calling in question the accuracy of a statement made by Dr Wells in the Glasgow Presbytery in response to the action of the Irish General Assembly at its last meeting. The republished statement of Dr Wells is correct. Dr Montgomery's letter gives an utter misreading of what took place, though I am sure he has no desire to misinform the Scottish public. The government committee of the Irish Presbyterian church, in violation of the rules for the guidance of the committee, introduced three paragraphs reiterating and reaffirming the decisions of the General Assembly in '86 and '93 in reference to Home Rule. During the first two days of the Assembly the abettors of the paragraphs in the Committee's report were in the seventh heaven of delight, asserting that the report in its entirety would be carried by six to one, threatening that the vote in the Assembly, they would insist, should be an open one though contrary to the standing orders, and informing all and sundry that any minister who voted against the report would have his name published in an ecclesiastical Stubbs's Gazette. But on Wednesday forenoon a subject in which the supporters of the government committee's declaration against Home Rule were interested came up for discussion and when the vote was taken they were beaten almost three to one. This was an eye-opener making it plain to all that the Assembly of 1912 was not the Assembly of '86 or '93. Hence despair followed on the heels of a delirium of expected triumph for the Committee's report. Those responsible for the report were informed by many of their friends that the report with the paragraphs *in re* Home Rule would be rejected by the Assembly or that the minority against it would be such that their victory would be a Pyrrhic one. On Thursday evening I was approached to see if I would consent to a conference with a view to prevent a discussion in open Assembly. The grounds put forward for the conference were that a public discussion in the Assembly would split the church from top to bottom and would ruin religion. The conference lasted nearly two hours. The amendment on the agenda paper standing in my name to delete the paragraphs referring to the resolutions of '86 and '93 was unanimously agreed to and the paragraph correctly given by Dr Montgomery, though he has missed its meaning, accepted by the conference became the unanimous deliverance of the Assembly. The deliverance without manner of real doubt meant that the Presbyterian church as a church refused to allow a discussion on a political issue in the Assembly and that the General Assembly does not reiterate the resolutions of '86 and '93. The question of Home Rule for Ireland so long as that deliverance is on the books cannot legally be brought before the Assembly—a sign that the church as a church has travelled far since '86 or '93. The convention about which so much has been said was reduced to its true proportions. The unanimous opinion of the Assembly is that the convention was an assemblage of Presbyterians without the sanction or the authority of the General Assembly. It was "a wise and honourable compact"—the phrase is not mine: it came openly from the other side. It is with regret that I have to add that the moderator was the first to break the compact. Immediately after the Assembly he whirled to London to take part in a purely political gathering as the representative of the Irish Presbyterian church. This action of his seems to me and even to some who agree with him politically a distinct breach of a public compact. He speaks of Home Rule in his letter as a religious question. If so, he gave the go-by in his speech in the Albert Hall, as reported, to the religious aspect of the question. Perhaps in the presence of the Duke of Norfolk and other sincere Catholics he got the hint not to beat the Protestant drum. I have a sincere admiration for Dr Montgomery as a man and for the work he has done, but many of us who appreciate his evangelising efforts are sorry that he as moderator of a great church, in face of a decision he declared carried, should have lent the weight of his name to a political crusade.'

LETTERS FROM J. B. ARMOUR TO HIS WIFE AND SONS

D.1792/A3/1/1-34

1903-1910

Originals of letters from Rev. J. B. Armour to his wife and sons (principally to W. S. Armour).

D.1792/A3/1/1

1 October 1903

Part of a letter to his wife from Armour, [London],

describing a visit to London, including a trip to Hampton Court, attendance at four different religious services and an expedition to the theatre to see a performance of Shakespeare's *Richard II.*

D.1792/A3/1/2

[n.d. 1907 ?]

Part of a letter to his wife or son, William, from Armour, [Dublin],

written from Dublin where he had gone to visit the Dublin Exhibition, describing an interview with Lord Aberdeen, the lord lieutenant. Armour was one of Aberdeen's personal chaplains and was on friendly terms with him as a fellow Presbyterian. The account of the interview reveals Armour's hostility towards T. W. Russell, the former Liberal Unionist who had been given office as vice president of the department of Agriculture and Technical Instruction in the Liberal administration. Despite Armour's expressed distaste for T. W. Russell's manipulation of patronage, he is clearly anxious to exploit his relationship with the Aberdeens on behalf of his friends and political associates such as Thomas Shillington of Portadown, who had contested South Tyrone in 1895 as a Liberal/independent nationalist. The reference to the vacant chair of Latin would seem to date the letter definitely to 1907, since there was indeed such a vacancy at Queen's College, Belfast, in that year—a vacancy that was to be filled by R. M. Henry.

'... he had become a high and dry Liberal Unionist, which meant a Tory, more Tory than the Tories and that in almost all the elections in the North, he had acted as if he was the leader of an all powerful party, issuing manifestos commanding the Presbyterian folks *nolens volens* to vote for the one, he as king delighted to honour, and that consequently he had disgusted and alienated a good number of the older members of Assembly and certainly most of the coming generation. This seems as far as I could gather a satisfactory explanation of the problem. Then he asked particularly my opinion about T. W. Russell, saying that I was to give my real opinion. I stated that while I respected his ability, I thought he was a bit of a humbug and a fraud and that he was going about posing as if the whole power of the state rested on his shoulders and that he was doing his level best for his friends, shoving them into honour and power and allowing men who had done twenty times more for the party than ever he had done, to be passed over, I told him as plainly as I dared that Master T. W. R[ussell] ought to be kept in his place and that whatever virtues he had or had not, he had no sense of humour which was essential for anybody who claimed the role of statesman. I then got my chance to put forward Tom Shillington's claims for a knighthood, reminding his ex[cellency] that he (Tom) had contested S. Tyrone against T. W. R[ussell], that I had stumped the co[unty] for the former who, though an honoured Methodist before, had become *anathema maranatha* with the fraternity in consequence of his politics which made him an Ishmael in the Methodist camp. I put the case strongly and his ex[cellency] replied that he would be glad to do what he could for him especially as he was a Methodist, adding that he (his ex[cellency]) was accused of doing nothing save for Presbyterians. He said that Balfour had taken the power from Lord Dudley of making knights and that it had not been restored yet. I have to run now to the exhibition and may not be able to finish (read the parable of building the tower). After some other talk on the university question, we joined her ex[cellency] in the drawing room and somehow or other the chair in Latin in Q[ueen's] C[ollege] B[elfast] came about which gave me the chance of putting in a word indirectly for R.K.McE. I told them the story of Dr O'Neill and the president at which her ex[cellency] laughed very heartily and mentioned how the Tory government had shoved in Dr [R. F.] Dill—the coroner—to a chair in the College over the head of the president at the time and his ex[cellency] asked what would happen if a similar thing took place now, to which I replied "there would be a three days tow-row in the papers and that would be all". There were several other things but I have no time to relate them. The interview at the local government office today was in a way interesting but if I did little ill, perhaps I did little good but more of this anon. Expect us on Thursday, at the exhibition all day—tired (?), love to all and a double dose for yourself.'

D.1792/A3/1/3   **Letter to W. S. Armour from Armour,**

3 March 1910   the first of a very lengthy series written to his son William who had just taken up an educational appointment at Queen's College, Benares, India, in which Armour recounts local, family and ecclesiastical gossip and comments in some detail on current political developments. This letter refers to a financial dispute concerning Professor James MacMaster of Magee College, Londonderry (Armour's wife's brother-in-law), who has been asked by his colleagues to 'hand over to the funds of the college a proportion of the £400 a year he had received from the Royal [University] and a proportion of the retiring allowance' and includes Armour's advice to MacMaster 'to sit tight and bid them go to the devil'. It also contains some comments on the position of Asquith's government in the aftermath of the January 1910 general election which had left the Liberals dependent on the support of Redmond's Irish party, forcing Asquith to tackle the reform of the house of lords before the 1909 budget, and a warning to William to take care of his health. All of these letters are written from Ballymoney, unless otherwise stated.

'Your ma is writing you and she will likely give you details of the events of the days since your departure. ... I write a note to you direct to Port Said but I have doubts about your getting it. However, I may repeat part of it. ... There is nothing exciting about here. The govt. has got round an ugly corner in the meantime but how long it may last is quite another matter. Asquith had to change his tactics and put the veto first to the delight of the Radicals and Nationalists but it is another whole and rather perilous role. How it may work out is beyond the ken of man. ...'

D.1792/A3/1/4   **Letter to W. S. Armour from Armour,**

10 March 1910   recounting a visit to Dublin in his official capacity as chaplain to the lord lieutenant and discussing a conversation with Lord and Lady Aberdeen which had ranged over the death of their son and the various attacks made upon the Aberdeens by some in Ireland who were opposed to them politically. As always, Armour had also taken the opportunity to press home a patronage request concerning an appointment to the magistracy.

'... I was in Dublin taking a service at the [viceregal] lodge on Sabbath evening. Their exc[ellencies] and especially his exc[ellency] much changed and cut up by the calamity of their favourite son's death. We did not speak of it directly as it is difficult to know what to say and anything one could say would be vacant chaff well meant for grain. They were evidently riled by the ex-moderator's manifesto and they asked me what I thought thereon. I replied without hesitation that it was a mean and contemptible production and deserved the scorn of all honest men. His exc[ellency] was much annoyed on hearing that some responsible person has been circulating that her exc[ellency's] crusade against consumption was working mischief in the sense that the feeling was spreading that the Irish had a double dose of consumptive germs and thereby Irish girls specially were refused as servants *etc.* and the responsible person had said that Jacob and Co., biscuit manufacturers, had turned off a number of workers, girls and men—a story which was without foundation in fact. I smiled and said he should not worry over statements of that kind, reminding him that nobody can do good in this world without having their good spoken evil of and that the better feeling of the community would discount statements of the kind. He is a little nervous over any criticism of the countess—naturally, but I fancy the best way to meet his nervousness is to belittle the cause. ...'

D.1792/A3/1/5   **Letter to W. S. Armour from Armour,**

5 May 1910   commenting on the death of J. J. Shaw, his close
                                      friend since university days who had unsuccessfully
contested the North Antrim seat with Armour's support in 1892; discussing the resulting
vacant recordership of Belfast and his efforts to secure the appointment of his favoured
candidate, Robert McIlroy, K.C.; and analysing the failure of William's brother, Max, to obtain
a vacant Presbyterian congregation in Bangor, Co. Down.

'... You will have heard by this time of [J. J.] Shaw's death which was an awful shock, specially
to me as I had known him so long and fairly intimately. He was wonderfully able and ought to
have been as far as mortal promotion was concerned among the foremost at the bar. [Sir James]
Dougherty is shocked as he was his closest friend in Dublin. Said D[ougherty] certainly stood
to him and got him the position in Belfast which he filled with conspicuous success but alas
for too short a time. The question of his successor has reached an acute state and I was in Belfast
yesterday trying to find out how the land lay. Thus I interviewed [Thomas] McDowell
[secretary of Ulster Liberal Association], Sir Charles Brett and Sir Hugh Mack [president of
Ulster Liberal Association]. I have just posted the result of my researches to Sir J[ames] B.
D[ougherty] who will, I fancy, send it on to [Augustine] Birrell. ...

Max did not get Bangor, as I suspected he would not—his father's politics stood in his way. He
may find that in other places also but it will draw out his pluck. ...'

D.1792/A3/1/6   **Letter to W. S. Armour from Armour, 3 Crescent
                                      Gardens, Belfast,**

12 May 1910
                                      describing his attendance at a number of committee
meetings; commenting on the opposition to the teaching of scholastic philosophy in the Queen's
University of Belfast and on the enmity of Presbyterian leaders to the whole institution;
attempting to analyse the possible consequences for national politics of the death of Edward VII;
and repeating some favourable remarks made by Dr Alexander Martin about Max Armour's
abilities.

'I have been here for two nights attending through the day a variety of committees. I have no
time this morning for more than a greeting. I see in this morning's paper that Robert
McIlroy, K.C., has been appointed as recorder of Belfast in room of the late Judge Shaw. I told
you something of the business I think in last week's note [*see D.1792/A3/1/5*]. The matter is
settled now beyond dispute. I interviewed Vice-Chancellor [Thomas] Hamilton on the resolutions of convocation in the matter of scholastic philosophy. He seems to be living in a fool's
paradise, imagining that the senate will not mind what the convocation may think. I told him
that in my judgement the senate would be frightened and would practically adopt the attitude
of convocation. He thought I was too pessimistic but I then went to see [R. M.] Henry—
prof[essor] of Latin and he quite agrees with my view, asserting that [Sir Samuel] Dill and he
have come to the conclusion that only ten or twelve on the senate will have back bone enough
to vote for the retention of scholastic philosophy. Hamilton filled the senate with weaklings
and he will be beaten with the rod he cut out for himself. The leaders of the Presbyterian
church have made up their minds to wreck the university and perhaps they may succeed. ...

The king's death will make a difference on the political situation—it will postpone the veto for
a season and perhaps may lend itself to the Tories. You are too hard on Asquith—he has a very
difficult drill to hoe. Strange to say [John] Morley has become very conservative and he and
Haldane and Grey have given a deal of trouble in the cabinet and therefore Asquith had not a
free hand but he, up to the king's death, managed fairly, that is he got his way or rather the
was of the chief section of the cabinet.

Truth has a good deal of insight but it is not always possible to carry out its views of matters political. I see parliament is adjourned until the 7th of June. That will be a breathing space and many things may happen before that. [Lloyd] George is credited with being a Tory of the Tories which may lead to an uncomfortable situation for himself in a few years. ...'

D.1792/A3/1/7   **Letter to W. S. Armour from Armour,**

26 May 1910   discussing the political repercussions of Edward VII's death; commenting on the degree of influence which he can bring to bear on government appointments such as that of Robert McIlroy to the recordership of Belfast; and indicating Max Armour's continuing problems *vis-a-vis* securing a Presbyterian congregation.

'... The death of the king has supplied the papers with material for the last fourteen days continuously and certainly the event has stirred the community to its depths. No king's death in the history of this world has produced such a wave of sympathy as this has done. How Geordie Pordie [*sic*] may conduct himself in his new sphere is a matter of conjecture. He may have a mind of his own. The Tory papers are rather overdoing the business and it is amusing to read how they are dwelling on his youth—he is forty-four years of age—as a reason why the veto question should be dropped. They are scared and would like things to go on as Lord Halsbury and old fogies of that ilk would like. It will be interesting to watch the situation in its political aspect. There may be a lull in the show but certainly not for long and "the lad of forty-four" ought to get a chance of making up his mind without unnecessary delay. Perhaps he will get a chance sooner than is expected in Tory quarters.

Robert McIlroy has entered on his duties, getting compliments from the bar and press ... [Sir James] Dougherty and myself put McIlroy there—that is fact, though it cannot be said in public. I am trying to run Dr Robert Boyd of Belfast, a youth from Forttown, second cousin of the family, for an appointment as surgeon and agent for the Admiralty in Belfast. I wrote Lord Pirrie and Dougherty on his behalf and also to the vice-chancellor of the Q.U.B. [Thomas Hamilton] who may be asked his opinion on the point. I know not how it may go but I have done what I could for him. I hope he will get it. Max is to preach for me on Sabbath at both spells of worship as a supply for St James's [Presbyterian Church, Ballymoney]. Some of the people there would not be adverse to giving him a call but it would produce ructions and would complicate the affairs of the church generally in the locality. Therefore I think he will not preach on trial at all there—the wise course for him to pursue. ...'

D.1792/A3/1/8   **Letter to W. S. Armour from Armour,**

23 June 1910   largely devoted to the politics of the scholastic philosophy issue, and in particular describing Armour's efforts to secure a compromise and the course of events in both the Queen's University senate and the General Assembly. There is also some further pessimistic comment on Max Armour's inability to obtain a congregation.

'... We had a meeting of senate to consider a resolution of the board of studies to give *three* courses for scholastic philosophy. The speeches against by Martin (R. T.) and [R. M.] Jones were so interminably long that [W. H.] Dodd and Mrs [Mary A.] Hutton who were in favour of the proposal had to leave by the 5.30 for Dublin, with the result that the resolution was rejected by fourteen to thirteen. I was a little annoyed at the result but not surprised. Tom Sinclair referred to it in the Assembly in a triumphant tone as Martin had evidently told him of the voting. He referred to me (without naming me) as giving notice to have the resolution rescinded and went on to say that we were pawns in the hands of the bishops. I resented this rather [?] and I looked and felt a little flabergasted [*sic*]. To make a long story short I have been trying to get a compromise in this way—to allow scholastic philosophy to count *two* courses instead of *three* which the resolution refused contemplated. ... Perhaps you will [stern ?]

when you learn that your daddie in his old age goes in for compromise. Things must be got to work in this world. ...

We got the licensing of students for the ministry by the General Assembly knocked on the head. Henceforth it is to be by presbyteries as formerly. I managed to make a speech, pointing out that it was unfair to exclude fathers who gave their sons to the ministry from having a voice in the licensing. I said that I had advised my son to go into one of the Scotch churches as he never would get a place in Ireland owing to the supposed sins of his father. ...'

D.1792/A3/1/9   **Letter to W. S. Armour from Armour,**

30 June 1910   discussing in great detail the case of a Liberal Pres-
                                   byterian layman called Bailey who had been suspended
from a congregational eldership on an indictment for alleged blasphemy. Armour was a member of a church commission which met in Portrush to hear Bailey's appeal and found in his favour. The letter also reveals the beginnings of Armour's association with, and interest in, the Independent Orange Order which was of course by this time well-established in the Ballymoney area.

'The Independent Orangemen wanted Max to preach to them in our church on the 10th July ... but he is not willing and I am in a fix. They hardly want me to address them and I am at my wit's end to find a substitute which would be acceptable—I am trying to find a man. If not, I will take the service myself. ...'

D.1792/A3/1/10   **Letter to W. S. Armour from Armour,**

7 July 1910   containing some church and family gossip and further
                                   discussion of the proposed service on 10 July in
Armour's church for the Independent Orange Order. Armour had suggested a subject for the sermon and was endeavouring to find a preacher to deliver it.

'... I have been under fire in the house for over a week in consequence of the service to be held on the evening of the 10th in the church for the Independents. In consequence of Max refusing to rise to the occasion, I had to promise to get somebody to hold the fort, but the somebody was an unknown factor. I had suggested the subject. What is Protestantism? What are its principles? and why are we Protestants? The Demosthenes for the subject was the quest. I could not tell because I did not know and therefore the bills were printed without any name. I have been under cross-fire every day and almost every hour since—your ma and Max drawing bows at every turn to find the secret. I was not to be drawn and therefore this Thursday nobody here knows. I had written [Rev.] Heney of Mossside as he had gone for [Sir William] Baxter [Liberal candidate in N. Antrim] at the election but he was unwilling to embark on the troubled sea but he added that if it would relieve me of a difficulty he would come. I took the hint and wrote him to say that if he came and had no objection I would sketch the line to be pursued and that as we all had to get material for our harangues from different sources there would be no lowering of his dignity in accepting an outline from me. Like a decent man, he said "certainly not" and I have sketched a literally big outline of the discourse, advising him to add thereto or substract therefrom whatever seemed good in his sight. He wished that his name should not appear on the bill but I have written to him to say that there is nothing in the outline he need object to as there is no attack on any man's religion save indirectly from first to last. I expect to see him [?] today to get his approval of Hamlet appearing in the play. That is the story but how I have had to endure pin-pricks for fully seven days. A thick hide is a wondrous defence. I was sad but said nothing. ...'

D.1792/A3/1/11   **Letter to W. S. Armour from Armour,**

13 July 1910   commenting on the Boyne anniversary celebrations in the area on 12 July, outlining his role at the service in his church on 10 July for the Independent Orange Order's local lodges and discussing the reactions to the government's proposed alteration to the royal declaration on religion. There is also the usual local and ecclesiastical news, including an approving comment on the award of a K.C.B. to Sir James Dougherty.

'... We have got the 12th over—the quietest 12th for many years, the Catch-my-Pal business [a temperance movement] having reduced drinking to a vanishing quantity in the meantime. How long that state of matters may continue remains to be seen. We are thankful for the mercy in the meantime. There was a big demonstration today in Ramoan Hill, Portrush, but I did not venture down. ... [Rev.] Heney's sermon approved itself to the brethren and the strangers. It raised more money for the order than any address has done, hence one of the reasons of its popularity. The high priest [Rev. D. D.] Boyle [grand chaplain of the Independent Orange Order], as James Cameron would say, never had a better audience. The hands were the hands of Esau but the voice was Jacob's—has been the comment but no information has been vouch-safed. The sermon must take its place as to authorship with the letters of Junius. He did his part very effectively as a whole. ...

The political situation is in a curious position. The altering of the declaration is stirring up strife: of the course the Irish Unionists—that is the Ulstermen are striving to appeal to the [?] Ulster folks but the fact that Balfour, Long and even Campbell are in favour of the change is a bitter pill for the fire eaters. "The Protestant religion" is trying to the nationalists—as the religion by law established is annoying to the non-conformists and others. It is supposed that the king almost refuses to accept the old formula—hence Balfour and the responsible Tories have to accept things as they are. ...'

D.1792/A3/1/12

21 July 1910

Letter to W. S. Armour from Armour,

commenting further on the reaction in Ulster and Scotland to the proposed change in the royal declaration [*see D.1792/A3/1/11*].

'... The proposed change in the royal declaration is stirring the north of Ireland and apparently Scotland enormously but whether it will have any effect on the measure remains to be seen. The king insists on a change and therefore Lord Rosebery whose son is stumping the country against the change, or against the change proposed, will find himself in a difficult position when the matter comes before the lords. He can hardly afford to go against the king's wishes, though his son must have taken the cue from him. ...'

D.1792/A3/1/13

28 July 1910

Letter to W. S. Armour from Armour,

describing a visit to Belfast to attend the Queen's University graduation ceremony and the Campbell College prize distribution (where Armour's youngest son Kenneth was a pupil). He also briefly refers to a meeting of the Q.U.B. senate at which scholastic philosophy was again on the agenda.

'... At the senate I withdrew my motion to rescind the resolution passed by fourteen to thirteen at the late meeting which practically confined sch[olastic] phil[osophy] to one subject as against *three* for Scottish philosophy. In withdrawing, I stated that I had proposed to both sides a compromise—namely to allow [Rev. Denis] O'Keefe [lecturer in scholastic philosophy] to present students for a degree in two subjects as against three. I fancy if the board of studies proposes that we can carry it but I know not what they may do. ...'

D.1792/A3/1/14

[n.d. c.3 August 1910]

Part of a letter possibly to W. S. Armour from Armour,

covering somewhat similar ground as D.1792/A3/1/13—

describing in rather more detail the Queen's University graduation ceremony and the Campbell College prize distribution and discussing Max Armour's refusal of a congregation in Bangor, Co. Down.

<table>
<tr><td>*D.1792/A3/1/15*</td><td>**Letter to W. S. Armour from Armour, [written on Royal Portrush Golf Club notepaper]**,</td></tr>
</table>

17 August 1910

mainly devoted to a discussion of the banning of a Hibernian demonstration in Garvagh, Co. Londonderry, by the government because of threats that it would be attacked by Protestants opposed to it. He stresses the influential role which he has played in persuading Sir James Dougherty to ban the procession.

'... The Garvagh meeting was proclaimed on Friday morning. I sent two letters of Sir J[ames] B. D[ougherty] to aunt Jane [MacMaster] requesting her to transmit them to you. It was a trying week for me for the authorities in Dublin were strongly of the erroneous opinion that the Orangemen were bluffing and they were on the eve, but for my letters, of allowing the Hibernians to go to Garvagh. Sir J[ames] B. D[ougherty] was not far from the edge of the razor. Bloodshed would have been the result had the meeting not been proclaimed. Every old gun, pistol and blunderbuss, all the powder and shot in Ballymoney, Coleraine and Garvagh had been bought up by the Orange and Ribbonmen here. Captain Welch told me on Tuesday last—I sent down specially to see him—that in every house in Garvagh there were four or five guns and in one house no less than *sixteen* for which licence was taken out. The intention was to snipe the Hibernians and even the police from the windows, retaliation being difficult and [?] and identification impossible. The authorities also had this information supplied but they seemed to harbour the idea that they could allow the Hibernians to get *beyond* Garvagh without mischief—a mere delusion which they recognised at the eleventh hour and forbade them to go beyond Kilrea. They held their demonstration—a tame affair—at McLaughlin's corner. The Hibernians were altogether in the wrong. They might as well have selected Sandy Row for their meeting as Garvagh and to select a field beside a new Orange rector was enough to madden the Orange fraternity. If the Orangemen had selected a field beside a priest's house for their display and played the "Protestant Boys" and "Kick the Pope", the indignation through Catholic Ireland would have known no bounds. However, "all's well that ends well" and the nine tenths of the Orange and Green are more than pleased that the meetings were proclaimed. Sir J[ames] B. D[ougherty] I am sure is inwardly thankful for having put down his foot. [Augustine] Birrell fortunately was away. He has a theory that all pocessions should be allowed and protected—a theory which looks just on paper but often turns out unfortunate in practice. ...'

<table>
<tr><td>*D.1792/A3/1/16*</td><td>**Letter to W. S. Armour from Armour,**</td></tr>
</table>

24 August 1910

containing church and local gossip and an account of a motor car trip with Sir James Dougherty to Garvagh and Portrush. He also makes reference to press criticisms of John Morley's tenure of the India Office.

'... We called on auld acquaintances in Garvagh and they all congratulated him on proclaiming the Garvagh gathering, each having some new tale to tell of the preparations made for giving the Hibernians a warm reception. I don't know whether he is yet convinced how near he was to the edge of the razor, as Oedipus would say. ... He is well out of a bad business. [Joseph] Devlin and John Muldoon advised the Hib[ernian]s to go elsewhere. They are not anxious for a row at the present juncture of affairs.

I see the Tory papers are pitching into John Morley for his government of India. He is fighting the officials. They are specially grieved at the statement of Montagu that Morley is simply using [Lord] Minto [viceroy of India] as an agent. The new grievance is the appointment of a commercial man, I forget his name, to the Indian Council. ... I suppose it is the doldrums at present in politics and Morley is taking the place of the sea serpent—that convenient subject for summer holidays. ...'

D.1792/A3/1/17   **Letter to W. S. Armour from Armour,**

1 September 1910   discussing Max Armour's continuing efforts to secure a congregation and the implications of the death of John Cooke, in particular the vacancy which this creates on the senate of the Queen's University of Belfast, and also the problem of selecting a suitable Liberal to succeed Cooke as his majesty's lieutenant for Co. Londonderry.

'... This is the close season in politics and therefore there are neither meetings nor speeches, save among a few of the Irish warring sects. John Cooke, whose death leaves the *custos rotulorum* of Co. Derry vacant will be much missed and by nobody more than Prof[essor] M[acMaster]. The government has a difficult job in selecting his successor as the gentry of Co. Derry are all violent Tories and there is no outstanding Liberal in the co[unty]. I have had a letter from the Liberal association of Belfast asking me to use my influence on behalf of Sir W[illiam] Baxter of Coleraine [who had unsuccessfully contested North Antrim in January 1910]. I fear the powers that be will hardly look at him, as he is, as your ma would say, bourgeois, and belongs to the middle class [Baxter owned a chemist's shop in Coleraine]—which would be no objection for me. Besides he is a seller of drugs. I hardly know what will be done. I would not like a reactionary Tory to get it but I don't see any way out of the wood otherwise. A successor will be needed for him on the senate of the Q.U.B. If [Augustine] Birrell takes [Thomas] Hamilton's nominee he will be sure to be wrong as Hamilton has filled the senate with men without backbone—narrow creatures who cannot see an inch before their nose, many of them hopeless reactionaries with only one article in their creed—let no papish enter the building save he conforms to its thirty-nine articles. ...'

D.1792/A3/1/18   **Letter to W. S. Armour from Armour,**

8 September 1910   containing family gossip in the main and recounting the contents of letters to *The Times* newspaper on current unrest in India.

D.1792/A3/1/19   **Letter to W. S. Armour from Armour,**

15 September 1910   describing the continuing saga concerning the vacant lieutenancy for Co. Londonderry and indicating the key role played by Armour as an important link in Birrell's patronage chain.

'... I also interviewed Sir Hugh Mack and some prominent Liberals over the successor to John Cooke as his majesty's lieutenant for Co. Derry. Sir Hugh gave me a lunch in the Reform Club—an eatable repast—and the trio discussed the business along with other matters for quite a while. They had been urging Sir W[illiam] Baxter's claims and had sent me a resolution in his favour to be transmitted to Sir J[ames] B. D[ougherty], which I sent forward, adding that [David] Hogg, brother-in-law of John Cooke and father-in-law of McNeill of Dublin, the staunchest Liberal in Ireland, ought to get the honour, though I had nothing but favourable wishes for Sir William. Sir J. B. D. wrote back that Hogg's appointment appealed to him more strongly than the Coleraine man's [Baxter]. It appears from Sir Hugh Mack that the Liberals are [?] in favour of Hogg and that they nominated Baxter only because they had heard on good authority that Hogg would not accept. They urged me to write to Sir J. B. D. again to further Hogg's claims and to his son-in-law McNeill to urge his father-in-law to go in for the honour and to accept if appointed—both of which I have done by this post. Hogg is a very big man and when [Christopher] Palles, the chief baron [of exchequer], contested the city of Derry [in

1872] a mob assaulted him but Hogg put his corporation in front of him and saved him from violence—an act of kindness the chief baron remembers gratefully to this day. ...'

Letter to W. S. Armour from Armour,

22 September 1910   describing the next stage in the delicate manoeuvering to secure David Hogg's appointment as his majesty's lieutenant for Co. Londonderry.

'... I was in Derry for the day interviewing David Hogg with a view to get him to consent to accept, if offered, the honour of H. M. L. of Co. Derry. Derry, says Sir J[ames] B. D[ougherty], is a county without gentlemen and very few Liberals and the government is in a fix about the appointment, as a Tory in Derry has the position for the honour and the Liberals are up in arms against the idea of a Tory getting the honour. Sir W[illiam] Baxter the Liberals recommended but as he is in the *retail* trade the government funks and won't give it to him. I, in sending forward Sir W[illiam]'s claim, mentioned very strongly the claims of Hogg, brother-in-law of John Cooke and father-in-law of [Rev.] McNeill of Adelaide Road [Church, Dublin]. Sir. J.B.D. took up Hogg's case. As I was in Belfast last week, I consulted Sir Hugh Mack and others and they were all in favour of Hogg. They put forward Baxter on the understanding that Hogg would not accept. They besought me to write Sir J.B.D. and McNeill and either to write to Hogg or go and see him. I wrote McNeill and to Sir J.B.D., and ... I went to see Hogg and after a talk he consented to accept the honour if offered. I have written Sir J.B.D. a letter on the subject which he may perhaps send on to Asquith who has the appointment in his sole power. There may be a court intrigue in favour of Chichester, a relative of the late marquis of Donegall, and Asquith's hands may be tied. I will send you Sir J.B.D.'s letter if I can find it. Hogg is a very big man, six feet three, but he has not much of the social instincts—a courageous man who kept his Liberal legs under him amid all the gusts of Toryism and terrorism which have been sweeping through the gates of Derry for the last fifty years. You see I cannot keep from the diplomatic service, though it brings little advantage of any kind. ...'

Part of a letter possibly to W. S. Armour from Armour,

[n.d. October ? 1910]   containing a mixture of gossip; a report of a meeting of the Queen's University senate at which the high failure rate at matriculation had been discussed; and comments on the appointment of a Protestant to a chair at University College, Galway.

'... averred that, if they had been in the Royal [University of Ireland], eleven out of the thirteen would have been stuck. I told them that if in three or four years there were not at least 1500 students in attendance that the university would be a failure, for a degree from a university having only four or five hundred students, though it might be a good one from a literary point of view would be utterly worthless in the eyes of the public. ...

I then asked "Had the senate not the power and right as in the Royal [University of Ireland] of appointing a standing committee to receive and consider the reports of the different examiners and say who should or should not pass or get honours?" It appears that the statutes do not give the senate any such power. Then said I, "are we to understand that the senate must accept without comment the conclusions of a board of examiners who have shown themselves hitherto utterly without common sense?" If that is so what is the use of a senate? This talk was a trifle plain but I could gather from Sir Otto Jaffe, a bald-headed, high-minded Jew, that the talk was by no means displeasing at least to him. ...

There is nothing known as yet about H.M.L. for Co. Derry. It seems a little strange. Your friend Anderson B.L., who stops in Mrs Taylor's, and who was in Winnipeg all last winter, has returned and he has been appointed to the chair of political economy and jurisprudence in Galway.

That is the second appointment of a Protestant to Galway by the authorities of the National University—a good precedent for the Q.U.B. to deal a little generously with Catholic claims. I wrote [Sir James] Dougherty a sympathetic letter about Anderson and he has done the job whereat Anderson's glad, as he may well be, seeing that the emoluments will keep the staff in the well. He is a clever chap and very modest. ...'

D.1792/A3/1/22   **Letter to W. S. Armour from Armour,**

13 October 1910   containing almost entirely family, church and local news, along with some favourable comments on the establishment of the new Portuguese republic. He also draws his son's attention to the appointment of Sir John Simon as the new Liberal solicitor-general at a very youthful age and suggests that perhaps William had been unwise to go to India, thus abandoning any possibility of a political career at home.

D.1792/A3/1/23   **Letter to W. S. Armour from Armour,**

[n.d. c.October 1910]   discussing a letter which he had received from Sir James Dougherty which had suggested that David Hogg was likely to be appointed his majesty's lieutenant for Co. Londonderry, 'unless court intrigue forces Asquith's hands in another direction'. He scathingly describes the visit of Anthony Traill, the provost of Trinity College, Dublin, and Armour's old political enemy, to Ballymoney to present the prizes at a school prize distribution and to have lunch at Trinity Manse. Armour also refers to his son Max's desire to become assistant minister at Fitzroy Presbyterian Church, Belfast, and the political apostacy of Rev. David Dorrington Boyle, former minister of St James's Presbyterian Church, Ballymoney, Co. Antrim, and Downshire Road Presbyterian Church, Newry, Co. Down, and grand chaplain of the Independent Orange Order.

'... Max is very anxious to hear if he has got the assistantship in Fitzroy. He preached there on S[unday] and he will possibly hear tomorrow the result. He seems anxious to get it but I would not grieve if he did not as I hardly approve of assistantships. I would rather he would try to get a charge for himself—which is the best kind of training. ... I would like him settled before the Home Rule scare is set going again. [Rev.] D. D. Boyle it is said will get the McQuiston Memorial Church [Belfast]—Ballantine's old charge. It is said he has gone to Canossa and taken the oath never to say a word on politics save on the orthodox side. If so he is an incarnate ass. ...'

D.1792/A3/1/24   **Letter to W. S. Armour from Armour,**

19 October 1910   containing church, local and family gossip; a further optimistic assessment of David Hogg's chances of becoming his majesty's lieutenant for Co. Londonderry; and a discussion of Armour's efforts to secure the appointment of a Liberal to a vacant seat on the senate of the Queen's University of Belfast.

'... [Thomas] Hamilton wants [R. J.] McMordie, the l[ord] mayor of Belfast, John Cooke's successor on the senate. I have tried to put a spoke in Hamilton's wheel, pointing out that McM[ordie] is as narrow as they can be made and that if he gets it we may close up as the gang already in will make the university the most denominational one on this planet. Sir J[ames] B. D[ougherty] is not in favour of McM[ordie] which is a point in favour of somebody else, though who that somebody else may be is not known. I have suggested, though not strongly, [Samuel] Keightley who deserves a higher honour at the hands of the government than a mere seat in the senate as he has fought S[outh] Derry twice in the Liberal interest [in 1906 and 1910]. I also suggested [Alexander] McDowell of Carson and McDowell's but Sir J[ames] B. D[ougherty] is not over sweet on Alexander. ...'

D.1792/A3/1/25   **Part of a letter to W. S. Armour from Armour,**

27 October 1910   almost entirely devoted to social chit-chat and family
                                    news, although there are the by now familiar references
                                    to the dispensing of government patronage.

'... I have had no communications from the Castle since writing last week and can say nothing
about how the land lies in reference to several matters of public importance. W. J. Johnston is
a candidate for a county court judgeship but I fear his chances are not bright chiefly owing to
the absence of K.C. to his name. He has been asked to stand for S[outh] Derry at the next
election and I have hinted to him that it might be well to consider it as it would certainly
strengthen his claim for a berth. ...'

D.1792/A3/1/26   **Letter to W. S. Armour from Armour,**

[n.d. November 1910 ?]   discussing a presentation to Alexander McDowell in
                                    the Ulster Hall, Belfast, which both he and Mrs Armour
had attended. He comments on the participation of Lady Aberdeen and on the unpopularity
of the Aberdeens and the Liberal government in general amongst Ulster Unionists. He also
describes his continuing efforts in the Queen's University senate to get matriculation standards
lowered from their current high level which is, Armour believes, strangling the university virtually
at birth.

'... We were at the McDowell presentation on Tuesday, an account of which you will find in
the papers sent by this post. Your ma went though her eye is still closed, resolved not to desert
Mr Micawber. Minus or barring the eye, she looked very well among a large number of females,
a percentage of whom appeared only passibly good looking. It was a great gathering. Her
exc[ellency] came from Dublin to take part in it as well as to address health meetings and open
the [?]. She made a very good speech, tactful, kindly, apparently sincere with many graceful
and gracious compliments to Alexander. His reply with a few sentences in addition was
"schrgut". The other speeches were very poor in my opinion. ... There was a deal of hypocrisy
running through the most of the references to her exc[ellency] was a majority of the speakers,
as I said earlier in the day to [Rev.] Simpson of Dungannon, "would send her to Jericho or to
that [?] region to which you, Simpson, are in the habit of consigning the pope". It is too true:
the hatred of the present regime in Belfast is intense and the feeling is growing that the Unionists
of Ulster will be betrayed by the Tories no less than the Liberals. ...'

D.1792/A3/1/27   **Part of a letter to W. S. Armour from Armour,**

[n.d. November 1910 ?]   discussing his continuing struggle to persuade the
                                    Queen's University senate to force the matriculation
standards down somewhat and gloomily commenting on the probability that the young lawyer,
William Macafee, will contest the North Antrim seat in the Liberal interest in the forthcoming
general election.

'... We will soon be in the throes of an election ... it is said [William] McAfee [*sic*], B.L., is to
contest N[orth] Antrim, a hopeless sort of fight. Dr [Thomas] T[aggart] could win no election
[Taggart was the Liberal election agent]. If [R. G.] Glendinning would stand he might have a
chance as he knows how an election can be won but I hear he has no [?] for political life. The
other standing under Dr T[aggart] means beaten by 1,000—though the youth is clever enough. ...'

D.1792/A3/1/28   **Letter to W. S. Armour from Armour,**

23 November 1910   containing local gossip and further comments on the impending general election, in particular on the effectiveness of the Liberals' national campaign and their efforts in North Antrim and South Londonderry.

'... We are in for a month's excitement over the elections. I don't see how the Tories can win but by how many the Liberals can return with depends on the ballot boxes. Asquith, Lloyd George and Churchill have set the ball a rolling very well—the clever speeches they have given already. The tow-row about Redmond's dollars will not have much effect as the brewers, landlords and licensed victuallers have contributed possibly five times as much to Tory coffers and Lloyd George's reminder to some of the lords that their palaces and estates have been underpinned by American dollars is a palpable hit which like humocea touches the spot. It appears that barrister [William] McAfee [*sic*] has been chosen to fight N[orth] Antrim—which seems to me a poor choice. I have no objection to the youth but in the first place he has not money to spend on a campaign and in the second place [Thomas] Taggart could win no election as he has no head and will take no advice from anybody. If he had any *nous* he might have won the last in spite of [Peter] Kerr-Smiley's dollars. If Glendinning had had his hand in the business, he would have pulled through all right. If he had been properly approached this time, he would I fancy have faced the music but what can one do with a muddle-headed creature with his hand on the tiller. I have no hope of success for McAfee [*sic*] whereat I am sorry. W. J. Johnston, B.L., is to tackle S[outh] Derry, a forlorn hope also I fear. He wrote me to go and speak at some of his meetings but I was compelled to decline on the score of health, not but that I would like the chance of edging in a few words on his behalf—in return for his father's great kindness to me. ...'

D.1792/A3/1/29   **Part of a letter to W. S. Armour from Armour,**

30 November 1910   discussing the financial problems of the Kilraughts Presbyterian congregation and the developing general election campaign in both Ulster and North Antrim. He expresses regret at not taking part in the struggle, because of poor health but also presumably because of the antagonism existing between him and the North Antrim Liberal leadership.

'The political temperature will soon reach boiling point here. It is creeping up beyond boiling point in England already. To change the metaphor, it is a *"sair fecht"* in most of the constituences throughout the three kingdoms. How it will end you will know from Reuter [*sic*] before this reaches you. It is a sore trial to be in the background of life and only to view the fight from a canoe among the reeds and rushes. [William] McAfee [*sic*] has begun his campaign and great regret is expressed that Max is not to the fore. He is well out of it perhaps. But I fancy a fibre of "the ould fellow" in him may long for a meeting or two to harangue. It is a good discipline even for a preacher to take a hand at the political wheel. It teaches him how to speak and wipes out of his constitution any starchy matter cleaving to him and a few knocks stiffen the sinews—at least the mental. I have not very much hope of a victory here as the Home Rule scare has reached the howling point. The banshees are out and are making night and day hideous with their yells. The Unionists started and stirred the witches' cauldron on Monday evening in the Ulster Hall but a very peculiar thing was observable. There was not a Presbyterian parson on the platform with the exception of the moderator of the Assembly who certainly was transgressing by his presence all the rules of moderatorial life. As moderator he had no right to be present as he was insulting a large section of the Presbyterian community. It showed a lack of common sense, as it was a breach of the ordinary courtesies of civilised life and he deserves a slap across the knuckles which he may get. It was a stupid sort of act. ...'

D.1792/A3/1/30   **Part of a letter to W. S. Armour from Armour,**

7 December 1910   commenting on early election results in Britain and on his inability to accept invitations to speak on behalf of the Liberal candidates Shane Leslie in Londonderry City and W. J. Johnston in South Londonderry. (He had sent a letter of support to both of them instead.) He analyses the progress of William Macafee's campaign in North Antrim and in particular notes that he is more attractive to Roman Catholic voters than either Sir William Baxter in January 1910 or R. G. Glendinning in January 1906. He is critical of the Unionist candidate Peter Kerr-Smiley's oratorical abilities and in discussing Kerr-Smiley's supporting speakers, he denies the assertion made by Dr McKean that he (Armour) was the original inspiration and source of the radicalism of the Route district.

'... The elections are going on; the Liberals lost a few the first two days—that is they lost more seats than they gained but the tide has turned this morning to the great chagrin of the Tories. The [*Northern*] *Whig* had no headline about Unionist triumphs and the [*Belfast*] *News-Letter's* headline was "a sad day for Unionism". What the morrow may bring one cannot tell but as far as the omens indicate the gov[ernmen]t will be back as strong as in January, if not stronger. I have been asked to go to speak in Derry for Shane Leslie and in South Derry for W. J. Johnston but I had to refuse both, though I sent a letter in each case—a copy of the letter to Derry you will find in one of the papers sent. "Julius Caesar" [Mrs Armour] I gather is not pleased with it but it would be hard for me to write a letter of the kind which would pass this *"censor meum"*. However, good or bad, it was sent and there it is. College Avenue [The MacMaster family] and other places in Derry will not like it which is a testimonial in its favour. [William] McAfee [*sic*] is doing very well here but the Home Rule bogey will frighten the timid. The other side is not spending as much money as in January and the enthusiasm for [Peter] Kerry-smiley is not yet at the boiling point. McAfee [*sic*] will have a larger Catholic vote than either [R. G.] Glendinning or [Sir William] Baxter. On Thursday evening last Smiley had his innings in the Town Hall when the speaking was reported very bad. This is the opinion of a supporter of Kerr-Smiley. He cannot speak but he had Crawford from the Curran of Larne—[Rev. J. L.] Donaghy from the Cutts of Coleraine—[Hugh T.] Barrie [M.P.] with Dr McKean from Belfast. McKean, according to reports, took to criticising me, asserting that I was the original inspiration of radicalism in the Route—a compliment indeed but I have no claim to the honour. However, I had my chance at him tonight. He was coming off the train to hold forth in Dervock. I shook hands with him and said, "Well, McKean, you have become a banshee." Thoughtlessly he replied, "they usually are heard before a death or funeral". "Yes", retorted I, "I accept that as a sign of the death of your man and certainly of your party". He saw how he had given himself away and took his departure without further parleying. A decent, big, good-natured man but I fancy the Smileys have been kind to him. ...'

D.1792/A3/1/31   **Letter to W. S. Armour from Armour,**

[n.d. c.December 1910]   expressing thanks for a large sum of money sent to help pay for younger brother Kenneth's continuing education; retailing a variety of family gossip; commenting on the election results, in particular the defeat of William Macafee and also on the appointment of David Hogg as his majesty's lieutenant for Co. Londonderry. He describes a meeting of the Queen's University senate which he had attended on the previous day. At the meeting he had reiterated his opposition to the seventy per cent failure rate at matriculation. He had also objected to the regulations restricting the award of a master of arts degree to students submitting a thesis based upon original research.

'... The election here is over—[William] McAfee [*sic*] defeated by a big majority. I expected this as the Home Rule bogey was the only plank in [Peter] Kerr-Smiley's platform. You will see the result weeks before you get this letter. However, N[orth] Antrim does not count—[?] speaking the Liberals are back as strong as in January and the veto of the lords will get its *coup de grace* and then we shall have changes here or at least attempted changes. His exc[ellency] has sent me a very friendly letter over [David] Hogg's appointment as h[is] m[ajesty's] l[ieutenant], Co. Derry. I will send it to you next week. I would send it today but Max has not seen it, nor aunt Jane [MacMaster] who claims a share in matters domestic. We had two hours almost at the senate. I gave them a piece of my mind on the regulations, saying that with these regulations interpreted nationally no university could thrive, attacking them again for rejecting seventy per cent at matriculation which was an insult to the teachers and students of Ulster and then specially attacking the regulations for the M.A. degree which is to be a thesis forsooth or by original research—which means that not five per cent of the graduates will face the absurdity. I pointed out that it would be a disgrace to send ninety-five per cent of the students into the world with a B.A. stuck to their tail—a degree which Dickens ridiculed in Mr Feeder B.A.—that the Scotch universities had abolished it certainly and that I preferred the Oxford and Trinity method of granting M.A. after two years on the payment of £10. The whole senate was in my favour and the matter is to come up at next meeting when my motion for the amendment of the statutes is to be sent to the Commission. ...'

D.1792/A3/1/32   **Part of a letter to W. S. Armour from Armour,**

22 December 1910   making further mention of correspondence with Lord
                                              Aberdeen concerning the appointment of David Hogg
as H.M.L. for Co. Londonderry [*see D.1792/A3/1/31*]; discussing the political apostacy of Alexander McDowell and the likely reaction of Lady Aberdeen to his desertion; commenting on the general political situation in Ulster and Great Britain and in particular on the failure of Ulster Unionist propaganda to sway Scottish Liberal voters.

'... I directed Max to send aunt Jane [MacMaster], who was in turn to transmit to you, his exc[ellency's] letter to me *in re* [David] Hogg's appointment as h[is] m[ajesty's] l[ieutenant] for Co. Derry. It was a triumph. You will find my answer to his exc[ellency] dealing with that and with his letter to Henderson who was contesting Aberdeenshire.

I need not enlarge on that as the letters explain themselves. You would see my letter to [W. J.] Johnston [who had contested South Londonderry in the Liberal interest] in the [*Coleraine*] *Constitution* sent you last week. Johnston under the circumstances made a very good fight. I am sending you the *Irish News* with a letter from [Alexander] McDowell therein to [Peter] Kerr-Smiley—a letter which McDowell would give £100 not to have published. How the *Irish News* got hold of it is a mystery. McDowell has been caught with his leg before wicket. His friends have been bothering me for long about some honour for him, declaring that he was a sound Liberal and I did my best to get him nominated as a senator [of Queen's University] in room of John Cooke but [Sir James] Dougherty had doubts about his Liberalism and he was right, as is now apparent—and thereby proved himself the better judge of human nature. He (McD.) has joined the Carson circus and he has revealed himself as a party intreaguer [*sic*]. "Being let go, he has gone to his own company". It was a mean thing for him and his entourage to ask her exc[ellency] to grace by her presence the presentation of the painting to him [*see D.1792/A3/1/26*] while in their hearts they would have liked to send her to Jericho. I suspect she has learned a lesson about the value of the lip-loyalty of the scaliwags of Ulster. You have no idea of the bitterness at present. Purdy's Burn Asylum [Belfast] will need enlargement soon—in fact lunacy is in the ascendant. But fortunately the emissaries in the shape of [Rev.] Tommy Thompson and [Rev.] Wright of Newtownards who scoured several—many parts of the constituencies in the Tory campaign of slander did the Liberals good and not harm. One might expect such fire-eaters to be taken at their true worth by hard-headed Scotchmen who listened to their harangues with a smile and then voted solid against their party. The Liberals are in stronger really than before and they will be in for probably four years at the time of calculation. Hurrah. ...'

D.1792/A3/1/33   **Letter to W. S. Armour from Armour,**

29 December 1910   almost entirely devoted to family and local news,
                                              along with a brief reference to an interview he has
given to a representative of the *Daily News* and Max Armour's fears about its possible effects on his clerical career.

'... Arnold, your old friend from Dunmurry, came in for a hour today and is gone. He wants for the *Daily News* my views on one or two points but Max is getting into a state of panic lest anything I should say might compromise his position in Belfast. He need not be alarmed. You may get a copy next week of the *D[aily] N[ews]*, if what I say appears. Meanwhile I send you some papers which though old will keep you abreast of the goings on in the political world. ...'

D.1792/A3/1/34   **Part of a letter to W. S. Armour from Armour,**

[n.d. 1910 ?]   entirely concerned with Armour's activities as an
                                     insurance commissioner for Co. Antrim (under the
terms of 1911 national insurance act) and with his role as a defender and advocate of the
Queen's University, Belfast. He relates how in his first capacity he and two other commissioners
had met with the Antrim County Council to find out what provision the council proposed to
make to deal with tuberculosis amongst the uninsured section of the population. Wearing his
other hat, he had accompanied the Right Honourable John Young, Professor E. A. Letts and
Sir William Crawford in an attempt to persuade the Antrim County Council to establish
scholarships for students from the county attending Queen's University, Belfast.

D.1792/A3/2/1-46

1911

Originals of letters from Rev. J. B. Armour to his wife and sons (principally to W. S. Armour).

D.1792/A3/2/1

Letter to W. S. Armour from Armour,

5 January 1911

discussing his state of health; commenting on the educational progress of William's younger brother, Kenneth, at Campbell College, Belfast; recounting a variety of family gossip; and analysing the reasons for the appointment of Thomas Shillington of Portadown, Co. Armagh, to membership of the privy council.

'... I enclose a letter from [Thomas] Shillington of Portadown who has been made a member of the p[rivy] c[ouncil] —a high honour. It is remarkable that all people as a rule when they gain some honours set it down to their own merits, though friends have been moving heaven and earth on their behalf. Two years ago I urged Shillington's claim to recognition on his exc[ellency, Lord Aberdeen] who promised to keep the matter in mind and now it has come whereat I am glad as he suffered a deal of boycotting from his co-religionists about '93. He had been a power among the Methodists then but they refused to listen to his sermons after he had become a home ruler. How he is treated now there I have no means of knowing. He is pleased. ...'

D.1792/A3/2/2

Letter to W. S. Armour from Armour,

12 January 1911

briefly mentioning the McCann kidnapping case and Unionists protests about it; discussing reaction to the publication of an interview with Armour in the *Daily News* [*see D.1792/A3/1/33*]; and passing on a number of items of family news.

'... The great event of last week was the big meeting in Belfast over the kidnapping case and the publication in the *D[aily] N[ews]* of my interview. The [*Northern*] *Whig* published part of it on Friday morning and reprinted the old manifesto of '87 with my name attached thereto [this was the notorious anti-Home Rule broadsheet, allegedly written by Armour during his Liberal Unionist phase] and wrote what it regarded as a flaming article on me. If I can get the paper I will send it to you though your ma is in distress about Max and you and thinks you will be both annoyed beyond measure with their father. But as I have committed no moral offence, it seems well for my boys to learn to stand fire. The interview was not given in full but sentences were cut out which do not give the full account of the case. Unfortunately the parcel of *D[aily] N[ews]* did not come to B[ally]money on Thursday or Friday and therefore I am indebted to some friend for the cutting enclosed. Some Englishman called Wilson from Wilts[hire] sent the cutting with a decent kind of letter asking if it was fairly given in the *D[aily] N[ews]*. I wrote back that generally it was correct but that a good deal had been omitted and that there was one misprint—"crimes" should have read "ironies". It was on the whole moderate and the curious thing is that while I said this idea of collecting arms and ammunition to resist Home Rule was wicked, the Protestant bishop of [?] wrote in next day's [*Northern*] *Whig* that the idea was stupid and wicked. I said—the sentence was not published—you cannot shoot an act of parliament signed by the king with guns—you cannot shoot the soldiers who try to enforce this act, or the administrators, and therefore there was a vision of a repetition of the Phoenix Park business with capital punishment on the perpetrators, with a possibility of an anniversary of "the Belfast Martyrs" as a rival of "the Manchester Martyrs". Another sentence was omitted: "Just as after every election there were cases of boycotting and persecution so a change in the government of Ireland such as was contemplated by a Home Rule bill might lead to sporadic cases of persecution but persecution for religious opinions on a general scale was improbable and impossible under the terms of the bill". I gave my reasons for this view which may or may not be valid. ...'

D.1792/A3/2/3 **Letter to W. S. Armour from Armour,**

19 January 1911 discussing his protests to the *Northern Whig* over its
publication of the broadsheet allegedly written by
Armour in 1887 [*see D.1792/A3/2/2*] and outlining further reactions to the *Daily News* interview. Armour also gives his view of the state of Protestant feeling on Home Rule and expresses
some concern about the possible impact of the McCann kidnapping case on the terms of the
final Home Rule legislation. He comments on Kenneth Armour's unhappiness and lack of
educational progress at Campbell College, Belfast, and on the efforts he and Mrs Armour have
made to use their influence with various individuals to push the application of Marian Armour
for the post of matron of the Richmond Hospital, Dublin.

'... I have written to the editor of the [*Northern*] *Whig* to tell him in covert tones that he is
liable for a serious action for republishing the manifesto with my name. I pointed out that the
document (1) was never published by me; (2) when it was published it did not bear my name;
(3) that it was republished seven years afterwards with my name forged to it; and (4) that the
forger bungled the business, as most forgers do, for he had signed my name in full—a form of
signature I never used to any document sent forth by me. He has written a rather feeble reply
in a way and I have replied, hinting broadly that he had neither the moral nor the legal right to
append my name thereto. The lawyers say it is actionable. I have not got his answer yet but
may. If I was a few years younger, I would not take it lying down but one need not worry over
things of this kind. I had two letters from a man called Wilson from Wilts[shire] over the interview appearing in the *D[aily] N[ews]*. His second letter—the first did not disclose his politics—
evidently showed his Tory proclivities. He was anxious to know the real state of feeling among
Protestants over Home Rule, asserting that if the majority of Protestants were against it that
would be its condemnation. I replied that he did not understand Irish politics, saying that when
the Union was proposed the vast majority of Protestants were very hostile while the vast majority
of Catholics were in its favour—the successors now of the Protestants of that time admitting
that their forefathers were entirely wrong. The same thing occurred at the disestablishment of
the Irish church, the vast majority of Protestants thinking it would ruin religion whereas now
the members of the late established church confessed that religion had benefited by the act.
The ballot bill and the universities bill met with this same hostility but now not three per cent
would vote for the repeal of either act. The Boer War was an illustration of the same truth but I
forget that instance until the letter was posted. I pointed out what I fancy is perfectly true,
that no act of parliament ever did as much good as its abettors fancied it would do and certainly
not a tithe of the evil its enemies prophesied about it if passed. I said also that Home Rule might
do some good but not the amount of good Redmond expected from it and on the other hand
it might do some evil but not a tenth of the evil the Unionists predicted. That seems a tolerably
correct view of the situation. I have not heard from him since. Possibly he has nothing to say
in reply. There are two letters in the [*Northern*] *Whig* this morning—one from [Rev.] George
Hanson and another from some man called Douglas, a home ruler, dealing with the kidnapping
case. I will send them to you. I can see that this unfortunate matter may modify the terms of
Home Rule. ...'

D.1792/A3/2/4 **Letter to W. S. Armour from Armour,**

26 January 1911 commenting on Marian Armour's failure to secure the
post of matron of Richmond Hospital, Dublin, and
on the *Northern Whig's* apology over the re-publication of the 1887 anit-Home Rule broadsheet.

'... The editor of the [*Northern*] *Whig* has come down a step from his high horse and says he
has given directions that no reference in the future is to be made to my connection with the
manifesto—a tacit acknowledgement that past references were not justified. Whether I may rest
satisfied with that is another matter on which I have not come to a definite decision as yet. ...'

D.1792/A3/2/5   **Letters to W. S. Armour from Armour,**

2 February 1911   commenting critically on the hostility of Unionists in
                                   Ulster towards Lord and Lady Aberdeen and in particu-
lar on hostility in the Coleraine district towards a visit from Lady Aberdeen to attend a meeting
on public health, an issue in which she was particularly interested. Armour expresses his disgust
at the attitude of Ulster Presbyterians towards the lord lieutenant, especially since Lord
Aberdeen had, as a Presbyterian, done his best to appoint and promote Presbyterians in the
public service.

'... Her exc[ellency] —the countess of Aberdeen came to Coleraine for a health meeting about a
week ago but the powers there did not wish to have her—political insanity has reached its zenith
there as elsewhere in Ulster. She had promised to come a year ago and Lady Bruce [the Bruce
family were Unionists who owned an estate of 20,801 acres in Co. Londonderry] had volunteered to lunch and keep her but in the meantime the Bruces had got very cool and practically
had said they would not have her. They are sore over H.M.L.s of the county [David Hogg, a
Liberal Presbyterian of Londonderry city, had been appointed his majesty's lieutenant for
Londonderry in 1910—*see D.1792/A3/1/31*]—that is where the shoe pinches but their real
grievance is the Unionist, that is they make this their reason though the other is the real
annoyance. However, somebody wrote the countess about the meeting and its date and the
countess telegraphed Lady Bruce to say she was coming and hoped it would not inconvenience
the Bruces to extend hospitality. Lady B[ruce] could not refuse, therefore she had to be at the
meeting. [Hugh T.] Barrie [M.P. for N. Londonderry]—the wretched little scut—cut up rough
and would not appear on the platform, as if that mattered. He too has a personal grievance of a
serious kind but he makes the Union as his divine principle and could not appear on a platform
when the lady l[ieutenant] was a speaker. He is down in the mouth as he fully expected the
Tories would come sailing into office and he would be the successor of T. W. Russell [vice-
president of the department of Agriculture and Technical Instruction]. "O Earth what a
multitude of hypocrites thou dost bear on thy kindly bosom." The most of the committee had
made up their mind to boycott the meeting but as Lady Bruce was to be in the chair they dared
not stay away. Therefore they came but objected to having the stairs carpeted for her
exc[ellency]. She was worse than a common person in their estimation. But several of the
Unionists saw the utter absurdity of their spleen and the stairs were carpeted and her exc[ellency]
entered to the strains of the nat[ional] anthem and got a hearty cheer. The thing passed off well
and some of the mad caps are sore over the reception which they tried to mar. The people of
Ulster are fit for an asylum. A decent man, a Presbyterian, the assistant in Purdy's Burn [Asylum,
outside Belfast] now wants to be appointed as chief in the public department of lunatic asylums
and [Rev.] Gibson of Broadway wrote me to further his cause. It was the opportunity I had
been waiting for—Gibson being a crusted Tory—I wrote him to say that I had recommended his
candidate but that his chances of success were vanishing as I refused to stir a foot for him
further owing to the disgraceful conduct of the Belfast Presbyterians—that at a meeting lately
his exc[ellency] has publicly hissed though there were four or five of his exc[ellency]'s chaplains
including the moderator of Assembly present and that none of them had the manliness to
protest—that these chaplins knew the politics of his exc[ellency] before accepting office—that
if they onjected thereto they should not have accepted the honour—that if they objected afterwards the manly, courteous course was to resign and that for them to sit in silence when hisses
were heard was conduct unworthy even of "uncircumsised Philistines". I added further that his
exc[ellency] had given more places of honour and emolument to Presbyterians during his reign
than all the Tory l[ord] lieutenants for 100 years, that I had done my best for my co-religionists
in the past but that those "baptised Pharisees" had put it out of my power to do anything
further. Gibson would squirm when he read the letter but it was deserved. ...'

D.1792/A3/2/6   **Letter to W. S. Armour from Armour,**

9 February 1911   commenting on the continuing controversy over the
                                   '*Ne Temere*' papal decree on mixed marriages and its

application in the Alexander McCann kidnapping case; suggesting that he had been fortunate in not being appointed to the Magee College professorship of church history in 1890 as this would have severely limited his freedom of expression; emphasising the loss of influence of the Belfast Unionist Presbyterians over government appointments; and indicating his determination to force the senate of the Queen's University, Belfast, to agree to restore the award of a master of arts degree by examination and to open all exhibitions and scholarships to competition every year.

'... The "*Ne Temere*" controversy is still in full blast. The Ulster Unionists have raised the question in the h[ouse of] c[ommons] and have given their say but [Joseph] Devlin [the Irish Nationalist member for West Belfast] whose speech I send has put several holes in the [ballad?]. The general opinion among those who know the woman and her family history is that she is no great shakes and to use her case for purely political purposes shows the straits to which the Ulster Tories are reduced. The *Manchester Guardian* which I will send takes a sane view of the "*Ne Temere*" and thinks it should be treated by Irish Catholics as a weapon no longer to be used. The [*Northern*] *Whig* and [*Belfast*] *News-Letter* of course did not publish Devlin's speech, thereby showing their vehement desire for fair play. ... When I look back over the years, I see it was a fortunate thing for me after all that I did not slip into the Derry professorship. It would have been my grave—a sort of blinding imprisonment. The fates were kind to me, however annoying the matter was by the rejection ... . There is a vacancy for an inspectorship of lunatic asylums worth £1,200 a year and the candidates are as numerous as the leaves in Vallambrosa. A Dr Ruttledge from Derry was here on Saturday for an interview and a Dr Patrick from Belfast was here on Monday. Ruttledge is in a state of despair as he let it be known that he voted for Shane Leslie [unsuccessful Nationalist candidate for Londonderry City in January and December 1910] which is as big a sin in the eyes of the Derryites as it would be to curse the Pope in the Vatican. He thinks his goose is cooked in Derry and he is sighing for a change of habitat. I fear his chances are not bright though he has a deal of backing, being an Episcopalian. I had to tell Patrick that the attitude of the Belfast saints to the government was practically a slamming of the door in the face of their co-religionists. A recommendation from Belfast would not further the interests of anybody at the Castle at present. Patrick went off in due course, not over hopeful but still without special depression. He seems to have a sense of humour. ...'

D.1792/A3/2/7   **Part of a letter to W. S. Armour from Armour,**

16 February 1911   apart from recounting family news and commenting critically on the running of Campbell College, Belfast, the letter is devoted to reporting a series of senate and convocation meetings which Armour had attended at the Queen's University, Belfast. In particular he describes how he had succeeded in getting the rules for conducting business in convocation changed, since some of the rules proposed 'seemed to have come from the Tsar of Russia for the guidance of the Duma'.

D.1792/A3/2/8   **Part of a letter to W. S. Armour from Armour,**

23 February 1911   discussing the possible repercussions of a meeting of the Literary Society of the Queen's University of Belfast to be held that evening to discuss the Irish question; indicating his reluctant decision to refuse an invitation to an Irish Nationalist party banquet in London; giving his views on the '*Ne Temere*' decree and its significance for mixed marriages in the future; recounting a variety of church gossip; and mentioning the possibility of a visit to Dublin on 13 March to preach at the viceregal lodge.

'... Tonight Lord MacDonnell is to give an address in the Literary Society, Q[ueen's] U[niversity], B[elfast] on the Irish question—I forget the actual title for the moment—and [Rev.] MacDermott, the Right Hon[ourable] T[homas] Shillington, Dr Hanson and somebody else are to speak thereon. I was asked to go but ... I thought it too much to start off for another meeting at which there would be the temptation to put in my oar and therefore I had to decline. They may have a storm as the feelings in Belfast are a trifle intense and last night's vote in the h[ouse of] c[ommons] over the veto will not sooth the madheads to any extent. I'll try to send you an account of the proceedings next week. I have just received an invitation to be present at the banquet in the Hotel Cecil on the 16th of March. It is to be a grand manifesto of the Irish party. John Redmond is to be in the chair. I suppose I must resist the temptation though I should like to hear the salvo of the Irish cannons. The *"Ne Temere"* business is the main spoke in the wheel of the Unionists in Ireland as they are twisting it for all it is worth. It will give trouble as I thought from the first. Whatever is the upshot of the business politically, it will prevent mixed marriages considerably in the future and therefore will have served the public good as these marriages almost without exception have turned out failures, not being conducive to domestic harmony. To introduce a bone of contention at the start of wedded life is not a hopeful outlook for the future ... .'

D.1792/A3/2/9   **Part of a letter to W. S. Armour from Armour,**

2 March 1911   dealing entirely with appointments in the Presbyterian church and government patronage. Once again Armour describes how he is using his influence with Sir James Dougherty, the under secretary of state for Ireland, on behalf of a police sergeant whom he considers to have been rather unfairly reduced to the ranks and on behalf of another constable in the Royal Irish Constabulary whom he considers worthy of promotion to the rank of sergeant. As to a chaplaincy in the Presbyterian church, Armour gloomily concludes that '[Rev.] Tommy Thompson, that baptised Pharisee, will get it through the local board for services rendered to the Tory caucus'.

D.1792/A3/2/10   **Part of a letter to W. S. Armour from Armour,**

[n.d. March ? 1911]   discussing the merits of a variety of candidates for the vacant chair in church history at Magee College, Londonderry; passing on some family news; enclosing a batch of newspapers, including the *Manchester Guardian*, 'the only Liberal paper worth reading these coster monger times'; and recounting the details of a motion to increase the number and value of scholarships which Armour proposed to introduce at a forthcoming meeting of the Queen's University senate on 6 April.

D.1792/A3/2/11   **Part of a letter to W. S. Armour from Armour,**

[n.d. March ? 1911]   containing the usual local and family news and further speculation about the vacant chair in church history at Magee College. In the letter Armour gives his reasons for declining the invitation to attend an Irish Nationalist party banquet in London on 16 March and analyses the possibility of Max Armour being able to move from his assistantship at Fitzroy Church, Belfast, to a vacant congregation at Ballykelly, Co. Londonderry.

'... I enclose you a letter from London which explains itself. I wrote to say that owing to health considerations I could not accept the courteous invitation. Chronic illness sometimes serves a purpose. The excuse was valid enough. But underneath there was another reason. It might have made the mad-caps of Ulster furious if I had appeared either as a speaker or auditor at a Home Rule nationalist gathering and therefore for appearances sake it seemed more prudent to say "no". ...

Max was mentioned as a candidate for Ballykelly when Paton was before going to Newry. Somebody objected to his name going on the list as he was the son of a notorious home ruler. Is this the sin of the father being visited on the children or is it a sign of the stupidity of men in regarding an unpopular opinion as a crime to be punished by excommunication? We are a peculiar people (not in the scripture sense) in this part of the world and our moral notions get a trifle confused. He (Max) does not think Ballykelly an El Dorado and therefore is likely not to disturb the Christians there over a controversy as to whether or not he is a home ruler. He likes Belfast and [Rev.] Coloquhoun [minister of Fitzroy Presbyterian Church, Belfast] and in the meantime inclines to hold the fort there. ...'

D.1792/A3/2/12   **Part of a letter to W. S. Armour from Armour,**

[n.d. 16 March ? 1911]   reporting in detail a visit to Dublin on 12 March to hold a service at the viceregal lodge in his capacity as one of Lord Aberdeen's chaplains. He discusses Aberdeen's increasing hostility towards Ulster Presbyterians and the government's desire to retain Sir James Dougherty's services as under secretary of state for Ireland. He analyses the mediating role which Dougherty plays between Lord Aberdeen, the lord lieutenant, and Augustine Birrell, the chief secretary. He also suggests that Lord and Lady Aberdeen lack the ability to judge character accurately.

'I got back from Dublin last evening (Wednesday) to find all here in health and good humour. The service at the lodge on S[unday] night passed off fairly. There were only about twenty-five present as there are few at the lodge now. I had not much talk with his ex[cellency], as Lord Carrick and his countess were present at the dinner which, being at 9 o'clock, left little time for talk. The presence of Carrick made conversation a trifle constrained as I did not know whether he was a hard-shelled Tory or not. Her ex[cellency] is always much interested in you—was asking particularly about you and was pleased to say she grudged you to India but hoped you would soon return to plunge into the turbid stream of political life here. His ex[cellency] is very much annoyed with the way he has been treated by the church and naturally and rationally as the conduct towards him has been scandalous. First of all the Belfast Presbytery acted illegally in sending off their own bat such a letter. The law of the church being that the government of the day can only be approached through the government committee [Committee in Correspondence with Government of the General Assembly]. Then it is said—I have no means of verifying the statement as yet—that Lowe wrote on the *official* paper of the church which implied he was writing in the name of the church for which he had no authority whatsoever. Officials have no right to speak for the church save as directed by the church. This will be heard of one day. Then they were asking the gov[ernmen]t to do what the gov[ernmen]t had no power to do, to arrest a man without reference to legal formularies—which naturally was refused. The whole McCann case has become a piece of political scoundrelism in the name of religion unparalleled in the history of the world and it will turn out the biggest mistake ever committed by a church.

Sir J[ames] B. D[ougherty] was in London and only returned on Monday morning. I went up on Monday morning and stayed all night. His two years of extended service are up in Nov[ember] but Birrell has asked him to continue another year—which he has consented to do on one condition—namely that he be informed of the extension in reasonable time. It appears that he did not know of the extension of service until a *fortnight* before his legal tenure was up. [Charles] Hobhouse it appears was dead against the extension for some reason or other with no cause given, so that both Birrell and his ex[cellency] had to appeal to Asquith on the subject and the matter was not settled until the very last minute. I have no doubt he will be continued another year as they have nobody to put in his place and then they will need him badly when the Home Rule bill is on the stocks. He is the essential element in the running [of] the machine. I gather that he is the mediator between his ex[cellency] and Birrell. His ex[cellency]'s candidates for office seldom commend themselves to B[irrell] and B[irrell]'s are liable to taboo by his ex[cellency]. His ex[cellency] and the countess are the most kindly of people. But they have little *nous* in judging character and therefore they are imposed on by a bevy of intriguers who have been swarming around them. One case in point. His ex[cellency], contrary to advice, appointed Max Green his private secretary. Green was a failure at the prisons board—a failure at the local g[overnment] board where he left things in a mess and he has turned out as everybody expected an utter failure where he now is—an empty-headed creature with much pomposity but without brains, such an unconscionable liar that he seems to believe his lies as truth. Her ex[cellency] confided to Sir J[ames] B. D[ougherty] that he was getting on his ex[cellency]'s nerves and as the royal visit is coming on they are at their wits end to know what to do with the helpless incompetent. I think if I was over the business I would retire him, pension or no pension. But their ex[cellencie]s are endowed too much with the milk of human kindness. ...'

D.1792/A3/2/13   **Part of a letter to W. S. Armour from Armour,**

[n.d. March ? 1911]   discussing the success of his marriage, now twenty eight years old, and commenting in detail on the articles in an issue of *Scribner's Magazine* which he encloses, including one on the caste system of India and the activities of Christian missionaries there.

'... We have managed to hit it off fairly and the tsar of all the Russias has driven the domestic machine with very few hitches. The *mater Gracchorum*, as Kenneth [Armour] likes to hear your maternal relative called, has magnified her office and as they say in the house of lords—at least some of them—over a measure *"placet"*. I may say the same. ...'

D.1792/A3/2/14   **Letter to W. S. Armour from Armour,**

30 March 1911   containing almost entirely local and family news including a lengthy account of the opening of a new hall for Ballywatt Presbyterian Church, Co. Antrim, at which Armour had been present. 'There is a strong contingent of Radicals about B[ally]watt and they insisted on having me asked.'

D.1792/A3/2/15   **Letter to W. S. Armour from Armour,**

5 April 1911   discussing in great detail the serious illness of aunt Jane Armour of Lisboy, Ballymoney, Co. Antrim; referring again briefly to his proposed attempt at a forthcoming meeting of the Queen's University senate to reduce over-severe matriculation standards which are 'an insult to the teachers and pupils of Ulster'; claiming that the *Manchester Guardian* is the only daily newspaper worth reading; and reporting a meeting of the Unionist Women's Association in Ballymoney.

'... We had a Unionist meeting of the women this week, when as a cynical person says, all the frumps gathered together. Most of them would have liked a union of another kind but providence had mercy on some males. ...'

D.1792/A3/2/16   **Letter to W. S. Armour from Armour,**

[n.d. April ? 1911]   conveying the news of aunt Jane Armour's death and the details of her will and of some £1,200 which has been left to Armour to divide amongst the various relatives.

D.1792/A3/2/17   **Letter to W. S. Armour from Armour,**

20 April 1911   containing details of aunt Jane Armour's funeral and the division of her inheritance which Armour is determined to carry out fairly and justly. He also reports the meeting of the Queen's University senate at which he had attacked the conditions laid down for scholarships and had succeeded in getting the whole issue referred back to the academic council.

D.1792/A3/2/18   **Letter to W. S. Armour from Armour,**

27 April 1911   almost entirely devoted to local and family news. He
comments on various obituaries of aunt Jane Armour,
including one by Samuel Craig McElroy, editor of *Ballymoney Free Press*, which had appeared
in the *Weekly Whig*.

'... S. C. McElroy had a paragraph on Jane [Armour] in the *Weekly Whig*. He is much pleased
with it himself—though Max [Armour] did not enthuse over it. The old man—S.C.—is dottering
on his feet. He is verily on his last legs. I have stopped reading his editorials. They are like the
sermons of the immortal bishop of Toledo in *Gil Blas*—a trifle musty. ...'

D.1792/A3/2/19   **Letter to W. S. Armour from Armour,**

4 May 1911   completely devoted to local and family news and to
anticipation of W. S. Armour's forthcoming home
leave.

D.1792/A3/2/20   **Letter to W. S. Armour from Armour,**

10 May 1911   containing local and family news and details of two
trips to Belfast to attend a variety of church committee
meetings.

D.1792/A3/2/21   **Letter to W. S. Armour from Armour,**

29 June 1911   entirely devoted to the problems surrounding the
premature retirement of a Presbyterian minister,
Rev. Jones of Killymurris.

D.1792/A3/2/22   **Letter to W. S. Armour from Armour,**

5 July 1911   anticipating W. S. Armour's imminent return on leave;
discussing the Jones retirement; and explaining his
reasons for accepting an invitation to attend the royal *levee* during the forthcoming visit of
George V and his wife to Dublin. 'I would not go to it but for the fact that people here would
say I had not been asked.'

D.1792/A3/2/23   **Letter to W. S. Armour from Armour,**

12 July/13 July 1911   containing an account of the royal visit to Dublin and
of Armour's attendance with nearly one hundred
other 'Presbyterian parsons' at a garden party, as well as at a *levee*; there is also a report of a
conversation between Armour and Thomas Hamilton, vice-chancellor of the Queen's University,
Belfast, which had taken place at a dinner party in W. H. Dodd's house in Dublin. Armour had
reiterated his views about the over-severity of matriculation standards, the result of the university
having 'fallen into the hands of the Saracens'. 'I was like the fallen spirit in Milton—I forget his
name—for open war on the academic council.'

D.1792/A3/2/24   **Letter to W. S. Armour from Armour,**

20 July 1911   discussing the award of a K.C.V.O. to Sir James

Dougherty in recognition of his successful organisation of the royal family's visit to Ireland and describing a meeting of the Q.U.B. senate at which the struggle with the academic council had been continued.

'... I had a note from Sir J[ames] B. D[ougherty] yesterday. He is pleased with the K.C.V.O., though it means nothing more than a recognition by his majesty of eminent skill. ... Sir J[ames] B. D[ougherty] was the engineer-in-chief and oiler of the machinery to prevent friction between the two courts—the English court officials being tempted to disparage the Castle court entourage—the latter resenting the high and mighty manner of the Londoners. It required tact to keep things going smoothly, especially as the Aberdeens are not popular with the Londonderrys who seem to have the ear of the king—the one sign of weakness his majesty is displaying— a weakness which if persisted in may have consequences of a disagreeable nature in the future—said Londonderrys being of the hopeless Tory band and therefore the worst possible advisers of the court. However, the whole show passed off with wondrous success and the court left Ireland pleased with the attention shown and agreeably disappointed with the reception as there was a fear that there might be some signs of disloyalty. But there was nothing to mar the harmony of the visit. Sir J[ames] B. D[ougherty] scored. ...'

D.1792/A3/2/25   **Letter to W. S. Armour from Armour,**

26 July 1911   commenting on Kenneth Armour's improved progress at Campbell College, Belfast; speculating on the possible political repercussions of the death of Sir Francis Macnaghten, his majesty's lieutenant for Co. Antrim; and criticising the tactics of the new leadership of the Conservative party.

'... Sir Francis Macnaghten [of Dundarave, Bushmills, Co. Antrim] has died at last and who is to be his majesty's lieutenant of the county is the question. Efforts will be made to secure the honour for Lord O'Neill of Shane's Castle [Antrim] or his son who is married to the marquis of Crewe's daughter. We must prevent that if possible. The O'Neills have been forming and addressing Unionist clubs. One might have thought that the daughter of a cabinet minister [Lord Crewe was in Asquith's government] might have kept from identifying herself with the enemies of her father's policy. It is to say the least of it a trifle shameless and to honour her husband under the circumstances might be to throw a pot of dirty water in the face of the friends of the administration. The only one I can think of at present is Lord Pirrie but perhaps his property in Belfast might not count for property in the county. There is a point there but I do not know how much there may be in it. The political situation is in a critical position. The madheads of the Tory party under the leadership of [F. E.] Smith, Lord Hugh [Cecil] and Austen [Chamberlain] have taken a leaf out of the book of the Nationalists a few years [*sic*] and have made a scene in the h[ouse of] c[ommons] which is rather disgraceful and perhaps will not do their cause any good. The Nationalists in the past were denounced in all the moods and tenses as a disgrace to civilisation and as traitors of the worst kind and here we have the gentlemanly party copying literally their tactics. It is supposed the attack was quite as much against [Arthur] Balfour as against Asquith, as Lord Hugh never has forgiven his cousin for not preventing the Tories from sacrificing him for his free trade principles. But to imagine that Smith or Austen could lead the party is a little too ludicrous—they are both rather thin beer and the older Tories would not have either. Balfour they cannot do without as he is the only man of real ability on that side. ...'

D.1792/A3/2/26   **Letter to W. S. Armour from Armour,**

3 August 1911   outlining the continuing struggle to appoint a successor to Sir Francis Macnaghten as his majesty's lieutenant for Co. Antrim, in which Armour is backing Lord Pirrie, but fears the power of the two leading Unionist contenders, Lord Shaftesbury and Lord O'Neill. The letter also includes an assessment of the political situation at Westminster as well as the usual local news.

'... We had an abortive [*sic*] of a meeting of the gov[ernmen]t committee [the Committee in Correspondence with Government of the General Assembly] on Monday, called at the insistence of [Rev.] Haslett of Ballymena who, wanting to curry favour with John Young of Galgorm [Ballymena, Co. Antrim], was ready to propose said John Young as a fit and proper person as the successor to Sir Francis Macnaghten in the lieutenancy of Co. Antrim. A more senseless proposition never was made by anybody professing sanity of mind. Haslett's sanity is a doubtful quantity or rather a vanishing quantity. [Rev.] Lowe explained how reluctantly he had called the meeting and deprecated the idea of making the nomination especially as there were other Richmonds in the field. Somebody called out "name, name" but I said "clout", the only remark I made. It was reported that John Baxter was likely to be mentioned but, as I knew he would not have the ghost of a chance, being a grocer, I did not wish his name bandied about. At last Lowe said he understood that a former [?] of Dr MacDermott was among those mentioned and as everybody knew who that was, his name was not given. We, that is the Liberal association and myself, are running Lord Pirrie who cabled from New York whither he had gone in the "Olympia" that he would accept the honour if offered. It is said Lord Shaftesbury would like to exchange the lieutenancy of Belfast for the county. Of course the fact that he is a member of his majesty's household makes him a dangerous rival, supposing he really wants the honour. I have pointed out to Sir J[ames] B. D[ougherty] that the gov[ernmen]t, having made him a K.C., have done quite enough for him in one year. The other dangerous person is Lord O'Neill whose son is married to Earl Crewe's daughter. I have been trying to put a spoke in his wheel on the ground that the Ladies O'Neill have been organising the women's Unionist associations. It is almost disgraceful that Lord Crewe's daughter should be found lending her name and influence to associations whose direct object is to upset the policy of the cabinet of which her father is a leading light. She has lost all sense of the proprieties of civilised life and ought to be tarred and feathered. If her husband had the smallest amount of manliness, he would have forbidden his wife having anything to do with such associations at least publicly, however the private sympathies might have run. I heard from Sir Hugh Mack who insists on taking me to lunch with him in the Reform Club anytime I call on him that the Liberal Whip [Alexander Murray, master of Elibank] had assured them that Lord Crewe would not interfere in the appointment. That of course was in view of a vacancy which was expected but had not occurred. What may be his attitude now that the vacancy has recurred is another matter. It is to be hoped that he may not interfere on behalf of a daughter who is acting like King Lear's daughters. That is all that is known about the business but to nominate John Young, an old man of eighty-four and a crusted old Tory, for the honour was a piece of unparalleled impudence. It shows how stupid Haslett is and how destitute he is of the elements of common sense. He is hopeless. The political sky is clouded. Balfour, whose teeth Austen [Chamberlain] and [F. E.] Smith wanted, has shown that he is master in diplomacy has tabled a motion of censure in the h[ouse] of c[ommons] on the gov[ernmen]t for advising the king to create the number of peers necessary for passing [the] veto bill. One of the designs of the proposal is to give an opportunity to the recalcitrants for blowing off steam and thus preparing them for surrender without dying in the last ditch. He is, as Mrs C. used to say of yourself, "that able". How the vote may go is tolerably well known. The backwoodsmen will appear in force in the lords and work off steam by a tremendous vote, while in the commons even [William] O'Brien and Tim Healy will have to vote with the Nationalists. It will be a vote of the lords against the commons and the commons against the lords. You will hear the result long before this note reaches you. Said note will read stale, as if it has been trailed through the salt sea between this and Benares. ...'

D.1792/A3/2/27   **Part of a letter to W. S. Armour from Armour,**

9 August 1911   discussing a proposed holiday in Portrush, Co. Antrim, explaining his latest moves in pushing Lord Pirrie's claims to the lieutenancy of Co. Antrim; mentioning his efforts to persuade David Hogg, his majesty's lieutenant for Co. Londonderry, to appoint two Londonderry Liberals, Samuel Kirkpatrick and Thomas Finlay, as magistrates; and anticipating the successful passage of the parliament bill in the house of lords.

'... I wrote Lady Pirrie on Monday morning to ask her to exercise a little diplomacy on behalf of her husband. I wished her to choke off the Aberdeens who are friends of Lord O'Neill, the son of Lord O'N[eill] being married to Earl Crewe's daughter. She has sent me a long telegram of thanks—from said telegram it is plain she wishes her husband to get the honour though she sees she can do nothing in the business. I have written her again to say that it was a delicate subject for her to touch but to do nothing in the way of forwarding the claims of anybody else. I have no idea how matters may go but it is hard to keep out of the business. ...'

D.1792/A3/2/28

17 August 1911

Part of a letter to W. S. Armour from Armour, [written from Portrush],

examining the possible alternatives for appointment as lord chancellor and solicitor-general for Ireland and the likely political consequences of the elevation of Redmond Barry, the current Liberal attorney-general for Ireland, to the chancellorship, especially in North Tyrone. The letter also recounts the latest developments in the intrigue surrounding the vacant lieutenancy of Co. Antrim.

'... Of course Redmond Barry will either be chancellor or appeal Lord and therefore N[orth] Tyrone will be vacant. [A. M.] Sullivan threatens to contest N[orth] Tyrone in any case and he has followers there and therefore it is within the bounds of probability that the gov[ernmen]t candidate—not being Sullivan—may be beaten. [Augustine] Birrell insists that the solicitor-general must be in the house of commons. He cannot do without help. Therefore there are rocks ahead and how the ship may escape shipwreck is a problem yet to be solved.

About the H.M.L. for Antrim, I have heard nothing definite. I wrote Lady Pirrie to use her influence to choke off the Aberdeens from throwing their influence in the scale of the O'Neills—the relatives of Lady Aberdeen. She replied that it was too delicate a matter for her to interfere in but *she managed to inform his exc[ellency]* that I was strongly in favour of Lord P[irrie]. His exc[ellency] telegraphed to Sir J[ames] B. D[ougherty] to say, "Our friend Mr Armour is in favour of Lord P". Sir J. B. D. cross-questioned me to know if I had written his exc[ellency] but I could say I had written to nobody on the subject save to Lady P[irrie] and himself. Your ma would insist on me writing to his exc[ellency] on the subject but I absolutely refused and therefore I was glad to be able to inform Sir J. B. D. that I had not written to his exc[ellency]. Evidently Lady P[irrie] had taken the trouble to allow his exc[ellency] to know how the wind was blowing in B[ally]money. Women are fine diplomatists when anything personal is on the *tapis*. ...'

D.1792/A3/2/29

23 August 1911

Letter to W. S. Armour from Armour, [written from Portrush],

praising Max Armour's capabilities as a preacher, though regretting that he had decided to remain an assistant minister at Fitzroy Church, Belfast, for another year, since Armour would have liked him to have been settled before the Home Rule crisis broke; and commenting on Kenneth Armour's favourable performance at the intermediate examination. He discusses in some detail press reports that Lady Aberdeen, through Max Green, Lord Aberdeen's private secretary, had leaked to a *Freeman's Journal* reporter details of an itinerary planned for the 1911 royal visit by Lord Iveagh, Lord Londonderry and English court officials which would have omitted any meetings with the Catholic hierarchy and that this had resulted in the substitution of new arrangements by the Irish privy council. The letter also discusses Armour's continuing efforts to secure Lord Pirrie's appointment to the Antrim lieutenancy and contains his views on the recently concluded national railway strike and the Labour party.

'... The question arose in Dublin how the reporter of the *Freeman['s Journal]* got hold of the programme [Lord] Iveagh had drawn up for the king. Some head constable in the south sent word to some of the Castle officials that he could tell how the information was given to the reporter. It turned out that it was Max Green who gave the cue. Her exc[ellency] was suspected to have had a hand in the pie but Green asserted that she knew nothing about it—a statement which was received with a grain of salt but it had to be accepted though there were a few sceptics. However, all's well which ends well. ...

I have not heard about the H.M.L. for Antrim. I wrote Joe Devlin asking him to take the side of Lord Pirrie. He sent me a letter to say that he had heard Lord P[irrie] was appointed though he added he could not vouch for the accuracy of the report. I was asked to write him also in favour of Moloney as solicitor-general but he did not make any reference to Mr Moloney. I said to him that I really could not say who was the best fitted for the post but I added that Birrell would need in the house the ablest man to be got if he was to pilot a Home Rule bill through the commons. Moloney seems to me one of the dreariest speakers I ever heard but it appears he is sick and has always been true to the Nationalist cause whereas another candidate for the honour is regarded as a vicar of Bray. The best man, as I told you I think, would be A. M. Sullivan but as he is married to a cousin of Tim Healy, the Irish party would not touch him with a forty foot poll [*sic*].

You will have heard through Reuter [*sic*] that the r[ailwa]y strike is over. The men think they have gained a victory but one might be a sceptic on that point. It will depend on the commission very much and perhaps said commission may make the men's victory a Pyrrhic business. That they have a real grievance may be true but I fancy they did not set about the strike wisely. The madheads of the Labour party broke away from their leaders and they have turned away from their cause to a large extent the sympathy of the man in the street. The hotel here was very full last week but owing to the strike several who were to come could not come. Some fourteen were to be in the Osbourne [Hotel] on Friday but they telegraphed that they were stuck at Sheffield and the arrangement was off. It is reported today that Redmond Barry is to be lord chancellor but it is only a report. I go off to Ballymoney tonight but when the remnant may return I know not. ...'

D.1792/A3/2/30   **Part of a letter to W. S. Armour from Armour,** [*page torn*],

[n.d. 30 August ? 1911]

containing a variety of political gossip and a scathing attack on Campbell College, arising out of the poor showing of its candidates in the intermediate examination. Armour speculates as to who will be appointed to the recordership of Belfast, vacant because of the death of Robert McIlroy, especially in view of the shortage of able Liberal Protestant barristers and the inadvisability of the Liberal government appointing a Catholic to the post. He also considers the prospects for the by-election in North Tyrone, necessitated by the appointment of the sitting Liberal member, Redmond Barry, as lord chancellor.

'... Sir J[ames] B. D[ougherty] to say that a Catholic should not get the [recordership of Belfast ?], the two law officers Catholics and the four revising barristers within the power of the government to appoint—all Catholics, a Catholic appointed for Belfast would put the fat in the fire and would make Birrell's [Home Rule] bill impossible. It would give a new text to the Unionists who would make the welkin ring with the news that Home Rule meant home rule and that the government by their appointments intended that should be the case. I added that it would be like pouring a barrel of petroleum on smouldering ashes. Therefore that door should be barred. It is true that Protestant barristers of the first class are not on the government side—they being struck with political blindness which made them believe that the Tories would never be out of office. They were ready to believe a lie, with the result they are in the wilderness. I consulted on Friday several of the leading men, most of whom were in favour of [W. J.] Johnston but some sceptical about the wisdom of such an appointment. I urged his claims but hinted that if there was a decent Liberal Protestant county court judge in Ireland, he should be moved to Belfast, Johnston to get his berth. I hinted [*words missing*] Johnston but he flared up at the idea, practically saying he would not take [*word missing*] but Belfast. He would take his chance and contest S[outh] Derry again. That [*words missing*] very unreasonable, if not stupid. ...

Redmond Barry is lord chancellor and I suspect Ignatius O'Brien will be solicitor-general. The present master of the rolls has taken to drink and drugs and must resign soon as he is a downright failure. Therefore O'Connor who is now attorney-general will soon be on the bench, hence he will not contest N[orth] Tyrone which is now in the market. A nice kettle of fish may be found in N[orth] Tyrone, as it is possible a Healyite in the person of A. M. Sullivan may contest the seat against the government nominee. If the policeman's lot is not a happy one, the gov[ernmen]t's life at present is not happy but there is a providence ruling over all ...'.

D.1792/A3/2/31	**Part of a letter to W. S. Armour from Armour,**

[n.d. September 1911 ?] describing a game on Portrush golf course with three members belonging to a Liberal group from the Eighty Club currently touring Ireland, and in particular a conversation which he had had with Sir John Benn about W. S. Armour's presidency of the Oxford Union and his Liberal politics. He explains why he declined an invitation to a reception in Belfast for the Eighty Club members. He reiterates his concern about Max Armour's future career in the light of the impending Home Rule crisis and again discusses the political repercussions of the North Tyrone by-election and W. J. Johnston's chances of being appointed to the recordership of Belfast.

'... We had a pleasant game but the rain—an unusual thing for months—prevented us finishing the match. As Sir J[ohn] Benn was my companion we had some talk on things in general and particularly on young Gladstone. I explained in a few words modestly your connection with him and how you had engineered matters so that under your presidency of the Union a vote in favour of Home Rule was carried in the Union after Redmond's speech and how Lord [?] was deprived of the presidency. He was very interested and he had evidently communicated what I had said to Kellaway [Liberal member for Bedford] for the latter called out to me from the carriage the hope that [that] son of yours will come back to help us in England. They had a pleasant afternoon and I stood tea for them and sent them on their way rejoicing. I was not over keen in going to the reception—as it turns out to your mother's disappointment—for reasons, one of them being that Max [Armour] was not favourable, possibly afraid that he might have a snarl with some of the hide-bound Tories over my presence. He is a little sensitive but he does not seem anxious to get settled which I would like chiefly because I fear that the Home Rule scare which will be strong in a few months may stand in the way of his father's son. He, under [Rev.] Colquhoun's tutilage [*sic*] resolves to hold on another winter in Fitzroy [Church, Belfast] to meet a storm at its close. I have no doubt but he does not seem afraid. Youth is always confident. The r[ailwa]y strike in Ireland will almost make Sir J[ames] B. D[ougherty] crazy: the outlook is no better today. The strain at the Castle will be intense. [T. W.] Russell is to contest N[orth] Tyrone. There was a rumour that Dr Prenter [?] was to be his opponent which would have made Russell's chances absolutely certain but they have fallen back on [E. C.] Herdman, who being a great employer of labour, may run Russell very hard, especially as there is a section of the Catholics Healyites and a large number of publicans in the constituency that will hate Russell because of his temperance principles. I see they—that is the Tories—are circulating his old speeches against Home Rule—which speeches are very strong. On the whole one cannot be over-confident about the result. It appears that [Augustine] Birrell wants Russell in parliament and [John] Redmond has consented to accept Russell in return for some favour you may be sure. I have heard nothing *in re* h[is] m[ajesty's] l[ieutenancy] for Antrim, nor about the recordership in Belfast. It is thought that W. J. Johnston's chances therefore are improved by Russell's selection for N[orth] Tyrone as the Nationalists are in favour of Johnston. He is here as revising barrister and seems very excited over the business. Some fifty solicitors in Belfast, it is said, have signed a petition in his favour, several of them being Conservatives. How it will go "I dinna ken" but on the whole the appointment should be made. ...'

D.1792/A3/2/32   **Part of a letter to W. S. Armour from Armour,**

[n.d. 15 September 1911 ?]   discussing the appointment of Lord Shaftesbury as his majesty's lieutenant for Co. Antrim and the appointment of Lord Pirrie to the vacancy thus created in Belfast. Armour is clearly disappointed and puzzled, although he takes some comfort from Unionist suspicions of Shaftesbury.

'... The government has managed to give delight to the Tories of Antrim by giving the H.M.L. to Lord Shaftesbury—Lord Pirrie getting the H.M.L. of Belfast. I suspect the king had something to do with the business—Shaftesbury being a member of his household—but it means that the magistracy of Antrim, as of old, will be the *appanage* of the Tories. Your ma, from a conversation she had with Jeanne A., thinks Lord P[irrie] did not want the H.M.L. of Co. Antrim but that he really wanted the Belfast honour. If so, it was hardly fair of him not saying it out straight. At any rate I was a little flummoxed on reading the paper this morning with the announcement which did not please me by any means. It is true that L[ord] Shaftesbury is a little suspected by the local Tories because he voted for the veto bill [parliament act, 1911]. That however raised my suspicions as to his game. ...'

D.1792/A3/2/33   **Part of a letter to W. S. Armour from Armour,** [*page torn*] ,

[n.d. September 1911 ?]   rejoicing at the Unionist defeat in the Kilmarnock Burghs by-election and at the ineffective intervention in the Kilmarnock campaign of Rev. Tommy Thompson and William Moore, M.P., as Ulster Unionist missionaries. The letter comments on an attack by the *Northern Whig* on Sir James Dougherty and expresses the hope that he will not resign. Armour indicates his annoyance at Lord Pirrie's conduct over the Antrim and Belfast lieutenancies. He also intimates his support for T. W. Russell in his North Tyrone by-election campaign.

'... I am told that the redoubtable Tommy Thompson got rather a set down in Kilmarnock. He appeared on Rees' [Unionist] platform and began with a bitter attack on the Catholics and Rees got up and said, "Friend we cannot introduce the religious question into this contest", whereat Tommy collapsed. William Moore and he then, it is said, engaged a hall specially for themselves but it appears that project came to nothing as on the first night there were some women and children with only eighteen men—which meeting did not seem likely to make a new Thermopylae. ...

There is a gross attack in the [*Northern*] *Whig* this morning on Sir J[ames] B. D[ougherty] as being absolutely without a particle of back-bone—an absolutely unfounded charge. He is a little thin-skinned and will feel it. I wrote him on Monday advising him to lose no sleep over the pin-pricks he was getting. It is always a mistake to admit you are hurt. "Drink and let the parties rave. They are filled with idle spleen. Rising, falling like the wave. And they know not what they mean." If you substitute for "drink" the word "wink" or "sleep"—that explains the true philosophy of life. It may be that there is a dead set being made on Sir J[ames] B. D[ougherty] to get him to resign. It is said the gov[ernmen]t intended to appoint Sir Henry Robinson, an incorrigible Tory, as his successor in any case. I hope he will not think of resigning though he has had two years beyond the usual time. I think I told you about [Lord] Pirrie being h[is] m[ajesty's] l[ieutenant] for Belfast and [Lord] Shaftesbury being h[is] m[ajesty's] l[ieu-tenant] for Co. Antrim. I could choke the Pirries. It is said [Lord] Pirrie was offered either and chose Belfast. It is possible he may have been offered either with an intimation secretly conveyed that he was expected to select Belfast as [Lord] Shaftesbury wanted Co. Antrim. The only comfort in a business which I do not like is that the Tories are doubly mortified ... [*part of the page missing*] .

Russell has been making wondrous [*sic*] in N[orth] Tyrone. He has turned the tables on [A. L.] Horner and [H. T.] Barrie and a few other swash-bucklers. He gave Andy Horner rather a back set by telling the audience that a few years ago, he offered to contest N[orth] Derry as a Liberal against [John] Atkinson, the attorney-general of the Tories. I don't know how the election will go but I am sure [Sir Edward] Carson's harangues have not done much good to his own side as the upholders of [E. C.] Herdman have had to dwell principally on what Carson's scheme does not mean. I sent Russell a note expressing sympathy with him in his campaign.

There is no definite news about the recordership of Belfast. The rumour is that Jonathan Pim will be the man. Jonathan began lately to see that the Liberals were likely to have to divide the loaves and the fishes for some time to come and therefore set his sails accordingly ...'.

D.1792/A3/2/34   **Part of a letter to W. S. Armour from Armour,**

[n.d. October ? 1911]   describing a luncheon in the Grand Central Hotel, Belfast, given by Lord Pirrie for the visiting Liberal postmaster-general, Herbert Samuel, at which Armour was present. He also reports a meeting with the postmaster-general on Portrush golf course and the ensuing conversation in which Armour attempted to explain the reasons for T. W. Russell's extremely narrow victory in the North Tyrone by-election (Russell 3,104; E. C. Herdman 3,086). An attack by Lord Pirrie on the Belfast Harbour Board is also discussed.

'... The luncheon on Friday given by Lord Pirrie turned out a great success—a fine enthusiastic meeting—viands of the best and the postmaster's speech was one of the finest I have ever heard. It will take a wilderness of Carsons to answer it. I have sent you the [*Belfast*] *News-Letter* which contains the best report of it. You can read it for yourself. [Rev.] Dill thinks it one of the best he ever read. You will also see his impromptu speech at the golf club dinner on Saturday night, a very happy utterance, full of humour and beautified with lightness of touch. It went down well even among the hide-bound Tories. It is worth reading. I saw him for a moment on Monday at Portrush and congratulated him on his speeches which was not disagreeable to his feelings. He is rather a fine looking fellow, young and with a head on his shoulders. He has fine intellectual powers and it did not seem strange to me that he should be in the government. I explained to him why T. W. [Russell]'s majority in N[orth] Tyrone was only eighteen—a narrow squeak. The reason of it was there was a row among the Nationalists there. Some county councillor called [?], whom the Nationalists had made a county councillor, but they blamed him for kow-towing too much to the duke of Abercorn. The consequence was that at the last election they ran Gallaher against him and ousted him. He vowed vengeance and carried out his vow. He took his motor and canvassed the Catholics against T. W. [Russell]. The publicans who are numerous in the constituency all voted against T. W. [Russell]. It is clear that if the party had been united, T. W. [Russell]'s majority would have been over 100. The Tories are wild with joy at what they call a great moral victory but if it pleases them to look at it in that light, nobody may object, especially as T. W. [Russell] is the member and moral victories of the kind don't count in a division. [Rev.] George Hanson was at the luncheon to my surprise and [Herbert] Samuel took up a sentence of a letter of his to the *Non-Conformist* and used it with effect. I could not understand why George came but on Saturday morning there was a paragraph in the *Sunday Telegraph* to say that the call given to him from Montreal which he had refused was renewed and that he had made up his mind to accept it. That as I said to you ma explains the milk in the coco-nut ... .

I had a letter from Lady Pirrie this morning to whom I had written about the luncheon. She has sent a couple of grouse which I must acknowledge ... .'

D.1792/A3/2/35   **Letter to W. S. Armour from Armour,**

19 October 1911   containing church and local news; a discussion of Lord Pirrie's attack on the Belfast Harbour Board for their alleged unwillingness for political reasons to sell to the Harland and Wolff shipyard, of which Pirrie was managing director, surplus land for expansion and the harbour board's unconvincing reply; and a brief account of a bread strike in Belfast which has spread to Ballymoney.

D.1792/A3/2/36   **Part of a letter to W. S. Armour from Armour,**

[n.d. November ? 1911]   entirely devoted to local and church gossip.

D.1792/A3/2/37   **Letter to W. S. Armour from Armour,**

9 November 1911   describes the effects of a great storm in the Bally-
money area and discusses the resignation of A. J. Balfour from the Unionist leadership and the appointment of Walker Craig rather than W. J. Johnston as recorder of Belfast.

'... The political sensation of the papers this morning is the resignation of the leadership of the Conservatives by Balfour. It is a sort of bolt from the blue. The constant nagging at him within his own party and the fact that he lost three elections have brought about what will be disastrous to the party. He is the only man of real genius in the concern but I suspect his superiority led to jealousy by the smaller fry represented by Austen Chamberlain and such wind-bags as [F. E.] Smith. However, it appears to me that the resignation resembles a similar crisis in the party such as when Gladstone gave up the Liberal leadership and perhaps in no remote time may eventuate in his taking up the reins as did Gladstone. A few years floundering under Walter Long or Austen [Chamberlain] —it is not known which will be entrusted with the reins, though I suspect Walter Long will be the man, will give Balfour his opportunity and he will be recalled from exile which is not altogether voluntary. The dearth of real mental ability on that side of the house is fairly apparent ... .

The recordership of Belfast at length is filled. Walker Craig goes there and [W. J.] Johnston get his place in Monaghan and Fermanagh. The latter will be disappointed but he has been exceedingly fortunate and ought to bless his stars. I did the best I could for him though perhaps in his heart he may think that I might have obtained Belfast for him. The fact is I found that under no circumstances could be get Belfast—certain Liberals there and influential Tories being dead against him—and the next best thing was to get him a berth which was managed. ...

Craig is certainly the worst possible appointment for Belfast which could be made. He has a genius for fighting with everybody, solicitors, juries, magistrates, and his career in Monaghan has been almost a scandal. The one source of gratification is that Belfast has got its deserving and heaven help them. The chancellor [Redmond Barry] is credited with a desire to give the berth to a Catholic but I pointed out very early that with the chancellor, the attorney-general and solicitor-general as Catholics, to give a Catholic the berth would be ruinous from a political point of view. That mistake has been avoided which is something ... .'

D.1792/A3/2/38   **Letter to W. S. Armour from Armour,**

16 November 1911   containing an account of a visit to Belfast to attend
meetings of the General Assembly sustentation fund committee and of the senate of the Queen's University, Belfast. Armour discusses the various candidates who might replace Sir Robert Hart as pro-chancellor of the university—Lady Londonderry, Sir Donald McAlister, Sir Charles Bell and Armour's own choice, Sir Samuel Dill. Once again he expresses his discontent with the teaching standards at Campbell College, Belfast.

D.1792/A3/2/39   **Part of a letter to W. S. Armour from Armour,**

[n.d. November ? 1911]   principally devoted to local and family news but also commenting on attacks in the press on Dublin Castle officials and on Sir James Dougherty in particular.

'... Captain [James] Craig [M.P.] if likely to bring the whole business before the h[ouse of] c[ommons] and I expect Sir J[ames] B. D[ougherty] will instruct [Augustine] Birrell in such a way that the captain may wish he had let the matter rest. It is a little galling for Sir J[ames] B. D[ougherty] to be shot at from behind a hedge with poisoned arrows without a chance of returning fire. Still I expect his time will come and perhaps he may have the last word. He feels the business acutely as he is a little thin-skinned and feels unduly annoyed with the bite of clegs whose reign is very short. The cold weather gives them their *quietus*. [Thomas] Sloan is giving a lecture this evening on "Will Ulster fight?". I was asked to be present but as it was communion week and as I had too much to see after, I sent a letter instead. If there is a decent report in the [*Northern*] *Whig* tomorrow I will probably send you a copy: if not, not. It will likely be in the *Ulster Guardian* which unfortunately is not published until Friday evening. The usual gabble about the iniquities of Home Rule takes up the energies of the reporters and editor of the [*Northern*] *Whig*. The latter is a very contemptible creature of the would-be fire-eating type. If his ability was equal to his political bitterness he might be a power but his power only extends to the timorous and the fiendish. He is a gander among hissing geese ... .'

D.1792/A3/2/40   **Letter to W. S. Armour from Armour,**

23 November 1911   discussing the continuing difficulty in removing the absentee Rev. Jones from his charge at Killymurris; analysing the political consequences for the Liberals of the unpopularity of the national insurance legislation; and outlining the possible effects of continuing attacks on Sir James Dougherty.

'... The other excitement of a political, social nature is the loss of a seat by the government in Somerset—the first loss yet sustained—Oldham does not count as it was a three cornered fight and the two wings of the government phalanx out-topped the Tories by 5,000. I fear the insurance bill, not Home Rule, is the cause of the disaster. It is a fine measure, though very complicated, but as it insists on all classes—employers and employed—to contribute, one may be sure such a demand on the pocket cannot be popular. Human nature likes advantages but it refuses to pay for them. "Beer for the slave that pays" is a popular maxim and expresses the average attitude. I fear the government is really wounded in what ought to be the house of its friends. Sir J[ames] B. D[ougherty], from the extracts I enclose, is not out of the wood. He has been made the target for attack and as he is a trifle thin-skinned he must be suffering in the flesh more than an ordinary mortal would. It is very annoying that in the last year of a very successful reign he should have fallen on evil days and evil tongues. He must be suffering "dolorous pain". ...'

D.1792/A3/2/41   **Letter to W. S. Armour from Armour,**

30 November 1911   discussing the 'interminable' Jones case; the Queen's University scholarships issue; the vacant university pro-chancellorship; and the general state of the political world.

'... The political world is in a state of excitement over Sir Edward Grey's speech, the insurance bill, the suffragists' insanity and Home Rule. The material for keeping the country from sleeping is abundant. I always thought the insurance bill would cause trouble, not because it is a bad bill—it is the opposite—but because it compels all classes to pay and to pay is the very last thing people are willing to do. We all like comforts without any self-sacrifice. We have no serious objection for other people to pay but when it becomes a personal [equation ?] our selfishness gets the better of our love for our fellow man. It is difficult to know how the Home Rule business is going. One cannot trust the papers which are largely in the hands of the Tories and imagination runs riot in a case of this kind. The question is very thorny and there will likely be an election over the matter. It is difficult to see how it can be otherwise. ...'

D.1792/A3/2/42

6 December 1911

Letter to Mrs Jennie Armour or possibly to W. S. Armour from Armour,

reporting a visit to Belfast and in particular a conversation with Dr Kirk about the educational shortcomings of Campbell College, Belfast.

D.1792/A3/2/43

[n.d. December ? 1911]

Letter to W. S. Armour from Armour,

reporting a correspondence with Sir James Dougherty concerning the possibility of William Armour obtaining an educational post in Ireland, along with a variety of local news.

'I enclose you two letters from Sir J[ames] B. D[ougherty] which will explain themselves. In answer to the first I wrote to say that the family would be glad if the berth could be reserved for you—that you might count on strong backing, that even John Redmond whom you brought down to a debate in the [Oxford] Union on Home Rule would likely throw his influence on your behalf in memory of a victory that you and Gladstone got for him in the [Oxford] Union and that Gladstone, I was sure, would be a strong backer. But I pointed out that as Johnston was selected for the mathematical side, it would seem to me that his successor would require to be a mathematician. This in my judgement would stand in the way of your application at the first and likely it would be too steep a style [*sic*] to get over. I asked Sir J[ames] B. D[ougherty] to write to me before today—your letter day and the second letter came yesterday morning. It is rather an attractive business but I am half afraid the thing is not possible. You see what Sir J[ames] B. D[ougherty] from his second note intends to do. Meanwhile I suppose we can do nothing beyond thinking on the matter and mentally preparing the plan of campaign in case the barrier is removed. ...'

D.1792/A3/2/44

[n.d. December ? 1911]

Letter to W. S. Armour from Armour,

largely devoted to the continuing saga of the removal of Rev. Jones of Killymurris for being unfit to fulfil his office.

D.1792/A3/2/45

20 December 1911

Part of a letter to W. S. Armour from Armour,

commenting on the seemingly interminable Jones case and on the efforts of Presbyterian Unionists, led by Rev. MacDermott of Belmont Presbyterian Church, to rally opposition to the Home Rule bill. He particularly refers to their proposed meeting on 1 February 1912 and the possibility that they may use the General Assembly as a platform.

'... It is clear [*page torn*] and the many who are looking towards the Mecca of Presbyterianism for a berth in the future will flock thither on the first of February. However, their meeting will not have much, if any, effect on the issue of the question. The man of Belmont has never succeeded in upsetting any project that was before the legislature. He may carry his motion in the Assembly but that is nothing and has no weight in politics. The Assembly is in the back water among the reeds and rushes while the great world is moving on regardless of their cry of wolf which has been raised too often for any sane man to heed. ...'

D.1792/A3/2/46

[n.d. 28 December ? 1911]

Part of a letter to W. S. Armour from Armour,

discussing the Jones case, passing on a variety of local news and commenting on the unpopularity of Lloyd George's national insurance scheme with the medical profession.

'... The doctors are still raging and foaming at the mouth over this insurance bill but one cannot see why they should make such a tow-row. It is more political spleen than anything else. But they may find themselves in the wrong box as one may be sure there will, notwithstanding their rage, be many of their calling willing to offer their services to the state on the conditions proposed. ...'

D.1792/A3/3/1-43	**Originals of letters from Rev. J. B. Armour to his wife and sons (principally to W. S. Armour).**

1912

D.1792/A3/3/1   **Part of a letter to W. S. Armour from Armour,** [*pages missing*],

[n.d. 1911/12]

discussing developments in the Queen's University senate and in particular Armour's role in getting S. R. Keightley [unsuccessful Liberal candidate for South Antrim, 1903, and South Londonderry, 1906 and January 1910] and Professor R. M. Henry appointed to two vacancies, with the inevitable assistance of Sir James B. Dougherty.

D.1792/A3/3/2   **Letter to W. S. Armour from Armour,**

[n.d. 1912 ?]

anticipating a meeting of the Queen's University senate in Belfast the following day at which there are likely to be 'squalls', commenting on the sinking of the 'Titanic' and outlining the main arguments which he had included in an article which he had just written in support of the principle of Home Rule. These are very similar to the arguments advanced in Armour's contribution to *The new Irish constitution* (ed. J. H. Morgan).

'... I wrote the article for Graham and sent it off on Monday. Your ma criticised but accepted with a few verbal alterations which improved it in her judgement but left it much as it was. I took four points.

(a) Home Rule is the principle of Presbyterian church government applied to secular affairs, a principle which works well in all the colonies when it has been tried and how or why it should not work fairly in Ireland is not clear. I elaborated that point, meeting objections *etc*.

(b) Home Rule would undo many of the evils of the Union of 1800—which could not be called a success, pointing out that ninty per cent of the Protestants were quite as bitter about the discretion of the Irish parliament as their descendants were against its restoration. Were they fools? Then I showed that Ireland since the Union had lost fifty per cent of her people, though the sheep and cows had increased. How much is a man better than a sheep? I also pointed out that Ireland's prosperity only began with Gladstone's legislation which was democratic and Home Rule was the extension of the democratic principle.

(c) So far from Home Rule ruining Protestantism it would give it a chance of being recognised on its merits. Hitherto it had been identified with the landlords who were tyrants and with the bureacracy which was largely in the hands of one Protestant sect.

(d) Then Home Rule would help not hinder commerce and that the fear that an Irish parliament would overtax Ulster was [laughable ?] as any taxes would weigh as heavy on the other parts of Ireland as on Ulster. Irishmen of every creed are not fond of paying taxes. This is the outline of the heads of the discussion. Now that the first reading is passed [of the Home Rule bill] , I hear little of grumbling or foreboding save in the [*Northern*] *Whig* and [*Belfast*] *News-Letter*. ...'

D.1792/A3/3/3   **Part of a letter to W. S. Armour from Armour,**

[n.d. 1912 ?]

including local and family gossip but also discussing the effects of the refusal of some Presbyterian ministers to sign, or to hold a service for the signing of the Ulster Covenant.

'... MacLurg of Ardstraw [Co. Tyrone] told me that on refusing to hold a religious service and to sign the Covenant, the people brought down Prof[essor] Leitch who gave a blood and thunder address averring among other things that a Protestant home ruler was a man who had a thraw [*sic*] in his character, something I have often heard—as if Leitch had not a hundred thraws in his character according to Prof. Walker. The result of his harangues was that about one third of the heads of houses have never entered the church since; many of the women folks attend still. John Hamilton of Helen's Bay [Co. Down] says he has lost twenty-five per cent, the rapscallions being headed off by a violent Orangeman—some Dr Gibson. I heard of somebody else who did not find a single hearer in his church the day after the Covenant signing. Several other tales I heard of confusion which the Presbyterian priests ruling the church have caused. The most amusing thing I heard was from Dr Purves. It appears that in 1886 many Scotch parsons sent an expression of their sympathy with, and their fears for, the Presbyterian church in the threatening cloud overshadowing Ireland—Presbyterian Ireland—in the Home Rule proposal. Dr Purves's name was in the list of signatories—"that is", he added, "before I knew Ireland". His congregation, almost all Unionist, however behaved as a whole quite decently to him though he did not sign the Covenant. Scott of Banbridge [Co. Down] has also suffered to such an extent that there had to be a visitation presbytery which resulted in a peace patched up at least in the meantime. We have been fortunate in this part of the world. Only a few have growled but if they blaspheme in secret, they do it under the breath in public. Hamilton of Helen's Bay says what has saved him from utter destruction was the fact that the rector of the locality refused to sign the Covenant and therefore the [ragabrash ?] could not leave Hamilton and join the other conventicle. ...'

D.1792/A3/3/4   **Part of a letter to W. S. Armour from Armour,**

[n.d. 1912 ?]   describing a social function at the viceregal lodge, Dublin, and a luncheon engagement with Sir Hugh Mack and R. G. Glendinning at the Reform Club, Belfast.

'... I called yesterday on Sir Hugh Mack—he had asked me to call. He asked me to lunch with him at the Reform Club which I accepted. [R. G.] Glendinning also was asked by him. When we were seated at the table in walked Tom Sinclair. I whispered to the two—he will be mentally saying, "there sit three traitors, which of them will we get shot first". "Gentlemen, will my presence here compromise you or will yours compromise me"—a conundrum which could not be solved. ...'

D.1792/A3/3/5   **Letter to W. S. Armour from Armour,**

[n.d. January ? 1912]   discussing the problems arising from Winston Churchill's proposed visit to Belfast and the opposition which it has generated amongst Unionists and also a Presbyterian meeting to be held in Belfast on 1 February 1912 to protest against Home Rule. Armour feels that pressure is increasing on those Presbyterian clergy like himself and his son Max who are in favour of a measure of self-government for Ireland. As to the Churchill meeting, he expresses confidence that the Unionists will not in the end carry out threats to occupy the Ulster Hall beforehand. He feels that Sir James Dougherty, as under secretary of state for Ireland, must be under considerable strain in the face of these developments.

'The excitement in Belfast is growing with immense intensity, lunacy is in the ascendant. The [Ulster] Unionist Council is threatening to raise a riot and commit murder if Winston [Churchill] dares to speak in the Ulster Hall. Their decision came like a thunder clap on many of their followers here and elsewhere, as everybody knows that it is an attack on the right of free speech which they intend to put down and thus attack one of the citadels. We are getting on. Then the Presbyterian gathering on the first to protest against Home Rule has another motion to find out what ministers have ceased to believe in their shibboleths and bring to bear on them a little boycotting for the honour of God and the good of their souls. Uncle John [Hamilton] who with his *confreres* took my advice to drop the idea of the special [General] Assembly wrote a letter to say that over 100 ministers would refuse to be present. There was a meeting in Belfast last Wednesday—perhaps I mentioned it—at which there were some fifty present and about forty-seven pledged themselves not to go to the gathering. The three said their congregations were so full of Orangemen that for policy's sake they would go, though they would come back as they went. The Presbyterians are making an attack on the right of private judgement in matters political, declaring it to be a damnable heresy. So we are getting on. The question is, with the right of free speech tabooed and the right of private judgement declared to be of the devil, what remains of Protestantism worth keeping? If one hamstrings his religion is it a religion that deserves to survive?

Max, your mother reports—she was in Belfast yesterday—is in a state of panic and would like to proclaim that he is not the son of his father. I wanted him to run for a place anywhere, knowing that the time soon would begin when the supposed sins of the father would be visited on the children but he would not listen with the result that he will have no chance for any place in Ireland for years. If I resigned, I believe he could not be kept out of this church but nobody seems to want me to take the step. However, with his talents and powers of speech, he need not fear if he wishes to go to Canada or America. He will get a better crib than he is likely to get in Ireland. I have written him to avoid panic and not to mind if providence should say, "I will send you far off to the gentiles". It is fast coming about that no man of any independence of mind can have any prospect of a position in the Irish Presbyterian church, but thank heaven it is not the only church in the world. The honest thing for the convention on the first of February to do is to pass a resolution that "nobody who is an apologist for Home Rule or even a non-apologist, that is if he refuses to vote in the question, can ever enter the kingdom of heaven". Certainly there will be no chance for him getting much place in the kingdom on earth if the convention is to be the judge. That is the pass to which things are coming in this quarter of the globe.

The report is that Captain [James] Craig has gone to Monte Carlo, not willingly. It is stated that the War Office asked him how he could reconcile his position in the British army with his threats to stir up civil war in Ulster against the king's government, with the hint that if he did not mind his manners he would be cashiered—I supposed he is a captain on half pay. Under these circumstances he has retired to try his hand at the roulette table and the valiant captain will leave the fighting to somebody else. He is not likely to die in the first ditch much less the last. Such is the story and it is not unlikely.

There are all sorts of rumours about the Ulster Hall being filled the night before with Orangemen who will refuse to leave and of thousands surrounding the building but I hardly credit the stories. The government will line the streets I [?] leading to the hall with policemen and soldiers for which the city will have to pay and I expect wiser counsels will prevail and a little common sense and idea of fair play will find its way into the heads of the responsible part of the Belfast community. [Sir James B.] Dougherty is having an anxious time I fancy as Neville Chamberlain is not fitted to cope with an emergency of this kind—a noodle.

A new day has dawned—the papers are full of rumours of war and riot. It is hard to judge what may happen. ...'

D.1792/A3/3/6   **Letter to W. S. Armour from Armour, [completed by Mrs Armour],**

[n.d. January ? 1912]

describing a visit to Dublin to attend a *levee* at the viceregal lodge; reporting a discussion which he had had with the Presbyterian moderator, Rev. MacMillan, concerning the impending Presbyterian anti-Home Rule convention and the moderator's possible attendance at it; recounting a conversation with Sir James Dougherty and his son Gerald, an impecunious and unsuccessful barrister, on the possibility of William Armour's returning from India and either entering the legal profession or trying to secure a vacant commissionership of intermediate education; and describing the new developments connected with the Winston Churchill meeting, now rescheduled for Celtic Park in Catholic west Belfast.

'I am just back from Dublin from the *levee* to which few of the aristocracy came. ... Home Rule in some shape is bound to come either from the Liberals or Tories—the latter would give a deal to get the chance. The primate came but I saw no other bishop. Dean Webster was the only distinguished church man I saw—and only a few lords. I had not applied for an invitation until Saturday and hence my name is not in the published list. ... [Rev.] MacMillan, the moderator [of the Presbyterian church] was there and I gave him a talking to. The intriguers who have called the Presbyterian meeting for to-morrow were anxious to have him present with a view evidently to publish to the world that the meeting was a meeting of the General Assembly. He refused but at last consented on the condition that they would alter their resolution to read something like this—"Many taking part in this meeting are in sympathy with the legislation of the present government in every thing save Home Rule"—and further that the government would not be abused—conditions which they accepted but are merely written in [?]. The weak man consented. I told him that the moderator of Assembly during his year of office was like the speaker in the h[ouse of] c[ommons]. He might be a violent Tory or Radical but the speaker while in the chair belonged to no side and so should the moderator during office. I added that as the [Ulster] Unionists Council had denounced free speech—witness their assinine conduct *in re* Churchill—so this meeting over which he was to pray was called to denounce the right of private judgement and to institute a boycott on all who refused to bow the knee to the Tory Baal. Her exc[ellency], beside whom he sat at luncheon, also condemned him heavily. His exc[ellency] had a long talk with him and then sent word that I was to wait after the others left as he wanted to speak to me. He was almost effusive in his thanks for my being present. He was annoyed with the moderator and said, "he was going to give away the whole show". I comforted him by uttering a few strong words about the meeting, saying that they gave it out as a non-political gathering but when his exc[ellency] heard of a non-political meeting in Belfast in its present temper, he might expect to hear of an evangelistic service next day in the lower regions, and perhaps if the subject came before the [General] Assembly, if God gave me strength, I would have something to say about their folly and bastard Presbyterianism. He hoped I would get the chance. He was also much distressed about a letter which R. D. Megaw had published in answer to John Hamilton's letter saying that 100 ministers had refused to attend the gathering. Megaw had said that it was only a few of his exc[ellency's] chaplains who had been taking up that position as [Dublin] Castle hacks. His exc[ellency] was very wroth and said, "the Presbyterian chaplains who were asked to do duty during all the years of Tory rule in the Castle were few". I think they were. He was very much distressed lest Dr H[amilton], who, he said, had a character of eighty years without a straw, should be cast down about the letter. I told him not to distress himself as neither Dr H[amilton] nor Mrs H[amilton] ever lost a moment's sleep over R. D. M[egaw]'s letter as everybody knew R. D. M[egaw] was only a henchman of William Moore's, the latter deceiving R. D. M[egaw] by filling his lug with the idea of a berth from the Tories. I left his exc[ellency] in a calmer frame of mind than when I met him. Uncle John [Hamilton] sent a very strong letter last night to [Rev.] MacMillan. However, it is but fair to say on behalf of the latter that his congregation has vowed to wreck the charge in case he does not show up at the meeting. Such life is likely to be in our church in the future but this state of matters will not last for ever. Two hundred ministers refusing to come to their gathering will give them pause. I send you on the papers marked which you can read and you will see I have turned on my accusers from one of them. ...

I was stopped by two or three on Belfast streets to say how anxious they were to hear a speech from me on the situation. One of them was an elder in Dr McIlveen's who is quite indignant that the meeting should be held to-morrow. The other stopped me to say that he did not at first agree with me on the education question but that he was a convinced home ruler. ...

The Churchill meeting you will see is to be [at] the Celtic grounds up the Falls. The Orangemen are threatening a counter-demonstration on the same day. Whether that will come off or nor remains to be seen. The government has made up its mind to prepare for all contingencies, sending troops and policemen to guard against any assault. Lord Pirrie is a trifle nervous and

Lady Pirrie is in a funk. He asked me to speak to her to calm her perturbation. I told her not to worry as there would be more soon and that neither she nor Lord Pirrie would suffer any insult or assault. She thanked me for the interview reported in the *Irish News* and I told her that the Island men, despite their politics, would see that no hostile disturbance would be allowed. I told her to be of good courage. Lord P[irrie] probably has caught a trifle of her excitement but he seems calm. I called to see Sir Hugh Mack whose wife died about nine days ago. ...'

D.1792/A3/3/7   **Letter to W. S. Armour from Armour,**

11 January 1912   containing family news and a rejection of the idea of
                                       a special General Assembly to discuss Home Rule,
which had been suggested by Rev. J. D. Osborne and Rev. John Hamilton as a response to an anti-Home Rule Presbyterian meeting to be held on 1 February. He also indicates why he thinks it unwise to attend a meeting in Belfast to discuss the latter.

'... The anti-Home Rule Presbyterian meeting on the 1st of Feb[ruary] is being much talked of and the heat is rising. I sent a letter to the *N[orthern] W[hig]* But whether it will appear this week or the next I don't know. A letter appeared in it last week which bears the marks of [Rev. J. D.] Osborne though he does not put his name to it. I have had letters from him and [Rev.] John Hamilton asking me to join in a petition to have a General Assembly (special) called for April. I have been disuading them on two grounds, first because we would require four presbyteries to join in the business and as it would be the advanced wing which would make the request it might not be so easy to get the four presbyteries to fall in with the request. Then it would be bad tactics. Those responsible for calling the Assembly would have to lead off with a resolution. A minority should hardly ever move anything: its role is to criticise and move only amendments. We would be hopelessly beaten if we proposed any policy but we might get a respectable minority by criticising "the die Hards". That is my position and I wrote both in that strain. A few moderate men in the Assembly are to meet next Wednesday to decide I fancy whether they will attend the February gathering and possibly about the year's moderator. I have been asked to attend but I declined not from want of sympathy for the object but because my presence might do more harm than good. That is the state of matters. [Edward] Carson and [J. H.] Campbell are speaking very wildly and viciously, stirring up as much bad blood as possible. A movement of which the landlords and their henchmen are the chief organisers is not likely in these democratic days to result in much ultimately. ...'

D.1792/A3/3/8   **Part of a letter to W. S. Armour from Armour,**

[n.d. c.February 1912]   entirely devoted to personal, family and local news.

D.1792/A3/3/9   **Part of a letter to W. S. Armour from Armour,**

[n.d. March ? 1912]   containing church gossip and comments on the
                                       defeat of the Liberals in a Manchester by-election,
which Armour attributes to the national insurance scheme, even though it is being celebrated by Ballymoney Unionists as a defeat for Home Rule. He also takes comfort from the desertion of three prominent English Unionists and from his often repeated conviction that the Tories, once back in office, will introduce Home Rule.

'... The Manchester election is a bad blow to the government. The insurance bill is the principal cause of the disaster. The Tories have worked it for all it is worth. The drums are out here tonight in celebration of the victory which they vainly regard as an anti-Home Rule blow. The banshees are to have a meeting here tomorrow evening which will duly celebrate the event. The Ulster idiots cannot see that the question which has been debated for over twenty years has got to be settled and will be settled by the Tories if they get the chance. Sir Frederick Pollock, Lord Courtney and somebody called Jenks I think—three great pillars of Unionism in the past have during this week deserted the party—Pollock putting his conversion to Home Rule on the actions of Carson and Ulster. That does not look very hopeful about Ulster's ultimate triumph. The whole civilised world is against the banshees' position and a wide-awakening awaits the stupids [*sic*]. ...'

D.1792/A3/3/10   **Letter to W. S. Armour from Armour,**

[n.d. March ? 1912]   largely containing local and family news but also some
                          comments on the national coal strike then in progress
and on the increasing acceptance of the national insurance scheme by Unionists in Ulster.

'The coal war is still running its course. Everybody is suffering, specially the railway companies which are running as few trains as possible. We are being taught how dependent we are on our fellow-men, especially on those who work where the sun never shines. You will see a decent article in yesterday's *D[aily N[ews]* which is worth reading. I half expect the business will reach some sort of settlement today or tomorrow. The thing has got to be settled somehow and the sooner the better. ...

There is to be an address on the insurance bill tomorrow evening at which I am to preside. It will work mischief for the powers that be at present though it has come to stay. The Orangemen are taking up the scheme and so are the churches—Presbyterian and Episcopal—which means that many are getting tired of the Tory rot. It will seem all right some day, though it will bring its penalty on the authors. ...'

D.1792/A3/3/11   **Part of a letter to W. S. Armour from Armour,**

[n.d. March ? 1912]   containing local, family and church news and a critical
                          assessment of Andrew Bonar Law's leadership of the
                          Unionist party.

'... The political weather indicates storms if not earthquakes. This coal strike with other things may upset Asquith's fine team. Andrew Bonar Law is turning out a fiasco and [Arthur] Balfour is returning to take up the reins the die hards snatched from his hands. He is to move today the rejection of the minimum wage bill. Bonar is a reed shaken by the wind and his party begins to feel he is not the man for Galway. It will be interesting to watch during the next few weeks the silent deposition of the upstart from a position he has not the ability to fill. Brains are still a factor in political life and smartness is a poor substitute for mental ability. He is turning out a *roi faineant*—if that is the correct spelling of the idea. ...'

D.1792/A3/3/12   **Part of a letter to W. S. Armour from Armour,**

[n.d. March ? 1912]   reporting a meeting of the Queen's University senate,
                          at which Armour had successfully proposed a resol-
ution 'declaring that Intermediate pupils, who had passed the middle grade in subjects prescribed for matriculation in Q.U.B., should be deemed to have passed the examination in those subjects', and commenting on the prospects for Home Rule and on the Liberal government.

'... I am like the arch-angel in Milton, for war though a man of peace, stagnation is not good for the liver at any rate and my liver shows no signs of sluggishness. I have been examining schools on Monday and today as a kind of diversion.

There is no absolute certainty that the coal strike is over, though the bill will probably get through the [house of] lords tonight. It will gradually lead to resumption. Asquith has had a hard drill to hoe and he must be nearly worn done over the perplexing problem. His final speech in today's *D[aily] N[ews]* is as touching an address as one ever read. Even Bonar Law acknowledges its pathetic sincerity. Events are coming into view to make the Home Rule measure doubtful of immediate success though one has no doubt that the question must be settled in some form soon by either the one party or the other. It must be tackled and got rid of as discussions of this kind cannot go on *ad infinitum*. I suspect the Tories may have to settle it as this insurance bill is continuing very unpopular, though it has come to stay seeing so many strong societies are taking it up. ...'

D.1792/A3/3/13   **Letter to W. S. Armour from Armour,**

[n.d. March ? 1912]   pointing out the continuing hardships caused by the
                                 miners' strike; criticising the regime at Campbell
College, Belfast, yet again; and giving his views on the proposed Unionist rally at Balmoral, Belfast, on 9 April 1912, to be addressed by Andrew Bonar Law.

'... Preparations for the Balmoral meeting on the 9 April for Bonar Law are going on apace. The mass of humbug which will be foisted on the ears of the public will be immense. I suspect Master Bonar will have his tongue in his cheek while he is launching his anathemas against Home Rule and certainly as he listens to the spouters of buncombe [*sic*] . The meeting is being boomed muchly. ...'

D.1792/A3/3/14   **Part of a letter to W. S. Armour from Armour,**

14 March 1912   discussing the appointment of Rev. Pyper of Dervock
                                 to Portrush Presbyterian Church and analysing Max
Armour's limited chances of securing the now vacant Dervock congregation, in view of the opposition of the 'Orange element'.

D.1792/A3/3/15   **Part of a letter to W. S. Armour from Armour,**

[n.d. April ? 1912]   containing a considerable amount of church news and
                                 details of further developments on the Queen's
University matriculation question. It also comments on the hostile Unionist reaction to a Home Rule demonstration in Dublin on the previous Sunday, at which William Macafee, the young lawyer who had unsuccessfully contested North Antrim as a Liberal in December 1910, had spoken.

'... I send you the Freeman [*Freeman's Journal*] of Monday containing the speeches against the monster demonstration on Sabbath last. It is not necessary for you to read them. I did not. The Pharisees down here are gnashing their teeth on the fact that W. Macafee, B.L., was there as a speaker. Had I been in his place, I would have kept away but it is rather amusing to listen to folks here blaming him for taking part in a meeting on that day and having nothing but praise for preachers who spend the Sabbath [day ?] in political harangues against Home Rule. They have a curious idea of right and wrong, believing apparently that it is the acme of righteousness to denounce Home Rule on Sabbath but an iniquity to be punished with fire to say a word in its favour on that day. Their thoughts on morality have become topsy-turvy. "Oh wud some power the giftie gie us, to see ourselves as others see us." To preach Bonar Lawism next Sabbath will be the staple of many a harangue as Unionism has become a sort of fourth person of the Trinity with many here. It is a new world my brethren as well as a bad one. I say nothing on politics these days.'

D.1792/A3/3/16

Part of a letter to W. S. Armour from Armour,

[n.d. 11 April ? 1912]

largely dealing with church matters and with the continuing struggle between the senate and the academic council of the Queen's University of Belfast on the matriculation issue. There are, however, some brief comments on the Balmoral Unionist demonstration.

'.. I am sending you the [*Northern*] *Whig* of yesterday with the account of the Balmoral demonstration. I have not read any of the speeches save Bonar Law's. It is hard to find out how many were there. The deputation from Ballymoney, headed by [R. C.] Martin and [R. D.] Megaw, was cheered to the echo which I have pointed out was a tribute to the mother of the Gracchi [*i.e.*, Mrs Armour]. It is well to be regarded as a force in politics as well as gardening. ...'

D.1792/A3/3/17

Letter to W. S. Armour from Armour, [completed by Mrs Armour],

[n.d. April ? 1912]

explaining his reaction to a letter from Professor J. H. Morgan, requesting Armour to make a contribution to a forthcoming volume on Home Rule which Morgan is editing; commenting on current political developments; and passing on the usual family news.

'I enclose you a letter from a Prof[essor] Morgan requesting me to write a short article on Home Rule for some volume he is bringing out. As I was away when the letter came and as Easter was on when there are few posts, I did not reply at once. A telegram prepaid came on Monday evening to which a reply was sent. "[Holiday ?] prevented reply: regret inability though most sympathetic". I then wrote declining on the grounds of want of time and health considerations. Another telegram came urging compliance and strange to say Max thought I should comply and your mother was of a similar view apparently. It was partly for fear Max would be annoyed that I refused—I telegraphed that I would yield and send him something soon. Thus the matter stands. I expect to have it ready for dispatch on Saturday, that is if I can get a few hours to have my brain shired. There is little rest for the wicked in these coster monger times. You will likely have Asquith's speech as soon as we are likely to have it. He will have a fine audience and his speech will have many readers as well as critics favourable and unfavourable. I see Carson is to take up the parable after him—Master Bonar Law getting the back seat in the synagogue. It is clear the Tories in their hearts are not in raptures with Bonar and think him rather light a weight in a dress night debate. Carson will thunder. You will see the speeches but they will be late in getting to the sacred city. You will not be bound to read them. I could not read anything but Bonar Law's yesterday morning. ...'

D.1792/A3/3/18

Part of a letter to W. S. Armour from Armour, [written from Portrush],

25 April 1912

expressing severe criticism of Campbell College, Belfast; discussing the repercussions of the 'Titanic' disaster; and anticipating a forthcoming meeting of the Queen's University senate.

D.1792/A3/3/19

Letter to W. S. Armour from Armour,

20 June 1912

recounting a meeting of the Queen's University senate which had discussed and passed a motion to rescind a previously carried motion to elevate the lectureship in Gaelic to a professorship. Armour makes it clear that he doesn't 'think much of an attempt to revive Gaelic but I see no insuperable objection to it'. He remains convinced that the senate 'are choke-full of prejudice', and that the vote was 'a declaration of war on the Catholics'. He reports Sir Samuel Dill's verdict on the General Assembly debate on Home Rule—that it is the beginning of a revolution, 'as he looks on it as a warning to those who have been trying to boss the church'. Armour's rejection of an invitation on health grounds to chair a proposed Nationalist demonstration at Maghera, Co. Londonderry, is also mentioned.

D.1792/A3/3/20   **Letter to W. S. Armour from Armour,**

27 June 1912   discussing Max Armour's failure to obtain the Dervock
                                                       Presbyterian congregation; mentioning that he has to
prepare a sermon to be delivered by Rev. Heney of Mossside, Co. Antrim, at a service in Trinity Presbyterian Church, Ballymoney, for local members of the Independent Orange Order; and analysing the proposed Nationalist meeting in support of the Home Rule bill at Maghera, Co. Londonderry.

'Your ma will have told you of aunt Moore's disappointment about Dervock, which has not the good sense to choose Max. He had fewer votes than I expected but there is no need to say anything further than that his steps are not to be on that path. I cannot say I am much grieved, though I fear his chances of a place in the Irish Presbyterian church are rather small. But the world is wide and all the religion and chances for work in the church are not confined to the Pharisees of Ulster. ...

I have to sketch a sermon, or the heads of one, to be delivered by [Rev.] Heney on Sabbath week in the church here for the Independent Orangemen. I have some little jobs of that kind now and then. There is to be a meeting in Maghera on Saturday to pass some resolutions in favour of the Home Rule bill. A deputation came here last Thursday to ask me to take the chair. John Dillon was to be there, said they, a point on which I expressed a doubt. Next morning a paragraph appeared in the *Irish News* to say the meeting was put off until September. That seemed to settle the matter but a few of the mad-heads insisted on the meeting being held and I was approached again to go but I have declined. The reason of the business seems something like this. The leaders of the Nationalist party, in view of the Agar Robartes amendment, thought a meeting would do good but when it, that is the amendment, was rejected, it occurred to them that a meeting might be the occasion of a row and therefore they countermanded it. But the publicans had laid in a store of spirits for the occasion and fearing a loss if the matter did not [turn ?] they resolved to bolt from the leaders and carry out the project on their own hook. I had a letter from Sir J[ames] B. D[ougherty] informing me of the real state of the case. ...'

D.1792/A3/3/21   **Letter to W. S. Armour from Armour,**

3 July 1912   discussing Max Armour's continuing difficulties in
                                                       obtaining a congregation of his own, along with the
damaging repercussions for the Nationalist cause of the Maghera meeting and the violence which ensued from it, which Armour blames on consumption of alcholic beverages and the laying of a trap by local Orangemen.

'... The papers sent will give you an account of the aftermath of the Maghera meeting. It was a huge mistake and was held contrary to the wish of the Nationalist leaders who had declared it off but the publicans who had laid in a quantity of whisky and fearing it would lie in their cellars egged on the Irish leaders, that is the local crew—to hold it with a result which is decidedly bad. It gives the Orange party a cry for which they were longing—a better cry than even the McCann case. Drink was at the bottom of the unfortunate business but it is not at all improbable but that some of the mad Orangemen of the locality laid the bait for an attack on the children. It is hard to get at the bottom of an Irish *fracas*. Certainly it was a dangerous course to take children with banners into a district where the materials for a shindy were quite ready for a flare up. You can read the papers and possibly come to a sane conclusion which is hardly possible in a country where if you do not take a side you are persecuted by both parties. You can form your own opinion, if it is worth having one. ...'

D.1792/A3/3/22 **Letter to W. S. Armour from Armour,**

10 July 1912 indicating his intention of going to Dublin to take a service at the viceregal lodge and to attend a meeting to be addressed by H. H. Asquith on 21 July; and expressing his fears about the increasing amount of tension and political polarisation in Ulster.

'... The aftermath of the Maghera gathering has been bad. Insanity in Ulster which was brewing has burst forth and everybody that is not in connection with a Unionist club is a fit object for ill-treatment. It is feared there will be explosions on the 12th, though what is expected usually never happens. Perhaps it may happen that the 12th will be a day only of exciting oratory. It is certain to be that, but perhaps having released their feelings by cheering the orators they may restrain themselves and put off action to another day. Sir J[ames B. D[ougherty] is kept in Dublin over the blackguards of the north. He had arranged to go over to see the manoeuvres of the fleet but he has been pinned to his desk in Dublin. No man [standeth ?] to himself and this is illustrated in several ways by the present crisis. The Ulster people seem to me to be trying to commit suicide. The threatened split between Liberalism and Labour may lead to new developments. The uncertain is the only thing that is certain. ...

A letter from Sir J[ames] B. D[ougherty] in answer to five or six requests I had to make to him but he has to thunder back a no, as if from the mouth of a cannon. I expected as much but one has to send up all sorts of applications. It is part of one's fate in this world when there are only five barley loaves and a few small fishes for the hungry multitude. The Belfast chamber of commerce has been interviewing Asquith yesterday over the Home Rule bill. Master Asquith has to tell them that the gulf between their views and his is without a budge. *Non possumus* is their cry and *non possumus* is practically the answer. So they have to return as they went but doubtless with the consciousness that they have done their duty to their consciences and their country. Carson has a letter in the papers this morning entreating his followers to go it mild and give no offence on the 12th, hinting that the day may come when they may cast off restraint. His party I suspect have been telling him plainly that his hysterics are not furthering the cause which is perfectly true. I wish the 12th was over. [Rev.] Heney of Mossside discoursed to the Independents in Trinity [Presbyterian Church] on Sabbath evening. The gathering was large but the collection was small, only some £2 17 0. They go on the principle, "base be the slave that pays". The collection was for the Orphan Society. The service gave me some extra work, but it is over *"laus deo"*. ...'

D.1792/A3/3/23 **Letter to Mrs Jennie Armour and to W. S. Armour from Armour,**

20 July 1912 partly consisting of an account of Armour's visit to Dublin (20-22 July) to attend the Home Rule meeting addressed by Asquith and to take a service, which was followed by supper, at the viceregal lodge. There is also an account of a conversation which he had had with Lord Aberdeen about the General Assembly Home Rule debates in June and a reference to an *Irish News* attack on the Ballymoney, Co. Antrim, Unionist solicitor, R. C. Martin.

'I could not get a moment yesterday to scrawl a line as I was on the move all the afternoon and we were late in getting back from the biggest of gatherings in the theatre. The luncheon at 1.15 was a very enjoyable business. It was served in two rooms—the one opening into the other. I suppose there were some twelve or fourteen round tables in all. There were some twelve at the table at which I was. Mr Asquith and her excellency [Lady Aberdeen] were at that table so you will see I was at one of the chief seats in the synagogue. He of course was a considerable distance from me. I was placed between Lady Lynch, the wife of some solicitor who had been knighted, and the Hon. Amelia Stanley, whose father was a cousin of the late Dean Stanley. ...

I did not get any talk with Asquith though his exc[ellency] in introducing me said he would like a word to two with me. Dr Traill [of Trinity College, Dublin, and Bushmills, Co. Antrim] was there and was talking vigorously with Asquith and Birrell and as I was near, I went forward and shook hands with Mr A., saying, as Dr Traill is wishing you a long tenure of office as prime minister, I heartily do the same, whereat both Birrell and he laughed almost uproariously and Dr Traill seemed quite non-plussed. The evening meeting in dimensions and enthusiasm beggars description. If you could fancy over 3,000 people standing and cheering and waving white handkerchiefs for over four minutes you can picture the scene. The fluttering of the handkerchiefs was like thousands of birds flapping their wings. The harmony of the meeting was interrupted only for about a minute by some absurd idiot calling, "what about votes for women", but the interrupters had to go through a bad few minutes. The incident of the hatchet on the previous evening made sympathisers with the suffragists anything but popular. Mrs Leigh will be tried for arson and serve her right. I should have liked Max to have heard Asquith as he would have got a few tips in public speaking. Like all the big speakers, he spoke slowly, deliberately, no word out of place and every sentence telling. It was a really great speech and so were they all. Birrell's was quite different in a way as he was, rather unusually I thought, a trifle rhetorical. But he has the gift, though it is not Mr Asquith's line in a way. Lord St Ledgers also spoke well and so did Simon, not son of Jonas, but solicitor-general. Redmond's speech was remarkably well delivered. He and Asquith used notes freely. On the whole I have never seen any meeting like it. The theatre was filled with a very respectable looking audience. Gardiner of Kingstown, Craig, Clements, Hamilton, Armour were the only Presbyterian parsons, so far as I could see, present. ...

His exc[ellency] became very gracious—thanked me almost effusively for what I said about them at Wilson's installation and then I had to explain the whole business about the action of the General Assembly—which I did as graphically as possible, pointing out what had been gained and how it was regarded as a signal victory. They had been under the delusion that the victory was on the other side. He complained of the statements made by the moderator at the Albert Hall meeting but I pointed out that it was impossible to keep one's opponents from misrepresenting facts—a fact which to his cost he knows to be true. "Your exc[ellency] one cannot set every speaker right but I may have an opportunity of drawing a feather across the neck of the moderator." He talked a good while on various matters and at 10.45 the motor was ordered to convey me to uncle John's [Hamilton]. There was a lady in the drawing room to whom I was not introduced as there was nobody to do it, she standing in fine evening dress alone. I had a ten minute talk with her. I think she is a daughter of Lady Sheffield. ... Then she declared herself a Conservative and was launching out on the dreadful things which were to happen soon. I advised her to read a sermon of the celebrated Jowett in 1878, wherein he pointed out that every now and then the world was being frightened by the terrible things which were sure to happen if certain changes were made in the laws and how the terrible things did not take place, quoting to her what might be regarded as an axiom, "that no change in the laws of a country ever brought about as much good as the advocates of the change expected but not one 100th part of the evils the opponents of the change prophesied it would bring about". "That is perfectly true", said she. "Everybody expected that Lloyd George's budget would ruin the country but the country is richer than ever it was". ...

I enclose you a clipping from Monday's *Irish News* in which Louis Walsh calls in question R. C. Martin's knowledge of Irish history. You can read it if you have a mind. I do not insist on it as I am of a merciful disposition. He will be very mad over it as he cannot stand criticism but he is on the border line between sanity and insanity on matters political and therefore a real Orangeman. I also enclose you an invitation for Friday evening the 26th inst. in London. With reluctance I refused for two reasons, first I have not the time or means to go on expensive journeys, and secondly I do not sleep when away and come back over-tired. ...'

D.1792/A3/3/24

[n.d. July ? 1912]

Letter to W. S. Armour from Armour, [completed by Mrs Armour],

largely devoted to family and personal news, along with some discussion of Max's continuing plight, including a suggestion that he should go to the United States.

'... I see no good in [him] remaining here as his father's politics will pursue and beat him wherever he preaches. To cast one's pearls before swine is contrary to scripture and to be rent by crowds of half lunatics with whom Ulster is full—is not playing the game. He does not take kindly to the idea which is a proof that he is very young. His way here for years will be hedged with thorns. ...'

D.1792/A3/3/25

[n.d. August 1912 ?]

Letter to W. S. Armour from Armour, [written from Portrush, Co. Antrim],

largely containing local and family news but briefly referring to the difficulties of the Portrush Presbyterian minister, Rev. Pyper, in relation to the impending Ulster day in September.

'... I can see that Pyper will have a difficult drill to hoe in Portrush, though he is very popular with the manse here. The Ulster day which ought to be called the Protestant fools' day will put him in a fix. He does not believe in it but it is not at all unlikely that the mad-heads will insist on a service and the question is how will he manage to get out of it. If he held it and was only half-hearted in the absurdity he would come in for abuse and if he does not show up he will be denounced roundly as a traitor. ...'

D.1792/A3/3/26

8 August 1912

Letter to W. S. Armour from Armour, [completed by Mrs Armour],

containing personal and social gossip.

D.1792/A3/3/27

14 August 1912

Letter to W. S. Armour from Armour,

consisting mainly of detailed news about changes in the personnel of the Route Presbytery and a report of a meeting in Belfast which Armour, as an insurance commissioner for Co. Antrim, had had to attend.

'... I am not up to politics at present. It ought to be the close season and I am taking a holiday. Even the Manchester election is losing some of its piquancy already and Bonar Law is not going to head the Ulster fenians after all. ...'

D.1792/A3/3/28

5 September 1912

Letter to W. S. Armour from Armour,

discussing the possibly murky circumstances surrounding the death of Lizzie McElroy, wife of S. C. McElroy; and analysing in considerable detail the current political situation in both England and Ireland. He is doubtful that English public opinion is turning against Home Rule and he is confident that a bill will eventually be passed, by the Tories if not by the Liberals. He also analyses the Unionist plans for the signing of an Ulster covenant.

'... Your friends in India would be wise not to make too much out of the Manchester election as that particular constituency always votes Tory at a bye-election [*sic*] and Liberal at a general election. It is a Tory stronghold but the Tories there are not tariff reformers so at a bye-election [*sic*] they can vote Tory knowing that the question of tariff is not on the carpet but when a general election comes they are anti-tariffites. The late election means very little, if the insurance was not in existence the Tories would not have a look in anywhere. That act is their asset but they are careful not to commit themselves to its repeal. They harp on defects which they carefully refuse to mention. Anti-Home Rule is a spent force in the English constituencies and anti-disestablishment of the church in Wales gains only a very few votes for the Tories. Their *piece de resistance* is the insurance act and then at the close of the poll they say—if they succeed—so many votes are against Home Rule and disestablishment. It is a piece of sheer hypocrisy to claim Crewe as an instance of change of view when everybody knows the seat was gained because of a three-cornered contest. At a general election a thing of that kind can hardly occur. I think it is totally certain that Home Rule will pass the h[ouse of] c[ommons] this year but some catastrophe may overtake the government during the succeeding two years before it automatically becomes law. But if this catastrophe occurs and the Tories grasp the reins, they must, unless their majority is overwhelming, tackle the question and propose some solution as the thing cannot go on *ad infinitum*.

There was a very [*? page torn*] attack on their exc[ellencie]s in the *Irish Times* yesterday which is copied into today's [*Northern*] *Whig* which I send you, also a reply in today's *Freeman['s Journal]*, also enclosed. A letter appears in today's *Irish Times* flatly contradicting the leader. The fact is the Tories are becoming desperate and any stick is good enough to beat the dog with. Among the racing men and the fast set and among those—and they are many—who think that all the plums of office are intended for Episcopalians, their exc[ellencie]s are unpopular. Their exc[ellencie]s have not always been tactful but with the masses they are still popular. You can read the extracts. The Ulster [?] are bent on another explosion and have arranged for a great covenanting day when they are to vow not to acknowledge or pay taxes to a Home Rule parliament, should it be set up. "Dying in the last ditch" is spreading and it is clear it is beginning to dawn on their stupid intelligence that Home Rule in some form is coming. It is a climb down however. They were all to swear with uplifted hand that they would oppose Home Rule by violent methods but now it is only a *declaration*—for which nobody will be obliged to risk his skin—that they will not pay taxes *etc.* as if taxes were not almost all indirect and you can fancy if an extra duty was put on tea, tobacco and whisky—these idiots refusing to buy tea or tobacco *etc.* Of course the day will produce mischief in congregations as many ministers will refuse to hold services. The orange tail is wagging the Protestant dog. The people who never have attended any prayer meeting will feel annoyed doubtless because they cannot get identifying the Almighty with their *credo*. ...'

D.1792/A3/3/29   **Letter to W. S. Armour from Armour,**

12 September 1912   discussing the Liberal defeat in the Midlothian by-election and the local preparations for the signing of the Ulster Covenant. Ballymoney Unionist Club had assisted the Unionist electoral campaign in Midlothian.

'Midlothian has been lost—a regrettable incident in political warfare but it may be a blessing in disguise. Liberalism and Labour have each got a lesson which they ought to lay to heart. The jubilation of the Tories and specially the Ulster gang of blind bats is a screech of joy. This shows how impervious they are to common sense and if they represent Ulster it would not be a great disaster to civilisation if they disappeared. It does not seem to dawn on their slow heads that some 2,400 in Midlothian voted for Home Rule beyond the vote for Unionism. Magnetised by a majority of thirty-two over the Liberal who was handicapped by the Labour man, they forget that possibly and almost certainly at the next election Hope [Major Hope, the victorious Unionist] will be Hopeless. Midlothian will be in Ulster on the 28th [Ulster day] trotted out about a million beyond its value—a tree with fine-looking fruit which will be bitter for them some day—a tree without any root and therefore the kind of plant for their fool's paradise. The result of the business does not distress me in the least though the Tories here are quite jubilant. Political fools are many here and have no vision. They cannot read the handwriting on the wall, Ulster day is being boomed for all it is worth which is not much. There is to be a religious ceremony at Leslie Hill [the Leslie estate on the western outskirts of Ballymoney] preparatory to the signing the Covenant, which is not an oath-binding covenant but a mere declaration which means nothing more than a signature to a petition—not a formidable act. I hear Lewis summoned [Rev.] Dill and [Rev.] Nelson—he did not [dare ?] to ask me—to see if they would take part in a religious service on that day. It appears they both refused to touch his proposal with even the usual forty foot pole. John Pollock told me on Monday that Lewis had engaged the Town Hall for some meeting but I forgot to ask him for what day and for what particular purpose. It may be for Sabbath the 22nd but what the nature of the service will be is not known at least to me. The Leslie Hill gathering according to advertisement is to be addressed by several parsons but who they are is not announced. Probably McCammon, Crothers and Benson will sway the hosts of the Lord by their blatant oratory. "Squeaking" Leslie is to take the chair. I expect Martin will be one of the speakers ... .'

D.1792/A3/3/30   **Part of a letter to W. S. Armour from Armour,**

18 September 1912   discussing Kenneth Armour's continuing indolence in matters educational and Armour's efforts to secure Max Armour a post in the English Presbyterian church in either South Shields or Sunderland. The letter also comments on Unionist preparations for Ulster day.

'... I am corresponding with a few people in England with a view to get Max a place in the English Presbyterian church as in Ulster where political insanity reigns he would not have the slightest chance of a call in Ireland. The sins—or supposed sins—of his father are to be visited on the children. That part of the commandment is being carried out and obeyed more perfectly than any other part of the moral law. I wrote Dr McHarry, late of Crouch Hill, who replied in a friendly way. He suggested that I should get a few testimonials or something of that kind. I wrote Colquhoun, Purves, George Thompson and D. D. Boyle. They replied very cordially. Purves put the matter very nicely and sent a letter with it to me. I have sent on the whole business to McHarry. There is a vacancy in S[outh] Shields in which Andrew Faloon has some influence and one in Sunderland I think. He will likely get a hearing in both. [Rev. D. D.] Boyle seems to be suffering from the present insanity and being in the midst of the politically insane, his life as a preacher is not a bed of roses I can see.

It appears, according to the London correspondent of the *Irish News*, that the form of declaration for the 28th is giving the Carsonite gang a deal of trouble, how to keep from colourable treason. The K.C.s and privy councillors don't wish to endanger their status but it is not easy to save themselves and satisfy the feelings of their mad followers who want strong meat with some pepper thereon. The task is of unusual difficulty and perhaps they may illustrate the old words, "the way of transgressors is hard". ...'

D.1792/A3/3/31   **Letter to J. B. M Armour from Armour,**

24 September 1912.   commenting on the pressure being exerted upon the clergy to announce and take part in the events of the proposed Ulster day and critically analysing the content of the Ulster Covenant.

'... I feel a trifle annoyed with [Rev.] Wilson. I saw him on Saturday and he was decided not to announce the Saturday service. I wrote a note to [Rev.] Dill to tell him that neither Wilson nor I would announce the meeting, adding that it was only fair that he (Dill) should know. To my amazement Taggart told me on Monday morning that Wilson had announced the meeting, though in a half-hearted way. He must be a reed shaken by the wind. Dill made no announcement. Lewis—it was a trifle cheeky—had written me to make the announcement. I replied that as there were some in the congregation as strong in their views as he was in his, though their views were directly opposite to his, it would not be prudent to say anything on the subject and that there was no necessity as the meeting had been sufficiently boomed. As to your Saturday meeting, you had better be guided by Mr Colquhoun who I fancy will not be entirely enamoured about the performance. I think he should allow those who are convinced about the righteousness of the gathering to do the most of the praying—himself to wind up the business with a real Christian prayer as distinguished from a passionate lecture to the Almighty to turn Tory to oblige the fire eaters. He is level-headed and I suspect he is sceptical about the sincerity of the religious aspect of the gathering. Looking at the matter calmly, I cannot see how any really honest, religious man could sign the declaration as from its wording—"every means which may be necessary"—it might mean that everyone who signs it would be expected to commit murder if that was thought necessary, which in an acme of passion would be a possible order. I think [Rev.] Archer will be in a hole. I hear [Rev.] Hamilton of Lisburn refused to take part in a religious service in his church but he offered the church for a service if he could approve of the minister who was to conduct it. Whether the offer was accepted or not, I don't know. It was as good a way out of the difficulty as he could devise. It will be as bad a day for Protestantism in Ireland that ever dawned as it may lead to the ruin of the Protestants in the south and west and when the Orangemen seize the tiller as they are doing, the result cannot be good for the Protestant faith. Carson's victory—if it occurs—will spell an awful defeat. ...'

D.1792/A3/3/32 Part of a letter to W. S. Armour from Armour,

26 September 1912 further commenting on the preparations for Ulster day, and on the need to suppress riotous disturbances in Belfast. He also discusses the responses of a number of Presbyterian clergymen to the crisis.

'... The Ulster day is in full swing. You will see from the papers sent at least one aspect of the folly. The *M[anchester] Guardian's* articles are sane. But the northern papers have reached the zenith of absurdity and insanity. I enclose the reply of [Rev.] Ramsay to Lewis. The type writing was done by a junior. It is about the most absurd and insulting production ever published. If it means anything, it means a R.C. should not be permitted to live, much less have a vote. The inquisition in its palmy days was never more savage to heretics than [Rev.] Ramsay would if he had the power to [*sic*] R.C.s What makes the thing worse is that he is nominally the principal of the intermediate school and this precious production will drive away any R.C.s attending and prevent any from joining. ... He must be taken by the nose. It is a letter from a Christian minister with every particle of Christianity left out. He seems to think he has a mission to make the British constitution a Reformed Presbyterian conventicle—a rather large order but it is well to have a lofty ideal and a firm belief in one's self as an instrument for establishing righteousness universally. The difference between the Convenanting view of the church and the Ultramontane view is not apparent. They are the same in theory. The Ulster day will be comparitively quiet here I fancy. Only [Rev.] Crothers and [Rev.] McCammon are to spout of the Presbyterians, as far as I can gather, at Leslie Hill. Lewis wrote me—it was a trifle cheeky—to ask me to announce the meeting on the Sabbath. I wrote back civilly to say that as there were people in the church who held views on the question as strong as his, though theirs were contrary to his, it would not be prudent to make an announcement, adding that I had never consciously in the pulpit made the slightest reference to current politics. To ask me to refer to the matter, I said, was hardly playing the game. [Rev.] Dill did not announce the meeting and neither did [Rev.] Wallace. It was not given out in Garryduff. I saw [Rev.] Nelson on Saturday and he assured me decidedly that he would not announce it but [Rev.] Taggart told me on Monday morning that he had made the announcement. It is clear he is a reed shaken by the wind. Wallace thinks he will sign the Covenant after all. Weak people may do anything. ...

The new rector of Portrush [Rev. T. A. Harvey] is getting it loud and strong for refusing to announce the gathering, and for refusing to allow a flag to be put up on the tower and practically telling them he will take no part in the religious orgy. Portrush is much scandalised and the mad-heads may invoke the aid of the bishop to bring the rector, as they would say, to his right mind. [Rev.] Pyper is conveniently off for his holidays—I advised him thereto some months ago. It is as well to be out of the way when a storm might blow. I hope we will weather the cape of storms. I expect the government, if the hooliganism of Belfast does not cease, may have to proclaim Belfast and the northern counties and apply the crimes act which the Tories passed with a view to restrain the south and west in case of illegal practices. It would be one of the ironies of history if the act, which the north applauded and would not hear of its repeal, should be brought into force in Ulster to restrain the youth and fools who are going about with pistols threatening to shoot anybody supposed to be lackadaisical about the Union or a crypto-home ruler. I would not be astonished if that was to take place, which would be amusing at least. Certainly something must be done in the near future if life and liberty are to be protected in the metropolis of rowdyism. ...'

D.1792/A3/3/33 **Letter to W. S. Armour from Armour,**

3 October 1912 describing the events of Ulster day in the Ballymoney district and more generally in the province, and commenting critically on Sir Edward Carson's leadership of the Ulster Unionist cause.

'... We have survived Ulster day which is over thanks be to God. It was rather a tame business here. The meeting at Leslie Hill was not inspiring—a meeting of Orangemen with a very few of any weight save Martin and Lewis. [Rev.] Crothers and [Rev.] McCammon were the chief speakers so you may guess it was lively oratory. The number of signatories was not the half what was expected and [?] tears are shed in secret over the big meeting which did not take place. [Rev.] Dill, [Rev.] Wallace, [Rev.] Wilson did not turn up. There was a rather awkward business at Finvoy. Some youths or men had barricaded the doors, windows *etc.* of the church. They had hidden away the bible and when [William ?] Moore with his ragged brigade appeared there was no admittance. Hence they had to call in the services of the crow-bar brigade and after a long effort they took possession of the building and with minds under the circumstances spiritually inclined, they held their service which you may be sure was teeming with charity towards all men, specially toward those who had "stoked" the door in their face. It was published next day in the [*Belfast*] *News-Letter* as an outrage by the nationalists by some "truthful Tommy". It was a protest against [Rev.] Craig who is not popular. There were few services in the Route which the Tories say is wholly given over to wickedness inspired from Trinity Manse. Is it right to speak of "inspired wickedness"? [Rev.] Henderson of Coagh it is said held a service and at the close announced that he could not sign the declaration and gave his reasons—reasons which he said were personal and that those present were at liberty to exercise their right of private judgement. How many signed I did not hear. It is said that [Rev.] Morrison of Aghadoey reluctantly gave the church and though he was present and read the portion of scripture, it is reported that he walked straight out of the church and allowed the rector to harangue the audience which was not overflowing. Carson has not set the Route on fire—a sheer mountebank, the greatest enemy of Protestantism in my opinion existing, inflaming men to violence whom he will probably leave and desert if any difficulty arises. The whole business is a disgrace to Protestantism and will give it a bad kick. To introduce religion into a purely political question is the old device of Hophni and Phineas of introducing the ark of the covenant into the battle against the Philistines—more than a doubtful policy and likely to have disastrous results for the ark of the covenant ... [*page torn*] ... If the design of the service was to pray God to send forth a spirit of evil, the prayers have been fully answered, as strife and ill feeling have been introduced into almost all congregations and the outlook is decidedly bad. It seems to be a repetition of the scene where the 400 prophets met to egg on Ahab to go up against Ramoth—Gilead and possibly the result will be the same. The old testament theories are being preached everywhere and there is a criminal forgetfulness of the words—"they that take the sword perish by the sword". ...

The new rector of Portrush has behaved like a man and a Christian. He was willing to read the prayers drawn up by the bishop for the occasion but he would not allow his church for signing the declaration or permit the union jack to be put upon the tower of the church. The Portrush people are seething with wrath and would like to stone him but he held to his point like a hero. [Rev.] Pyper has shown himself to be a stickley-back. He went away on his holidays really to get out of taking part in an organised hypocrisy but his father and brother got round him and compelled him to come back and hold or take part in the service. It was a contemptible act, cowardly in the extreme, and though it may gratify for the passing moment the passions of the mob, every honest man will despise him. If he had taken the side of the rector—which he should have done—he would have been worthy of real respect. He has sold himself for a mess of pottage. You will find in the *Manchester Guardian* three or four very good articles on the subject which are worth reading as are the accounts of Carson's histrionics during his career in the province. ...'

D.1792/A3/3/34   **Letter to W. S. Armour from Armour,**

10 October 1912   commenting on the excellence of the local harvest, his involvement in a newspaper controversy with the moderator of the General Assembly, Rev. Montgomery, his co-option on to the matriculation committee of the Queen's University of Belfast and the activities of 'King Carson'. There is also yet more criticism of the educational regime at Campbell College, Belfast.

'... The moderator of Assembly wrote a letter, which I am sending in a cutting to the *Glasgow Herald* and *Scotsman* quietly contradicting a statement made by Dr Wells *in re* the action of the General Assembly about Home Rule. Somebody sent me the *Glasgow Herald* which I took to mean I was expected to reply. I have sent a reply—a rather mild one for me. The reply ought, if the papers publish it, to be in today's issue. Of course I cannot send the reply as the Scotch papers do not arrive here until Friday morning. There will be some anger in some quarters likely.

I told you of the strict boycott of the rector of Portrush by his parishoners in consequence of his refusal to allow his church for the signing of the declaration. The hubbub over the matter is loud and almost threatening. I wrote him a note of congratulation on his manly courage and expressed sympathy with him, advising him to sit tight, preach his best and make no reference to the current insanity. He has sent me a cordial letter of thanks which I will enclose you in this letter or at least a copy thereof. ... The rector writes as follows:

"Dear Sir, I was deeply touched by your letter congratulating me on the stand I have taken about Ulster day and I thank you most warmly for it. It was not every one who would have the insight that sympathy would be most welcome to me under the circumstances and it is not every one who would have taken the trouble to convey their sympathy. I was almost entirely alone here in the position I took up which was based on the belief that 'it is not by might nor power but by my spirit', the church of Christ can best face difficulties. Under such circumstances a man is sometimes brought to doubt his own convictions. I have received three or four other letters also which have confirmed me in thinking that I was right in not bending to the storm. I hope I may live down the bitterness that my action has caused but I am told that some will never forgive it but they are mostly of a class, or rather of an organisation, from which to differ is an honour. Again thanking you for your kind letter which I shall always treasure—I am, yours very sincerely, T. Arnold Harvey." The letter is written on paper brought evidently from his late rectory, Lisadell, Ballinful, Co. Sligo. ...

I think the Carsonite circus has not proved a success. Immense money spent on the crusade without much results of a permanent kind. *Punch* was exceedingly good on the business. Ridicule usually kills and I think "King Carson" will turn out a *"roi faineant"*. Is that the phrase, if not correct it ...'.

D.1792/A3/3/35   **Letter to W. S. Armour from Armour,**

17 October 1912   discussing his public dispute with the moderator,

Rev. Montgomery, and commenting on the future of both the Balkans and the Home Rule bill as well as on an attempt to assassinate President Theodore Roosevelt.

'... I am sending you the letter in answer to the moderator and his reply. The reply is so weak that I thought it better not to take any notice of it. He rides off on a mythical horse and never touches any point I raised. As a fairly convincing proof of its weakness as a reply, neither the [Belfast] *News-Letter* nor the [Northern] *Whig* published the correspondence—an outward sign that it was not thought a crushing retort. If either of these papers had given the correspondences I would have sent a few words as a finale as far as I was concerned. ...

The Balkan imbroglio, the Home Rule bill and now the attempt on Roosevelt's life by a demented Bavarian are the staples of public talk. I suspect the Balkan uprising will be more thought of in India than the other two—as these two will be regarded as comparitively parochial issues. The Musselmen of India will naturally be excited as it touches them in almost a vital point. The authorities in India may have some "[?] on their rock". I fancy that when the war is over it is not easy to see how it can be kept back—the reign of the Turk in Europe will be a mere nominal asset for the Caliphate. The Balkan states have been badly treated by the great powers of Europe as the reforms in government almost guaranteed by the treaty of Berlin are merely as yet on paper. No attempt has been made to compel the Turk to keep obligations. The sword may be a mightier weapon than the nibs which signed the treaty—to borrow a phrase which *Punch* applied to the Carson histrionics. I cannot say but that I hope—with Lloyd George who has been called over the coals by *The Times* and your ma—that the outcome of the struggle will lead to an enlargement of the liberties of oppressed nationalities. I am in favour of the bag and baggage policy.

'... The Home Rule bill will pass the h[ouse of] c[ommons] but whether it will become law depends on whether the government can weather two years. At any rate what is certain is that a Home Rule bill must become law at no very far off period. Perhaps this war may have something to do with its passing. If the empire was involved in the event, it might lead to possibilities which are not dreamed of as yet. ...

Max preaches in Sunderland on Sabbath and in Manchester on Nov. 3rd. I suspect he will get a call to some charge in England. Ireland is out of the question in the meantime as a field for the exercise of his gifts ... .'

D.1792/A3/3/36

Letter to W. S. Armour from Armour,

24 October 1912   discussing some reactions to the General Assembly's compromise of that year on the Home Rule issue and commenting on the progress of the Home Rule bill on its parliamentary circuit.

'... *The Witness* had a very nasty malicious article in last week on me and [Rev.] Hamilton of Lisburn in reference to our letters in the *Glasgow Herald* and *Scotsman* in answer to [Rev.] Montgomery. It more than insinuates that we both broke the code of honour in revealing what took place at the conference—a charge which had no justification as far as I am concerned as I told nothing farther than that my amendment was unanimously accepted by the conference, which fact was made public by the disappearance of the Sinclair paragraphs from the report. The article accuses me of lying as it asserts that my statement in the Assembly of the paragraph in the amended report as "a wise and honourable compact", which statement I said "was not mine, it came openly from the other side", was false as I was the man to make it for the first time. It was [Rev.] Prenter's phrase—somebody in the conference said a wise and honourable compromise to which Prenter replied, "no: a wise and honourable compact". Then the article quotes some sentences which he says I uttered but which I never uttered. *The Witness* is becoming the yellow press of the Presbyterian church. The article is certainly libellous but it is hardly worth bothering about. Let them roar and be as malicious as they can. ...

The Home Rule bill is proceeding: [J. H.] Campbell has got an amendment excluding Trinity College and Q[ueen's] U[niversity] B[elfast] from the control of the Irish parliament—a most foolish move on the part of the Tories as it may lead a Nationalist parliament to largely endow the Nat[ional] University. The *Irish Times* seems dead against the business. The bill would be in my judgement far better without any safe-guards which will do no good and only lead to constant friction and recriminations. ...'

D.1792/A3/3/37   **Letter to W. S. Armour from Armour,**

31 October 1912   discussing a two day meeting of the senate of the Queen's University of Belfast at which a rearrangement of the conditions for scholarships was agreed and the possibility of seeking additional money for scholarships from borough and county councils was urged by Armour. The letter also comments on the implications of J. H. Campbell's amendment to the Home Rule bill to exclude Queen's University, Belfast, and Trinity College, Dublin, from the jurisdiction of a Dublin government. Campbell, a Unionist, represented Dublin University at Westminster.

'... There is a good deal of searching of heart about T.C.D. and Q.U.B. over Campbell's amendment excluding T.C.D. and Q.U.B. from any interference on the part of the Home Rule government. It is a serious mistake; some of us wished to have a special senate for considering the matter and getting Campbell's amendment withdrawn. It requires ten members to sign for a special meeting of the senate but we could only get seven to append their names. The curious thing is that the Home Rule Catholics on the senate would not sign on the ground apparently that it might embarass Redmond who had assented to Campbell's amendment. I fancy the real reason is something like this. As the co[unty] councils and boroughs have made such a splendid contribution to the National University, they think that, supposing when convocation gets the power in Q.U.B. and puts every difficulty in the way of Catholic students attending Q.U.B.—as is likely to be the case--they may get a college in Belfast for themselves affiliated with the National University. That seems to me to be the real reason of their refusal to sign and therefore, though it may not be in my time, it is one of the probabilities of the future that there may be a pure and simple Catholic college in Belfast. The Ulster people are preparing a stiff rod for their own back ... .'

D.1792/A3/3/38   **Part of a letter to W. S. Armour from Armour,**

7 November 1912   entirely devoted to family and local news.

D.1792/A3/3/39   **Letter to W. S. Armour from Armour, [written from Belfast],**

28 November 1912   reporting a meeting of the Queen's University senate and discussing some family business matters. The senate meeting had been a special one, called to discuss the Campbell amendment to the Home Rule bill.

'The senate meeting is over and [S. R.] Keightley's motion which I seconded was rejected by fifteen to nine. It was an entirely political vote. The Tories were whipped up for the occasion. They are hopeless and the result will likely be that if and when Home Rule comes—and come it will in some form there will be a social, religious boycott of the university and almost certain a college opened in Belfast for the Catholics in connection with the National University. They are as blind as a bat ... .'

D.1792/A3/3/40   **Letter to W. S. Armour from Armour,**

[n.d. December ? 1912]   largely devoted to family and local news, along with some retrospective comments on the decisions of the Queen's University senate and their implications for the university's future. He blames these decisions on the visionless Tories.

D.1792/A3/3/41   **Letter to W. S. Armour from Armour,**

11 December 1912   containing Campbell College gossip and a report of a meeting of the Co. Antrim insurance committee, of which Armour was of course a member, along with the usual local news.

D.1792/A3/3/42   **Letter to W. S. Armour from Armour,**

19 December 1912   which includes a brief critical comment on Bonar Law's political capabilities and the news that Max Armour is to receive a call to a congregation in South Shields.

'... Bonar Law seems an impossible leader and B[onar] L[aw] M[ust] G[o] will be the watch-word of the Tories as B[alfour] M[ust] G[o] got rid of Balfour, an infinitely superior man. B.L.'s policy seems impossible. He wants brains, though he has the gift of a kind of gab which pleases the Tory gallery or pit, or both, but the saner part of the party is shaking the head ominously ... .'

D.1792/A3/3/43   **Letter to W. S. Armour from Armour,**

25 December 1912   confirming that Max Armour is to go to South Shields and commenting on the withdrawal of the Campbell amendment to the Home Rule bill, in respect of Trinity College, Dublin.

'... The vote of the nine against the fifteen has carried the day after all. There will be tears in secret but the tears I fancy are tears of joy that they have been beaten ... .'

D.1792/A3/4/1-42

1913

Originals of letters from Rev. J. B. Armour to his wife and sons (principally to W. S. Armour).

D.1792/A3/4/1

[n.d. 1913 ?]

Part of a letter to Mrs Armour from Armour,

describing a visit to Dublin in his capacity as chaplain to Lord and Lady Aberdeen. He repeats a variety of court gossip which he has heard and recounts a conversation with Lord Pirrie and Sir Charles Brett about Alec Wilson and his speech to the anti-Carson rally in Ballymoney in October 1913.

'... I had with Sir Cha[rle]s Brett a talk with Lord P[irrie] about Alec Wilson. It appears he might have turned out a genius at ship-building if he had stuck to Harland and Wolff but Lord P[irrie] added that he had failed in an examination, I think for the Royal Engineers, and the failure had taken the spunk out of him. We—Brett and I—praised Alec's speech at Ballymoney and held that he had the elements of a successful speaker in him. He—Alec—is to give an address to-morrow somewhere in Dublin. I may go to hear him. ...'

D.1792/A3/4/2

1 January 1913

Letter to W. S. Armour from Armour,

arguing that although the Home Rule bill is likely to pass the house of commons, along with the bill to disestablish the Anglican church in Wales, their rejection by the house of lords is likely to damage the Unionist party in Britain. He suggests that some of the Unionists in Ireland are beginning to consider compromise. He also confirms that Max Armour's call to South Shields is now certain and comments on the surrender of the British Medical Association over the Liberal national insurance legislation.

'... You will find in the *M[anchester] G[uardian]* all that one can say on the political situation and on the collapse of the B[ritish] M[edical] A[ssociation] over the insurance act. It is literally apparent now that Lloyd George has got the victory and will be able to have his act in operation when this note reaches you. It is a hard nut to crack and one would need to get up early to get on the lee side of the Welshman. The real political situation seems to be that everybody has made up his mind that the Home Rule bill and Welsh disestablishment will pass at least the h[ouse of] c[ommons]. If the lords throw out both, it will not be good for the Tory party which is honeycombed with dissension already. It is beginning to dawn on the responsible Irish Unionists that their game of bluff is nearing its end. It is reported that Lord Londonderry was sent over to advise the Ulsterites to accept some compromise and that Carson is even getting doubtful about the idea of civil war. [Rev.] Wright of Newtownards is reported to have said to Lord Londonderry that he was a traitor to propose such a thing and of the race of traitors—a snapshot of his character which however containing the elements of truth could not have been pleasant for aristocratic ears to hear. Other strong speeches were said to have been delivered but perhaps the report is the effort of imagination. It seems true however that things even in Belfast are not as they were months ago. ...'

D.1792/A3/4/3

9 January 1913

Letter to W. S. Armour from Armour,

commenting on the death of the duke of Abercorn and on David Hogg's chances as the Liberal candidate in the impending Londonderrry City by-election, caused by the sitting Unionist member, the marquis of Hamilton, succeeding to the title of duke of Abercorn.

'... The duke of Abercorn, the author of the snatch "we will never have Home Rule", is gone and the Unionists are in mourning. Presonally he was very kindly and the sorrow for him about Newtownstewart is real but the race of which he was the big man was never very reliable as the members of the family always liked to play with both ends of the stick. Disraeli poked fun at him in his own way in "Lothair". Disraeli had no particular love at heart for the so-called aristocracy. I see that our friend—Mr Hogg— is likely to be run for Derry. If Marshal Tillie carries out his threat to stand as an independent Unionist, Hogg will go in in all probability. Independent of Tillie his chances are by no means bad. If he gets in there will be fewer bulky men in the h[ouse of] c[ommons] than he. It took me some trouble to get him to consent to be in the running for the h[is] m[ajesty's] l[ieutenancy] but having tasted the [?] of honour like Caesar he has become ambitious. The Professor [MacMaster] will not be allowed to vote for him unless he does it on the sly which is hardly likely as he is a man under authority. The males of the MacMaster house are not of the heroic build of the females of that paternity. If Hogg asks him to vote for him, he will clear his throat several times before saying "no" in a whisper. Would that I were stronger, I would be in the fray. You have the *M[anchester] G[uardian]*'s ideas on politics, insurance, Welsh disestablishment and therefore it is not necessary to add anything to what you find written there. One thing is certain, the doctors have been beaten and now as this has dawned on them a few are indulging in Billingsgate about the "wee Welshman" who must be greatly amused at their feckless wrath. They have not the grace to take a beating like men … .

I see from the [*Northern*] *Whig* this morning that Tillie has withdrawn from the contest in Derry and has promised to put his motor at the disposal of [Lt. Col.] Pakenham [the Unionist candidate]. This is very much what expected [*sic*]. Tillie is a lath painted so as to look like iron but he is only "a bourtrey" piece of wood. He is a drinking man and therefore is not to be depended on. It is as well as it will be a contest direct between the two parties. Hogg may not get the full Catholic vote as the priests were for another Shane Leslie [Leslie had unsuccessfully contested the Londonderry City seat in January and December 1910 as a Nationalist, whereas Hogg was standing as a Liberal]. …'

D.1792/A3/4/4   **Part of a letter to W. S. Armour from Armour,**

15 January 1913   discussing the opening of David Hogg's Londonderry City by-election campaign, as well as various family matters.

'… The only excitement will be the Derry election which formally opened last night by the appearance of David Hogg, H.M.L., on a public platform. Ure, the Scotch solicitor-general, if that is the right official title, and Mr Redmond, Shane Leslie and others spoke. I sent good wishes. If I can get a copy of the *Irish News*, you will have an account of the speechification. If you have time, be sure to read the solicitor-general, [Sir John] Simon, on tariff reform. It is like all his speeches, very, very able—a knockdown kind of utterance. …'

D.1792/A3/4/5   **Letter to W. S. Armour from Armour,**

22 January 1913   commenting on S. C. McElroy, the veteran editor of the *Ballymoney Free Press*, especially on his attitude towards Home Rule, and on the possible outcome of the Londonderry City by-election. He also considers the possible repercussions, especially in Ulster, if the house of lords compromises on the Home Rule bill.

'… S. C. McElroy owing to the Flint election is ready as a plenipotentiary to compromise on Home Rule. He speaks as if he was the right-hand man of Bonar Law and Lord Lansdowne. He would like to be a mediator. The Flint election has been a sore disappointment to the Tories who fought it on the Welsh bill and bishops and clerics did their best to represent the bill as a robbery of God and an insult to religion. The plural votes were there to the last man … .

The Derry election is an uncertain quantity as it is practically a toss up which side will win. H.M.L. [David Hogg] has a chance from all one hears. It is to take place next week. I refused to go to the Protestant protest meeting to be held in Dublin on the 24th. It is too far off for me, not to mention the fact that a political speech would take too much out of me ... .

The insurance act has well nigh ceased to be a factor in elections. It and Home Rule were hardly ever mentioned in Flintshire. Of course H[ome] R[ule] is the stock in trade in Derry. Nothing else is talked about. What if the lords come to terms over it? They may perhaps in June when it comes up a second time. What the Ulsterites will do then in such a case it would be hard to say. The reason for rebellion would disappear. We will wait and see... .'

D.1792/A3/4/6	**Letter to W. S. Armour from Armour,**

30 January 1913 indicating S. C. McElroy's return to the Unionist orthodoxy which he (McElroy) had espoused since 1906, commenting critically on the militant activities of the suffragettes and expressing some optimism about David Hogg's chances of success in the Londonderry City by-election.

'... You will see [in the *Ballymoney Free Press*] that S. C. McElroy has this week become thoroughly orthodox again. He was heterodox in the *F[ree] P[ress]* last week with the result that the [*Coleraine*] *Chronicle* refused to print in Saturday's issue what he had written for the B[ally]money audience. Your ma had a presentment that the *Chronicle* would give his article the go-by—which was the fact. He has learned this week not to stray into radical doctrines and therefore he will be received back into the fold ... .

One is sorry to note that Lord Hardinge [viceroy of India] is not recovering rapidly from his wounds. There may be some piece of lead or iron lodged in the [?]. In today's paper there is a paragraph stating the police is on the track of the rapscallions who are supposed to be Brahmins. A [?] of the kind is not to be wondered at when we read of the threats of the mad women of England who are resolved to stop at no crime in the furtherance of their purpose. They will get a keel-hauling or I am mistaken which will ruin their cause. All parties of the male sex are fairly satisfied with the withdrawal of the franchise bill. You may expect to hear of dastardly deeds, if not on the line of the attack on Lord Hardinge, at least a cousin germane thereto. Much as one might sympathise with a moderate measure for their relief, it must be said that to attack the males who have never concealed their agreement with the greater part of their programme smells of the devil ... .

It is generally believed that [David] Hogg will get in for Derry. At any rate from all accounts the Unionists are not only not confident but are almost in the Slough of Despond. In their meeting in the Guild Hall on Monday night the undertone of the speeches did not indicate hope of victory. However, there is no use in shouting until the ball touches the goal. The poll will not be declared until Friday. It is not usual to declare the poll in Derry on the evening of an election as the inflammable material is very abundant there on both sides. There may be a row on Friday night, no matter which candidate heads the poll. The wags about Derry say, "The Jews cannot vote for either as the one is a Packen*ham* and the other is a Hoggi" ... . The Jews are not numerous in that quarter, though Lazarus has a fine house. I suspect the joke will not have much effect. Hoggi certainly cannot speak but he can vote which is the main thing from the Nationalist point of view. He will do quite as well as an orator, of which class the h[ouse of] c[ommons] is not in much need. The talkers are a numerous tribe and silence is golden. If Hoggi gets in, the Unionists of the three kingdoms will be in a state of consternation as Ulster will have more Home Rule members than Unionists. It is said that [Rev.] McGranahan has lost some families because Hoggi is a worshipper there. That is the measure of toleration some folks are inclined to give, though as McGranahan has always been a Unionist it is not clear why he deserves punishment because Hoggi is a worshipper ... .

You will be able to read Asquith's speech at Leven. He is an extraordinary man—could give

Bonar Law without hurting himself as much brains as would make Bonar a passable statesman. The [*Northern*] *Whig* this morning is pretty confident about retaining Derry city. I am not over confident about Hoggi. One cannot tell what unknown factors may turn up at the last moment. The constituency is peculiar. The Tories have annoyed several of their former supporters. They cannot keep from blundering ... .'

D.1792/A3/4/7   **Letter to W. S. Armour from Armour,**

12 February 1913   analysing the intolerance of Protestant Unionists towards the minority of Protestants, such as himself, who sympathise with Home Rule.

'... The intolerance of those who have seized on the tiller of the church is almost unbelievable. If Home Rule, when it comes, manifests the same spirit towards the Protestants that the majority of the Protestants is doing to those who differ from them, well the Protestants will have no rational ground of complaint as that would only be following the example set them by the Protestants generally. [Rev.] Bain of Westport *eg.* was asked by T. G. Smith to address a prayer meeting last night and consented but the elders met and refused to let him come because he had written a letter to the Protestant Home Rule meeting [held in Dublin on 24 January 1913]. Writing a letter of this kind was a sign of leprosy which excludes from the camp of Israel. The same thing occurred with myself. A meeting in the interests of the Sustentation Fund was being organised in Ballymena. [Rev.] Mitchell of Broughshane, who was getting up the gathering, wrote me as being the convener of the fund for the synod to see if I would go and speak at the meeting. Though it was inconvenient and though I was on the point of refusing, fortunately I replied in the affirmative. The presbytery met and decided that under no circumstances should I be allowed to be present or speak. Mitchell had to write me. It was the most mysterious letter I ever got. I smelled that there was something up and I heard afterwards what had occurred at the presbytery. More than half of the so-called Unionists never gave a fraction to the fund. They damned it from the first. If my absence from the meeting of "the saints" was [*word missing*] to the success of the business, I will rejoice even at their intolerance. [Rev.] McClurg of Ardstraw ... has been boycotted to such an extent by his congregation that he has made up his mind to emigrate to Canada. He told me yesterday that though he could beat the rapscallions of his congregation, yet, as future advancement in the church here would be impossible, he thought it wise to give up the fight... .'

D.1792/A3/4/8   **Letter to W. S. Armour from Armour,**

26 February 1913   entirely devoted to family news and an account of a meeting of the Queen's University senate, held to discuss the establishment of a part-time diploma in commerce to be taught in the evenings.

D.1792/A3/4/9   **Letter to W. S. Armour from Armour,**

[n.d. February/March ? 1913]   critically discussing various tributes to Armour's one-time close friend, John Megaw of Ballyboyland, Ballymoney, Co. Antrim, who had just died, and anticipating a further trip to Belfast to attend a meeting of the General Assembly Committee in Correspondence with Government to appoint a Presbyterian chaplain to the army.

D.1792/A3/4/10   **Letter to W. S. Armour from Armour,**

[n.d. March ? 1913]   containing family and local news only.

D.1792/A3/4/11

Letter to W. S. Armour from Armour,

12 March 1913

entirely devoted to local and family gossip, apart from some discussion of the possible candidates for a vacant deputy lieutenancy in Co. Londonderry.

D.1792/A3/4/12

Letter to W. S. Armour from Armour,

[n.d. 18 March 1913 ?]

written on the occasion of his thirtieth wedding anniversary and commenting on the success of his marriage which had ironically taken place in a 'public house', the Imperial Hotel, Belfast. He also discusses a by-election result in Westmoreland and its possible political consequences.

'... You will have heard by this time of the triumph of [Weston ?] in Westmoreland, though he has been driven out of the Tory church with book and bell. I never before rejoiced in the success of a Conservative but I was inclined—perhaps mischief was the motive—to throw up my cap. Misfortune dogs the steps of Bonar Law and what he will do now, it is hard to predict. As [J. L.] Garvin says the dry rot has set in in the party. *The Times* will likely rejoice as one can see tariff reform is not a plank in its platform. I think the election will be the death knell of the Chamberlain propaganda. It will be interesting to read the Tory papers in the morning, some of the editors will gnash their teeth and many will silently rejoice that Joseph is getting a back seat in the synagogue. It will have its effect on the house of lords as it will show the members that if an election was to take place tomorrow the chances of a return of the Tories would be [scrimpit ?] ... .'

D.1792/A3/4/13

Letter to W. S. Armour from Armour,

27 March 1913

further discussing the lack of toleration currently characteristic of the majority of Presbyterians in Ulster, as well as recounting in detail a local evangelical meeting addressed by 'a fanatical Yankee Covenanter'.

'... I hear [Rev.] McNeill of Adelaide Road [Church, Dublin] is likely to get and accept a call to Birkenhead as successor to the Rev. Wm. Watson. The stipend promised is £1,000 a year. The Adelaide Road folks have hardly played the game with him fairly. He filled the church which required enlargement through his personality but they never gave him the whole of the seat rents which was mean, spending part thereof in improvements which became necessary through his power as a preacher and popular gifts. It is an illustration of the persecution to which any man who shows independence of judgement is subjected to in these days. Because he dared to differ politically with the bosses of the church, he would not get a hearing in any church in Belfast. His name was spurned in Duncairn [Belfast] and though he is undoubtedly the ablest of our preachers, some screeching Unionist with as much brains as a chattering sparrow would have polled him out of any congregation with a decent stipend. The Presbyterianism of the north of Ireland will soon hardly be worth preserving as any body who dares think for himself is sure to get the run. I am truly sorry that McNeill should go but I expect he must ... .'

D.1792/A3/4/14

Letter to W. S. Armour from Armour, [to be sent with a covering note via Jane MacMaster] ,

1/2 April 1913

describing a successful church bazaar and anticipating a trip to Belfast to attend a General Assembly meeting to discuss the 'rearrangement of the theological professors' of the Presbyterian church.

G

D.1792/A3/4/15   **Letter to W. S. Armour from Armour,**

9 April 1913   discussing a forthcoming meeting of the Queen's University senate at which revised arrangements for matriculation will be discussed, but possibly will not be passed, due to the absence of Armour and Sir Charles Brett at a viceroy's *levee* in Dublin. There is also some further comment on Max Armour's enforced English exile.

D.1792/A3/4/16   **Letter to W. S. Armour from Armour, [written from Portrush] ,**

26 June 1913   retailing some Portrush gossip, including the fact of the rector's continuing unpopularity with his congregation [*see D.1792/A3/3/32*] , and indicating the possibility of the Independent Orange Order holding another service in Trinity Church, Ballymoney, for which he will have to provide the basic outlines of the sermon.

'... Life has become very drab since the [General] Assembly and one is not up to politics or ecclesiastic issues at the end of June. The Independent Orangemen wish for a service in Trinity Church on the 6 July—Sabbath week and a deputation has come to me to secure them a preacher which will be difficult as the time is short. I may have to fall back on [Rev.] Heney [of Mossside, Co. Antrim] who has spoken to them on two occasions I think. If he comes, he will expect me to sketch him the heads of a discourse which will be difficult as I have written two already for the brethren. It is hard to polish off a third on the same subject ... .'

D.1792/A3/4/17   **Letter to W. S. Armour from Armour,**

3 July 1913   discussing the folklore of Co. Antrim as well as recounting the usual local and family news.

D.1792/A3/4/18   **Letter to W. S. Armour from Armour,**

10 July 1913   reporting a meeting of the Queen's University senate and discussing local political developments. The senate meeting had again been largely concerned with the problem of matriculation.

'... [Rev.] Heney preached to the Orangemen very acceptably [at the service for the Independent Orange Order held in Armour's church] . Saturday will be a day of tremendous excitement but perhaps it will pass off only with the escape of some bad gas ... .'

D.1792/A3/4/19   **Letter to [J. B. M. Armour ?] from Armour,**

14 July 1913   containing birthday greetings, family and local news, as well as some comments on a meeting of the Queen's University senate.

D.1792/A3/4/20   **Letter to W. S. Armour from Armour,**

23 July 1913   discussing a meeting of the Queen's University senate held to elect a new professor of metaphysics and commenting critically on Sir Edward Carson's anti-Home Rule campaign.

'... Carson's speeches and programme seem to be those of a lunatic or fanatic. The whole thing is becoming hollow and is bound to become a fiasco ... .'

D.1792/A3/4/21   **Letter to W. S. Armour from Armour,**

30 July 1913   recounting an experience during his student days at Queen's College, Cork, where an attempt had been made to convert him from Presbyterianism to Anglicanism. He also makes the claim that even Sir Edward Carson realises that Home Rule is inevitable.

'... When at college in Cork a lady of position tried me up and down to enter what was then the established church and offered to get for me the interest of the bishop of Cork and some other social personages. I refused but ... if I had listened to the siren I might have been by this time at least like [Rev.] Benson [Anglican minister in Ballymoney] a chancellor. In that case I might not have met the Canadian [Mrs Armour] and perhaps might have developed into a henchman of Edward Carson ... .

Unless some catastrophe occurs Home Rule will come. Carson even thinks so. His meeting in Ballymena was not marked by enthusiasm either by the audience or the speakers ... .'

D.1792/A3/4/22   **Letters to W. S. Armour from Armour, [written from Crieff, Perthshire, Scotland],**

28 August 1913
                                    containing an account of holiday experiences.

D.1792/A3/4/23   **Letter to W. S. Armour from Armour,**

4 September 1913   describing the last days of the Scottish holiday and the journey home; commenting also on the labour dispute in Dublin.

'... These riots in Dublin are giving the powers that be much anxiety. The police are blamed, being regarded as acting cruelly and as men will do when frightened. But I suspect there may be another side to the question. The *M[anchester] G[uardian]* and *D[aily] N[ews]* are rubbing in the idea that Carsonism has given the cue to [Jim] Larkin as he is bettering the instructions, being an apt pupil in anarchic strategy. Sir J[ames] B[rown] D[ougherty] will be at his wit's end, having been cast for no fault of his own on a bed of thistles ... .'

D.1792/A3/4/24   **Letter to W. S. Armour from Armour,**

[n.d. September ? 1913]   partly devoted to an account of a meeting of the Co. Antrim insurance committee, of which Armour was a member, but also commenting on Carsonism, 'Murphyism' and 'Larkinism'.

'... Carson and his merry men are back in Ireland. The *N[orthern] W[hig]* is choke full this morning of his speeches and his actions as commander-in-chief of the reactionaries. The business is larger in bulk than in reality. It is a compound of bluff and bunkum—a stage performance and though it may mean trouble in the future, being sound and fury it signifieth very little if anything. It will delude the silly. The saner part of the Unionists do not like his antics as they see the question has to be settled and Carson takes the position of the Pope with his *non-possumus* which never does any good as such an attitude is of a bedlamite colour. No good comes out of Bedlam ... .

The Dublin snarl shows very little sign of settlement. Murphyism and Larkinism are in death throes and which will become victors in the wrestle is not apparent. The public is suffering at any rate. It is difficult to say on which side one's smypathy should lie. Like Disraeli one would like to be on the side of the angels, but I fear the angels at least of light have little to do with the quarrel, though angels who belong to Satan's side of the house seem to be numerous on each side. Dougherty will be at his wit's end for of course the Castle people will come in for hard words from both sides. Hard words, it is true, break no bones but our friend is at bottom very sensitive and at his time of life, he will feel the strain much ... .'

D.1792/A3/4/25

[n.d. September ? 1913]

Letter to Mrs Jennie Armour from Armour, [written from the viceregal lodge, Dublin],

describing a trip to Dublin, his conversations with the Aberdeens and a visit which he had made with Lady Aberdeen to the new sanitorium being built at her instigation at Peamount. Also at her suggestion, he had met with the insurance commissioners to discuss the problems of the Co. Antrim insurance committee.

'... I had a long crack with his exc[ellency] over this Larkin business which has given him much annoyance especially as the *Aberdeen Free Press* published Larkin's side of the story and so also the correspondent of *The Times* repeated in a virulent tone the same story. He is very much hurt. It appears the king read the story in *The Times* and wrote to his exc[ellency] for an explanation of the business. It must have been a bitter pill for his exc[ellency] to write such a letter in his own defence. It appears the correspondent's wife had asked to be presented at the Drawing Room last year but those in the office ignored her request—hence this man has his knife in the Aberdeens. I quoted to him Hamlet, "you may be as chaste as ice and as pure as the snow but you will not escape calumny" and other tags which he repeated to her exc[ellency] ... .'

D.1792/A3/4/26

[n.d. 19 September 1913 ?]

Letter to W. S. Armour from Armour,

commenting further on the significance for the future of the Dublin lock-out and describing a visit by Captain Jack White, who was anxious to promote a meeting in Ballymoney of Protestants opposed to Carson.

'... The Dublin strike has given and is giving the authorities at the Castle no end of trouble. Mistakes in tactics have been made. It is a pure genuine fight between labour and capital. The religious question has not a look in in this quarrel. It is a kind of foreword for the future that the question before an Irish Parliament will not be Catholicism versus Protestantism—but labour against capital with a by-play, clericalism versus anti-clericalism ... .

Captain White, son of the late Field-Marshal Sir George White, was here on Monday evening to see if a meeting could be got up against the Carson policy. I have not heard what was done as Dr Taggart [the North Antrim Liberal electoral organiser] did not seem anxious for me to be present, though on what grounds I cannot say, as the captain is anxious to enlist a number of Protestants who may not be ardent home rulers but who are opposed to Carson's histrionics. I saw Captain White. He is strong for Home Rule and has been in communication with Lord Dunraven, though whether he is a Dunravenite pure and simple or not, I could not say. There was talk of holding the meeting immediately after Carson had discharged the last of his wooden guns in Ulster. His concluding play is to terminate during this month ... .'

D.1792/A3/4/27

[n.d. September ? 1913]

Letter to W. S. Armour from Armour, [*page torn*],

almost entirely devoted to reporting the planning of the proposed anti-Carson Protestant meeting to be held in Ballymoney. There is also criticism of Carson's proposal to set up a provisional government in Ulster if Home Rule is implemented.

'... Sir Roger Casement, the consul who exposed the atrocities of the slavery sanctioned by the late king of Belgium, who was a crowned villain worse than Pharaoh, [and there ?] the worse state of slavery in the rubber fields of Putumayo, had written to suggest a meeting here to attack the policy of Carson. Captain White, the son of the celebrated Field-Marshal Sir George White, had been down the week before on the same errand and interviewed a few on the feasibility of the project. He had gone away satisfied that a meeting was possible. I told you that I had written Sir Roger suggesting the lines on which the resolutions should be drawn. He had suggested that Lord Ashbourne, the head of the Gaelic leaguers and a Protestant who had turned Catholic, should be asked—a proposal that I vetoed quietly by saying that no Catholic should be asked to take part as a speaker. Sir Roger, wishing to survey the situation on the spot, wrote on Monday morning that he proposed to come here on Tuesday. We sent, that is the authorities and I, word to say come by the 12.25 from Belfast and lunch here on arrival. He came and after lunch we went to the Minor Hall where some fifteen of the stalwarts were gathered and I explained the object of the meeting, putting the points—Was a decent meeting a feasible business in Ballymoney? This was answered by a unanimous "yes". Then who were to be the speakers and some six names were mentioned—Captain White, Mrs Green, wife of the historian, Captain Crosbie, Mrs Finnemore—I think that is the name—and George Birmingham. These were to be asked, though it was not likely or even desirable that all should respond with "a yes". Then two resolutions were proposed and accepted as a basis. The question of who was to be chairman was held over. My opinion was that Sir Roger should be the man but he had refused when I put it to him in the manse and by his refusal there hangs a tale which reveals human weakness [*words missing*] not jealousy, in a peculiar fashion. [*page torn, further words missing—missing section appears to refer to Casement's description of a quarrel between Casement and Captain White about who should chair the meeting and about suggested speakers associated with the Gaelic League*] ... he opened on Sir Roger, accused him of every kind of crime winding up with the charge that he was not an *honest* man. There was a casting of the creels there and then. Sir Roger told me that and bound me over to secrecy. This may be the rift within [the lute ?] . Sir Roger's explanation of the matter is that there is a slate off. Certainly White is peculiar. I advised Taggart last night to write White to tell what had been done, to give a list of the speakers to be asked and the resolutions to be proposed or an outline of them. As he is to be in the forefront of the orators and as there is no mention of a chairman, perhaps the wrath of Achilles may be soothed. I am anxious to hear what he says. He wrote a letter on the subject of Carsonism which appeared in the [*Manchester*] *Guardian* and the *Irish News* on Friday. If I can lay hands on it, you will have it. It is not a bad letter but reading between the lines it is clear that he is not so enthusiastic over his project as he was when he was here.

Carson's provisional government is about as fantastic a piece of business ever put forward by a sane man. It lacks statesmanship and no sane Unionist could swallow it. Sir Roger told me, or rather read me, part of a letter from Sir Horace Plunkett in which he does not mince matters *in re* his opinion of Carsonism. Sir Horace is on the verge of kicking the traces and states that a change in Irish government must take place. I think the possibilities of a conference say about April are real but the proposal must come from the Tories. Much private talk is indulged in because no letter was read by Carson coming from Bonar Law or Lord Lansdowne. There may have been, it is surmised, but it was thought wise to keep such a letter in the locket. It is thought that part of Carson's speech was a threat to Bonar Law to keep him in the way Carson would have him go. Things are humming and will hum for a little but Carsonism is a *brutum fulmen* ... .'

D.1792/A3/4/28   **Part of a letter to W. S. Armour from Armour,**

[n.d. 9 October 1913 ?]   describing the continuing preparations for the anti-Carson rally to be held in Ballymoney on 24 October, including a further meeting with Captain White to discuss the wording of the resolutions and Armour's attempts to persuade John Baxter, a businessman and county councillor, to act as chairman. Local and provincial Unionist reaction is analysed.

'... The week has had its quiet excitements. The meeting is in progress for the 24th. There is to be a gathering tomorrow of the people from the country to see the part they are to take therein. Captain White called here on Saturday evening; his motor with his wife therein—a handsome woman a Spaniard it is said—stopped at the gate. She came in afterwards and talked to your mother. I found the captain in a civil mood—soothed him down by telling him that he was to have the chief place in the speaking as he would be called on first. He demurred at first but gave in. He did not say a word indicating that he had fallen foul of Sir Roger. There was a difficulty about the second resolution but finally he left the matter in the hands of the committee. He started about 8 o'clock but before he had gone a mile his motor punctured and he had to return to get it set right. His wife seemed to think the puncture was not of good omen. Sir Roger did not approve of my substitute of his second resolution and wrote out another which though a trifle vague the committee accepted. I have written him this evening to say that he has managed to get round the corner successfully. He has sent me the Blue Book containing his report on the Putumayo atrocities and a bulky kind of volume in a way but he has indicated the parts I am to read. There is a hitch about who is to be chairman of the gathering. I was requested to speak to John Baxter which I did on Monday night. He practically refused then, putting forth the difficulty that his chief man and R. C. Martin being shareholders in the concern would be offended. He was to give me his answer next day. He came down last night when I was out but waited my return. We talked over the business for an hour, every [particular ?] of which interested him. Finally I was to get him a copy of the resolutions which I did and gave them to him with a copy of the *Westminster Gazette* containing an able letter giving Lord Halsbury's idea of what constitutes high treason—which idea clearly points to Carson as guilty of treason; then there was a letter from Sir Roger on the state of Ulster feeling in regard to Carsonism. Baxter has given no sign as yet. He would like to be in the chair but he is very timid. That is the state of matters. Some of the mad-heads here have been trying tentatively to get the commissioners to refuse the Town Hall for the gathering. Cochrane I hear, not John, but the old furniture man, went to Robert Patterson, a town commissioner—on the subject but Patterson, it is said, bade him go uncomfortable quarters. The Tories are getting a trifle alarmed and there may be trouble, though I think it will hardly be serious. Baxter seemed to think that Captain White had some ulterior motive in the matter, to which I said—supposing he wants to contest this constituency the next time, should we not rejoice that somebody would give Kerr-Smiley a run for his money; his (Baxter's) objection then vanished. Capt. White thinks of organising a meeting in the Ulster Hall but I said to him—perhaps you had better see first that you could get the Ulster Hall; that had not occurred to him. He would hardly succeed in getting it after its refusal to Churchill. That Carsonism is not really popular outside the ranks of the Orange Lodges is true and that his provisional government is the most outlandish proposal ever made by a sane man is also true but the terror is so great that sane men prefer to sit silent and say nothing. The right of free speech does not exist in Ulster at present ... .'

D.1792/A3/4/29   **Letter to W. S. Armour from Armour,**

16 October 1913   containing church and Queen's University senate news
                                      and further details of threatened Unionist counter-measures against the anti-Carson meeting of 24 October. Armour reveals that he is putting pressure on his friend, Sir James Dougherty, to ensure adequate police protection.

'... I told you of the meeting on the 24th to protest against the lawless policy of Carsonism. The Tories here are in a state bordering on political insanity as they have a project in hand to summon from Coleraine and elsewhere a band of Orange rowdies with drums to drown the speakers or it may be to rush the hall the night before and keep it against all comers. They are furious and they talk of civil and religious liberty but they deny the right to everybody to think for himself if he dares to think differently from them. However, we will see. I have written to Dougherty quickly today to tell him to instruct the Co. Inspector to come down here and to tell him that the authorities will send down as many police as will make the rapscallions ineffective. I have advised him to instruct Morrison [the Co. Antrim R.I.C. inspector] to have a cordon of police above and below the hall and that nobody is to be allowed to pass from above or below the cordon without producing a ticket of admission to the hall. This was done for Asquith's meeting in Dublin with effect and ought to be done here. I also told him to tell the chairman of the town commissioners that the town would have to pay for the extra police. This will appeal with [more] force to [R. D.] Megaw than any possible argument. I have told Sir J. B. D. that the government is bound not only as a matter of safety but of policy to protect a meeting which has a right to be held and that if the meeting is protected and gets the liberty to discuss a pertinent question, it will encourage other places and will put a hole in Carson's drum. I shall hear how the advice is taken. Birrell is in Dublin or was yesterday. You know all I know now. I have not told to anybody save one which I have done. I wrote *sub rosa*. I think he will attend to it. He will, I fancy, speak very plainly to Morrison and to Davies [the Ballymoney police commander] here—both are worth watching but [*sic*] a little plain speaking ... .'

D.1792/A3/4/30   **Letter to W. S. Armour from Armour,**

22 October 1913   discussing a trip to Belfast to attend a tuberculosis meeting and a visit from the police to review the security provisions for the Ballymoney meeting of 24 October.

'... I told you that I had written J[ames] B[rown] D[ougherty] to say that threats were freely blowing that the followers of the pious and immortal memory have made up their minds to prevent the meeting by taking possession of the hall or by having drums in front to drown the voices of the speakers and that the government should instruct Morrison Co. Insp. to have a posse of police to guard the meeting and allow the right of free speech. Morrison and Davies appeared here on Saturday to talk to me first. I told them that there ought to be a cordon of police above the hall and one at the entrance to Townhead St[reet] and that nobody should be allowed within that space but those who had tickets. "Oh they could not do that." That is nonsense was my reply. At Asquith's meeting in Dublin there was a force of police and nobody was allowed near the hall but ticket holders. That bowled them over. Then I said nobody should be permitted to enter the Orange Hall opposite the Town Hall, as drumming there would disturb the meeting. "Oh they could not prevent people from entering their own hall." "Very well, you are sent to keep the peace and prevent rioting—suppose they insist on drumming and fifty people from the Town Hall go across and maul them, there will be a serious riot and where will you be?" This let a little light into their skulls tarred with political prejudice. Then how many police will be necessary? I said fifty at the outside. Morrison said 100. Davies thought none would be necessary. I hear he has ordered seventy. The fire-eaters have collapsed and now they say there will be no attempt from their side to disturb the gathering. The threat that the meeting would be protected has made them as meek as lambs. Of course they are ready to welcome what they could not prevent. Human nature is a curious study. Nearly 500 tickets are out already. There is a difficulty about a chairman. [R. G.] Glendinning [former member for North Antrim at Westminster] who was expected to preside is not back from the continent and will not be in time. It is said [R. C.] Martin [a local solicitor and Unionist leader] has closed up his house and is off somewhere until the row is over. It is like him—he is a piece of wood painted to look like iron ... .'

D.1792/A3/4/31   **Part of a letter to W. S. Armour from Armour,**

27 October 1913   discussing the organization of the anti-Carson meeting in Ballymoney Town Hall and criticising Dr Thomas Taggart, a leading Liberal in Ballymoney and North Antrim (he had acted as the Liberal election agent in the general elections of 1906 and 1910). The letter is evidence of the jealousy and animosity which existed between J. B. Armour and the Liberal 'establishment' in North Antrim, which may have been a factor in keeping Armour out of active participation in local politics at this time.

'... Friday night was got over quietly: the audience was fair and there was no want of enthusiasm:

the speaking was excellent. The arrangements for the gathering were perfect. Jas. Hanna did the lion's share of the work and though he will not get the credit, he thoroughly deserves it as whatever frailties [Dr Thomas] Taggart has, he is lamentably lacking in good management. A few on the committee made up their minds to prevent him from making a [?] of the thing. The question of the chairman was difficult. When it was expected Glendinning would be present, it was easy to select him as chairman but when he could not come the fat was in the fire. Taggart was strong for W[illia]m McAfee [*sic*] [unsuccessful Liberal candidate for North Antrim in December 1910]. I secretly put the veto on that by suggesting that if there was to be a McAfee [*sic*], his father was preferable to the son, as said son had given annoyance by attending the Redmond meeting on a Sunday and speaking. I was not particularly anxious for the father but by proposing the father, we got rid of the son. The real facts are Taggart was very anxious to be chairman himself and the majority of the committee were just as anxious that he should not be. John McElderry was chosen at last and he fully deserved the honour as he behaved as an ideal chairman. The meeting was not disturbed as a sufficient force of police was here, there and everywhere. The Unionists here are like innocent lambs saying there was no need of an extra constable as they were ready to receive and [?] the meeting. R. D. Megaw had threatened—so it is reported—that the Orange drums would be round the hall to drown the voice of the speakers and he made it known that R. C. Martin had a more drastic and effective way of making the gathering an abortion. What that way was cannot be known. At least I determined that the meeting would be held *nolens volens* and wrote to the Castle to instruct Morrison, the co[unty] inspector, to come down and see what was needed and to get peremptory orders to see the protection would be sufficient. He came with Davies to the manse on the 18th. He is an amusing cuss. That he is not prime minister—that he is not the director of the king's *navy*—that he has not all the portfolios of government—he thinks he could manage all with an efficiency much to be desired—is a puzzle to him and a mystery to providence. However, he condescended to ask what should be done. I informed him that he should consult Megaw and Martin and to tell them that he had got orders to protect the meeting but that the expense of extra police would come on the town rates ... .'

D.1792/A3/4/32   **Letter to W. S. Armour from Armour,**

[n.d. October ? 1913]   reporting his participation in two deputations to Antrim County Council, one on behalf of the county insurance committee to plead for funds to assist those of the uninsured who were suffering from tuberculosis and the other on behalf of the Queen's University senate to ask for money for university scholarships. Neither deputation had received an immediate answer.

D.1792/A3/4/33   **Part of a letter to J. B. M. Armour from Armour,**

[n.d. October ? 1913]   outlining the circumstances leading up to the anti-Carson meeting of 24 October and describing the events of the day itself.

'... That was the only way of allowing a spout of the tolerant spirit to enter their brains, moth-eaten by prejudice. It did, when they were told, cool their ardour for interruption. Touch uncle Willie's pocket and he becomes an amicable Christian. I told [county inspector] Morrison that there must be, to prevent a dash by the hooligans, a cordon of police above and below the hall through which nobody could pass save ticket holders. "Oh we cannot interfere with the liberty of the people: oh but you *must*: it was done at Asquith's meeting in Dublin and what was done in the green tree can be done in the orange". That was settled. Then I said "you must not permit any Orangeman to enter the hall opposite the Town Hall and begin a drumming to drown the speakers". "Oh that cannot be, we have not the right." That can and must be was the reply—suppose they begin drumming in the Orange Hall and fifty from the other meeting go across and lather them, splitting their drums—there will be a riot and you will be responsible for a breach of the peace. That settled that and to the question how many police will be needed

I said fifty—Morrison said 100—Davies thought from what he knew no extra force would be required. He ordered some seventy and with their arrangement—nine or ten at one end and some on the Kilraughts, Finvoy, Dervock and Coleraine roads, the hooligans took fright and everything in the town in all its parts was as quiet as on a Sabbath day. *Disturbance none*. The meeting was a success—the reports even in the *Irish News* are very poor. The speaking was high tone and earnest and everybody says it was the finest gathering ever held in the Town Hall. Captain White spoke well. As he and Sir Roger had had a tiff I insisted that he should lead off which he did. The only mistake he made was to make too much of T. G. Houston's [headmaster of Coleraine Academical Institution] letter which he read. He seemed pleased with his reception. Mrs Green, Sir Roger, Alec Wilson and young Dinsmore made very fine harangues. I liked them all but was specially pleased with Wilson's. It took a little management to hook him for the meeting. Sir Roger had brought him down the week before to a committee meeting and he was so much pleased with the earnestness of those present that he consented willingly to appear on the platform. Your ma and I got an ovation on entering and when Dinsmore in his speech was referring to the cowardice of the Presbyterian parsons, he congratulated the Route on the possession of "the grand old man" whereat there was a burst of cheering, enough to have lifted the slates from the roof. Your ma, while pleased, was a trifle piqued because the second in command was called an old man. The platform was crowded by a large number of good looking women, Marion A[rmour] being not the less distinguished looking of the females. Sir Roger, Mrs Green, Alec Wilson came here for supper which Susan [Green] had provided, being as aunt Moore would say a compleat cook. They did enjoy their meal and left for Ballycastle at 12.30 which they reached about two, as they mistook the road, landing first at Ballintoy. Sir Roger has written letters of thanks to Julius Caesar [Mrs Armour]. On Saturday we had a telegram from Portrush from D[ougherty] to say that the chief secretary [Augustine Birrell] and he would call on us. Your ma prepared a good luncheon but as they did not turn up on time, we went on. In the middle of the spread the motor appeared. They had been at Garvagh [Co. Londonderry], visiting the birth place of Sir J[ames] B[rown] D[ougherty]. They refused to stop for lunch but I said it is on the table and you may go further and fare no better. Birrell said "all right" and I ushered him into the dining room and Sir J. B. D. consented to follow. Sir J. B. D. is forbidden to eat meat and only allowed a small morsel through the day—consequently he hardly touched the viands. B[irrell] enjoyed the soup and was pleased to say that he had not had more tender mutton in his life—whereat Susan beamed. We then went into the drawing room as the study was taken up by the chauffeur at a repast. B[irrell] remarked that it was a pleasant room which had the look of comfort and cleanliness. He was in the pleasantest possible mood and I gave him what I thought on the situation, telling him that if the bill did not pass the Orangemen about Belfast would murder the Catholics and that there was bound to be more bloodshed if the bill was defeated than if it passed, adding that not twenty per cent of the covenanters really believed in Carson's lawless policy. He told us practically what Asquith said on Saturday. I took him to see the church which he said was neat and clean, the latter adjective he said he could not apply to the last church he was in at Garvagh where he had stood within the pulpit of James Brown's church and read a few verses of scripture. I amused them both by telling them that it was not often they were in a church twice on Saturday and that I was afraid they would not be twice to-morrow. They were hearing [Rev.] Pyper in the morning and I fancy they started for Dublin today, probably going by Kilrea and Dungannon. Birrell is really the pleasantest of men. His visit has set the folks a talking here. Sir J. B. D. seems very much worse ... . K[enneth Armour] is much pleased to hear of the meeting and wishes to sign the new covenant ... .'

D.1792/A3/4/34   **Part of a letter to W. S. Armour from Armour,**

[n.d. October ? 1913]   discussing the continuing repercussions of the meeting of 24 October and in particular the reaction of the local Unionist leadership.

'... I wrote an account of the meeting and its after domestic results to Max [Armour] who was to send it on to aunt Jane [MacMaster] at Aberdeen who was to send it to you. The arrangement was a saving of writing. Max likes to hear what is going on and so does the Lady of Stoke

[Jane MacMaster was matron of the Stoke-on-Trent Infirmary]. There is little else to chronicle … .

Sir Roger's speech which was very fine is reported rather fully in the [*Ballymoney*] *Free Press*. The speaking was all good. I have not seen [R.C.] Martin [local solicitor and Unionist election agent for North Antrim] since his return on Monday. Had it been my case, I think I would have faced the music by holding the fort at home. He is the most nervous of men. Your ma says she hears that Mr [R.D.] Megaw has hardly slept since he heard of the extra police for which the town will have to pay. It was stupid of him to say anything about interrupting the meeting, seeing that his nephew is a candidate for the co[unty] surveyorship and as there are four or five home rulers on the [Antrim County] Council, he will need the votes of the four or five. If it is known what he said, David will certainly miss votes which he will require. Then to make things worse, he stated that Martin was for more drastic measures than he proposed to make the meeting a fiasco. If Martin hears of the matter he will not be in the sweetest of tempers. He will not like to be given away by representing him as a fire-eater … .'

D.1792/A3/4/35 **Letter to W. S. Armour from Armour,**

5 November 1913 analysing new developments in the Home Rule crisis, especially Carson's advocacy of passive resistance towards a future Dublin parliament and the increasing possibility of a compromise involving some concessions to soothe Ulster opinion.

'... Balfour has made at Aberdeen a speech on the same lines as he made when the South African constitution was proposed, exhausting his abundant vocabulary of pet adjectives. Some are rascally enough to say he wishes to oust Bonar [Law] from the leadership and certainly he has thrown over Bonar's hint of a conference and a compromise. The merchants of Belfast had their innings yesterday but the merchants by means of cheap fares were drawn from all parts of Ireland. Charlie Pollock—bless the mark—was one of the orators. What is peculiar about the gathering was Carson's climb down. There is to be no civil war, then why all the drillings—but only passive resistance to the measures of a Home Rule parliament. As passive resistance tried in England of late years has in the lapse of time died down and has done little public good as a means of protest, the outlook for passive resistance in Ireland is not bright and seems not particularly favourable. Sir Edward Clarke and Lord Dunraven ridicule the idea of an election—the latter calling it a gamble while the former admits that an election could not be fought on Home Rule pure and simple, it is not likely Balfour's election or referendum will catch the public mind. Negations do not help to forward a cause. If there was an election tomorrow, it matters not what party should come in, the question has got to be settled. The one serious fault in the present bill is that the money for making the bill a success is grossly inadequate. Appearances are in favour of a settlement by giving the northern counties control—or the government of the three kingdoms on their behalf—of the police force and possibly more power over education and other things which would free these counties from the likelihood of over-taxation. Sara Wallace who is now on the high seas for Australia reports in a letter to the Rev. Samuel [Wallace] from Algiers that William Redmond and his wife, an Australian, are passengers by the same vessel and that said William in a conversation with her—she speaks of his kindness and good humour—affirmed that the question would be settled by a conference. It that is his opinion one might conclude, taking into account Bonar's speech and the articles in the Tory press, that this method of arrangement is almost certain … .'

D.1792/A3/4/36 **Letter to W. S. Armour from Armour,**

12 November 1913 commenting on by-election results in Britain and on a proposed Unionist reply to the anti-Carson Ballymoney meeting of 24 October.

'... There is nothing stirring here. The Reading and Linlithgowshire elections roused the spirits of the Tories to the highest point of the political barometer but Keighley, which Buckmaster retained by an even larger majority than before, has sent their spirits down to the direction of zero. Reading was fully expected, as it had been nursed by Wilson for some time, to revert to the Tories and so it did. Linlithgowshire could not be expected to show for Pratt the same enthusiasm as for Ure and the socialists it is said voted Tory. They are likely to become a nuisance and a thorn in the side of the Liberals and when they have done what mischief they can in that direction if they get the chance, they will do the same for the Tories, that is supposed these in the near future succeed at the polls. There is an article in the *Birmingham Post* from its London correspondent which you will find in the *M[anchester] G[uardian]*, worth reading though it cannot have been manna to some of the readers of the *Post*. There is to be the answer on the 21st to the meeting of the 24th Oct. in the Town Hall but I fancy it will be made up of a ragged political crew. The drums will be in evidence but who the speakers are to be I have not heard. R. C. M[artin] will likely fire off though perhaps in his heart he is tolerably sick of his *confreres* ... .

As changes will come in the government of Ireland at no remote period by the one party or the other, it is wise not to take a too violent opinion about those changes before hand ... R. C. Martin is to be in the chair on the 21st. The orators are [Peter] Kerr-Smiley [Unionist member for North Antrim], Captain [James] Craig and R. D. Megaw. There is somebody else but I only remember the two. R. D. M. will make the welkin ring.

D.1792/A3/4/37   **Letter to W. S. Armour from Armour,**

19 November 1913   discussing the proposed Unionist meeting in Ballymoney on 21 November and a number of other
political developments. In particular Armour gives his reactions to the possibility of partition which is now beginning to be suggested as a solution to the Irish problem.

'... The big meeting engineered by R. C. Martin as an answer to the one on the 24th Oct. is to come off on Friday 21st inst. I saw R. C. M. for a moment on Monday. He is in a state of funk over the prospects of Ireland and fully expects that we will all be in the poor house, if he cannot stop Home Rule by his orations on Friday. He does not put much faith in the oratory of R. D. Megaw to keep back what he thinks will be the catastrophe of history. To argue with a man in that mood is to waste breath and possibly temper and therefore as somebody described a visit of Dr Boyd to a patient [?]. When asked about the patient, he stopped, said nothing and then went away without saying anything. I said nothing and came away. I would like to hear the speaking nevertheless. Redmond's speech at Newcastle was exceedingly fine. Mrs Greer yesterday asked me if I had read it and then voluntarily said it was a very able speech. You will see it in the *M[anchester] G[uardian]*. The ablest pamphlet I have read ever on the subject is by Robert Johnston, F.T.C.D. The publishers likely at his request sent me a copy on Saturday. I have nearly got through it. It deals very ably with the whole question. Its title is *Civil War in Ulster—its Object and Results*. I must write him a note as soon as I have finished its perusal and will probably send you a copy next week if I can get one. The surmises and kites thrown up by *The Times* are very confusing but I suspect there can be no separation of Ulster as that would be a curse and not a blessing to Ulster. Of course the meeting on Friday in the opinion of the clans summoned from afar [will] settle the question once and for all time. Bob Megaw's oratory will set the heather on fire. It will be a new thing to see Mrs Thos. McElderry on the platform with R.C.M. as chairman of the gathering. She will likely blister her hands cheering her son-in-law that isn't. ...'

D.1792/A3/4/38   **Letter to W. S. Armour from Armour,**

27 November 1913   describing in detail the anti-Home Rule Unionist meeting held in Ballymoney on 21 November and also
reporting a meeting of the Queen's University senate held to deal with routine matters.

'... The anti-Home Rule meeting on Friday evening here in return for the meeting on the 24th was an omnimixum gathering. Very few of the town and neighbourhood were there and had it not been for 193 brought on the B[ally]castle R[ailwa]y and a similar number brought from Portrush with the Orange contingents from far and near, it would have been a ghastly failure in numbers. [R. C.] Martin presided but he violated all the rules of chairmanship by speaking some fifty-five minutes in all. He went over the whole shop, though said shop only contains an assortment of political rags and tags. [Peter] Kerr-Smiley was evidently quite as much a lover of John Jamieson as of his party and went through some speech written by [W. J.] Lynn of the [*Northern*] *Whig* as best he could, winding up with a doggerel, the refrain of which was at the end of each verse "to hell with Home Rule". The audience, it is said, had the good taste not to applaud an utterance worthy of a gutter sparrow.

The public houses profited by the meeting as many of them present forsook the orators preferring John Barleycorn. Even the [*Northern*] *Whig* did not publish Kerr-Smiley's ballad with its refrain. Captain Craig fell on Mr Alec Wilson for his statement, which is as true as the gospel, that thousands of Protestants were dragooned into signing for Carsonism and with that gentlemanly feeling and beautiful Christian spirit he said, half apologetically, to the ladies present, "Wilson is a damned lair". Dunville [Craig's father had owned the Dunville Distillery] in this case was clearly the inspiring spirit. William Moore had on his war paint. When he got up, so the story goes, somebody called out my name but he said that he refused to say a word against me as my opinions were not of today or yesterday. He treated me in a different tone from R. D. Megaw whose speech was the poorest of a very poor lot. D. J. McMaster, who was built without any backbone, thought it right to attend, forgetting that it was a Liberal government who gave him the right to have J. P. after his name. Frailty thy name is D. J. M. He is reported to have said that his cousin's speech was "guldering" from first to last. He is verily the worst speaker who ever mounted a platform and deserves the *sobriquet* the schoolboys gave him—"turkey Megaw". I sent an account of the meeting to the *B[ritish] W[eekly]* but whether Nicoll will publish it at all or only parts thereof I have no idea. Perhaps he may or may not. It is a matter which gives me no concern. The following is a matter on which I am pledged to say nothing but as you are far away you cannot make it known. [Rev.] D. D. Boyle and others drew up a series of questions— such as was the Covenant widely signed in your congregation—were there many signatures to the petition to the Gen[eral] Assembly of members other than Presbyterians? What is the opinion of what the feeling would be in your locality supposing the Home Rule bill became law and others of a cognate kind—I saw and helped to answer a paper of the kind. Some professor— I suspect R. M. Henry—drew up a strong statement on the views expressed—a deputation waited on Asquith—some say J. E. Hamilton, Alec Wilson and others, I did not hear their names—they were partly home rulers and some Unionists among them. Asquith complimented them on the ability of the document, cross questioned them on every point, taking notes of their answers, and said the document with the answers and explanations would be laid before the cabinet next day. He informed them that Bonar Law and Lansdowne were in favour of a compromise but Carson was inexorable but added the bill will go through in spite of Carson. That disposes of rumours about this or that change and one is half sorry to see that some apparently great authority has been putting forth proposals which the *M[anchester] G[uardian]* is half inclined to bolster up as far as I can see ... . I ordered a copy of the *Irish News* of today to be sent you containing a letter on Friday evening's meeting and dealing rather bitingly with R.C.M. and Bob Megaw. Nicoll did not insert in the *B[ritish] W[eekly]* my sketch on the meeting. He has written a note giving his reasons why not ... .'

D.1792/A3/4/39   **Letter to W. S. Armour from Armour,**

[n.d. December ? 1913]   largely devoted to local news but also commenting on the intolerance of Ulster Unionism and on the impact of Unionist tactics on other dissident groups in the empire.

'... You will see from Monday's or Saturday's [*Manchester Guardian*] that Prof. Henry was forbidden to distribute the prizes at the Sullivan schools in Holywood [Co. Down]. These pagans *are tolerant* and yet they babble about toleration. They are ceasing to be Christian and missionaries are needed in the Co. Down and elsewhere. I did not read Hardinge's speech *in re* S[outh] African affairs and therefore I have no opinion on its wisdom or folly. It is clear from MacDonald's speech that trouble is brewing in India. Carsonism has something to answer for in regard to Larkinism, Suffragettism and the Hindoo [*sic*] unrest. ...'

D.1792/A3/4/40   **Part of a letter to W. S. Armour from Armour,**

[n.d. December ? 1913]   describing a Co. Antrim insurance committee meeting
                                               in Belfast and commenting on the political difficulties
which Rev. Reid of Garryduff Presbyterian Church had got into as a result of a speech which he had delivered during the Wick by-election campaign in Scotland.

'... Poor Reid of Garryduff has fallen on evil days and evil tongues over his harangues at Wick. There was a leader in yesterday's *Irish News* on his [?] and another sub-leader today and many letters from Protestants calling in question his points that the Catholics of Cushendall had been persecuting Protestants. He is in a fix. He cannot reply in the sense of contradicting the letters and he is left in an awkward hole. He may have sympathy from the Tories but they can only indicate it in secret. I don't see how he can get out of what is the actual charge that he was maligning the people of Cushendall. He was a fool to take to the platform as he has not the preparation for standing a heckling and the hecklers since his return have been too many for him. ...'

D.1792/A3/4/41   **Part of a letter possibly to W. S. Armour from Armour,**

[n.d. December ?1913]   commenting on the possibility of a compromise over
                                               Ulster in relation to Home Rule and on the likely
consequences if David Hogg [Liberal member for Londonderry City] should die as the result of an illness from which he is suffering.

'... My own opinion is that Ulster in the long run would be better to claim no more representatives than it deserves from its numbers. There cannot be much doubt but that the O'Brienites will in nine cases out of ten be opposed to the Redmonite [*sic*] squad and therefore the Ulster members would naturally unite with them. However, nothing will be done in the way of compromise until the eleventh hour. But I fancy something will be cobbled up in the end. ... I hear Mr [David] Hogg is not likely to get through his illness. If he goes there will be another exciting time on Derry walls. Will Sir John McFarlane I wonder be selected to fight the constituency. It is possible the Catholics may decide to run a man of their own. ...'

D.1792/A3/4/42   **Letter to W. S. Armour from Armour, [completed by
                                               Mrs Armour],**

**[n.d. 31 December 1913/
1 January 1914]**   discussing the likely reaction of Scottish Presbyterians
                                               to Ulster Unionist opposition in the house of
commons to a temperance bill for Scotland and retailing various items of local news.

'... The Scotch parsons (outside the established church) and the people will not forgive the Ulster members for voting as a body against the temperance bill for Scotland. When the Irish missionaries say that Home Rule is a question of religion, the retort is the temperance question in Scotland is a religious one and every duffer from Ireland voted against religion in Scotland. The [General] Assembly was wild at me for saying that any Scotch Presbyterian or Nonconformist who voted with the Assembly's views was a renegade to his faith and a traitor to his country. The people in the north will find that what was said then hit the bull's eye. ...'

1914

D.1792/A3/5/1-39

Originals of letters from Rev. J. B. Armour to his wife and sons (principally to W. S. Armour).

D.1792/A3/5/1

[n.d. 1914 ?]

Part of a letter to W. S. Armour from Mrs Jennie Armour, [completed by Armour],

almost entirely devoted to local and family news with a few general political comments appended by Armour himself.

'... The political horizon is not any darker—Carson has delivered his soul and his followers are satisfied though a trifle in the dark. They are not hilarious. Poor Reid is in an ugly hole from which he cannot extricate himself with honour. His best course is to keep silence especially as he has nothing to say. I hear his folks are in a state of irritation in a subdued way. ...'

D.1792/A3/5/2

[n.d. 1914 ?]

Part of a letter [*pages torn*] to W. S. Armour from Armour,

discussing the circumstances surrounding the extension of Sir James B. Dougherty's tenure as under secretary of state for Ireland and the character flaws of Lord and Lady Aberdeen.

'... It is settled that Sir J[ames] B. D[ougherty] will get another year from Nov[ember] coming. Birrell has asked him to continue if he can get the treasury to sanction his remaining. D[ougherty] replied that he left himself entirely in his hands on one condition—that he be informed in time. It appears that the extension of two years was opposed by [Charles] Hobhouse and that his exc[ellency, Lord Aberdeen] and Birrell had to appeal to Asquith to choke off Hobhouse. D[ougherty] only knew of the extension a fortnight before his time was up. Hence the condition ... keeping off Sir J[ames] B. D[ougherty]'s real ability, the reason why Birrell and his exc[ellency] wish him kept on is that B[irrell] and his exc[ellency] hardly ever agree in their selection for any of ... [*page torn*] They [Lord and Lady Aberdeen] have little power of reading character, being over-weighted by sentimentality, hence they are imposed on— she being very able but very shallow—as shallow as a white plate. ...'

D.1792/A3/5/3

[n.d. 1914 ?]

Letter to W. S. Armour from Armour,

largely devoted to local gossip and the progress of the war, but it does contain some references to the current political situation, especially regarding the significance of the removal of Lord Aberdeen as lord lieutenant.

'... This Welsh church bill is causing anxiety among the radicals naturally. Asquith and Co. seem to be weakening in the knees and I would not be surprised if Redmond has not his nails pared, as it is almost certain they will whittle down the Home Rule bill in the vain hope of oiling the hair of the Ulster Unionists. The eviction of the Aberdeens seems an omen in that direction. ...'

D.1792/A3/5/4

[n.d. January ? 1914]

Part of a letter to W. S. Armour from Armour,

containing local and family news.

D.1792/A3/5/5   **Part of a letter to W. S. Armour from Armour,**

8 January 1914   discussing the possibilities of a compromise solution to the Ulster problem and commenting in particular on the suggestions of Rev. McMordie of Kilkeel regarding partition and the postponement of Home Rule for a twenty five year period.

'... There is nothing very stirring in the political world. I see Dr McMordie of Kilkeel has been opening his lips but I fear his statements of view will hardly satisfy the Carsonites and certainly part of his policy is impossible. He gives it out that the idea of separating Ulster in whole or in part from a Home Rule bill is nonsense [*page torn*] ... it is pure insanity and would turn out ruinous to Ulster and to Protestantism generally, as Ulster would show its intolerant spirit in regard to Catholics and thus create a spirit of intolerance towards Protestants in other parts of Ireland. The [persecuted ?] will not pass a vote of thanks to Dr McMordie. His other proposition, that the Home Rule bill should be hung up for twenty-five years, does not show much grasp of the situation. I suppose he thinks that by the end of the period he would probably be sleeping quietly with a wife on each side of him. Though perhaps the second venture may prefer to sleep among her kith and kin or beside some sound companion in the marriage market, and one can hope that his first love and he may agree better over there than according to reports they managed to do on this planet. His views however are a new rift in the Ulster lute but they will probably be ignored by his friends as his latter suggestion will be scorned by his political opponents ... .'

D.1792/A3/5/6   **Letter to W. S. Armour from Armour,**

29 January 1914   indicating his intention to attend a *levee* at Dublin Castle and analysing the current position of John Redmond and of Asquith's Liberal government.

'... There is to be a *levee* at the Castle next week and it is possible I may go thither for a day or two as one hears at the seat of events how the political barometer stands—how far the mercury is up or down. Redmond made a big speech last Sunday. The Tories profess to see in the speech signs of fear that all is not going well with his political gun but the ordinary reader can hardly detect any signs of trepidation in his words which are always clear and statesmanlike. He is an undoubted force. The [*Northern*] *Whig* has all sorts of rumours today about the retirement of Birrell from the chief secretaryship. He is to be made a peer according to the Victoria St[reet] oracle and [Sir John] Simon is to be the new chief in Dublin. The [*Northern*] *Whig* is becoming a nuisance to read and is copying the yellow press of America, going always one better. It is the oracle of canards. The great difficulty with the government is really this question of the navy which is costing too much money already. The baseless fear of Germany is the bogey and the cry is for more Dreadnoughts. If new taxation is necessary—that may upset the coach for the Liberal administration. Churchill may be the danger for the present regime. It is hard to see how he can go back to the old fold, though that is the hope of the die-hards ... .'

D.1792/A3/5/7   **Part of a letter to Mrs Jennie Armour from Armour,**
                                   [written from Donore, Dublin],

3 February 1914   mainly devoted to an account of a luncheon party which Armour had attended at the viceregal lodge.

D.1792/A3/5/8   **Letter to W. S. Armour from Armour,**

11 February 1914   describing a trip to Belfast to attend a meeting of the Queen's University senate, commenting on rumours that Lord Pirrie might be about to desert Liberalism for Unionism and discussing George V's appeal in the king's speech for a compromise solution to the problem of Home Rule.

'... Going up yesterday morning Mr Willie Young of Galgorm hailed me on the platform as he wanted to introduce the correspondent of *The Times*—a young looking fellow—to a Protestant home ruler. He informed the youth that he could count all the Protestant home rulers on his fingers. I said—you must have a large number of fingers as I know there are thousands of Protestant home rulers. I had not time to palaver with *The Times* man as there was a meeting at 11.30 ... .

Lord and Lady Pirrie attended the McMordie dinner, that is the dinner given by the corporation in their honour, though the correspondent of *The Times* gave the names of the principal people there but never mentioned their name. It was rumoured through Belfast that they *insisted on coming there*—a base suggestion as I told in the letter to your Ma from Dublin. It has also been spread abroad that Lord Pirrie was expected to make a speech, the purport of which was to be that he had seen the error of his radical ways and had become a convinced Unionist. That did not come off and therefore he missed as a Unionist would say a great chance and he remains under the shadow of suspicion. If he was so inclined, he could hardly make two somersaults within a few years. It is true—at least it is stated—that perhaps they think the Liberal party has not made enough of them, though it is clear the party has done a deal for them in the way of honours. They are likely maligned by such innuendoes ... .

[W. H.] Brown, son of the late Rev. Macaulay Brown of Limavady, has been appointed as quarter sessions recorder for Cavan and Leitrim and the appointment is very unpopular with the bar. He contested N[orth] Derry against [Hugh T.] Barrie at the last election but he disgusted many of his friends as they believed he had changed his politics for filthy lucre's sake, he being a sort of agent for [J. B.] Atkinson, the Unionist. He seems to be very well disliked and how he got the berth, of which he was much in need as his practice was almost nil, nobody knows. The chancellor was dead against him. I spoke to Birrell for him for Galway but he replied he could not appoint a man who had no practice to an important position. I begged him to give him something. He is called at the bar "the plumber"—the story going that Atkinson on one occasion when somebody was wanted to speak for him somewhere said "send for the gas-blower", meaning Brown, and hence he has been called "the plumber" ever since. I am glad he has got something as he and his friends have been boring me with letters for every vacancy for the last two years. He is now of the list whereat "*laus deo*". [R. D.] Megaw is specially hard on the appointment but he has the weakness of seeing nothing but failings in his fellow men. He never gives anybody credit for either ability or virtue—a characteristic which is not amicable. At the bar they poked fun at R. D. M. suggesting that he should get up a dinner in honour of Brown, preside thereat and communicate his many qualifications for the deserved honour. Like a goose he almost took the suggestion seriously. A man like him throws himself open to private ridicule ... .

It is said the Tory peers and peeresses boycotted the king yesterday as few of them showed up to honour him at the opening of parliament. It is reported further that it was he who wrote in the speech from the throne the passage begging all parties to combine in settling the Irish problem. There may be truth in both reports. It is probable that about May a compromise may be effected but not before that as the Tories are staking their fortune on the chapter of accidents—a perilous venture ... .'

D.1792/A3/5/9   **Letter to W. S. Armour from Armour,**

19 February 1914   paying tribute to Sir Thomas Sinclair, whose funeral
                              in Belfast he had just attended. Although Sinclair was
a Unionist, Armour makes it clear that he greatly respected him as a prominent Presbyterian layman and as a colleague on the Queen's University senate. He also reports a 'tedious' meeting of the senate and comments on the fears of Ulster Catholics about the prospect of the partition of Ireland.

'... The Catholics about Belfast are in a state of almost panic lest Asquith with the connivance of Redmond may sell them over the bill. They aver that if Redmond gives in his days as leader will be numbered. I told them—that is those who were speaking to me on the matter—that they might keep their temper as it was not likely that the principle of the bill would be tampered with. Asquith may be trusted to put the Tories in a fix. The exclusion of Ulster in whole or in part is an idiotic proposal from the Protestant point of view and no sane Unionist wants it. The party are putting the idea forward only with a view to wreck the parliament act. There is no seriousness in the proposal. We must wait and see how events may turn out ... .'

D.1792/A3/5/10   **Letter to W. S. Armour from Armour,**

26 February 1914   containing church and local gossip; yet again pouring scorn on the possibility of the partition of Ireland; and hinting at his possible retirement in the not too distant future.

'... If the letters of Mahaffy and Sir Horace Plunkett which appeared in *The Times* the other day are not in the *M[anchester] G[uardian]* of yesterday, I will cut them out and send them as they seem to be sensible letters shearing off the absurd proposal of the exclusion of Ulster or any part thereof—a thing which only a few madheads propose. They would be madder if it was carried into effect as neither bankers nor businessmen would like their operations confined to Ulster ... . I have been asked to go to London for St Patrick's day when there is to be a big Home Rule gathering but I must decline for reasons physical at any rate ... .'

D.1792/A3/5/11   **Letter to W. S. Armour from Armour,**

5 March 1914   discussing Co. Antrim insurance committee business and the problems of the telephone service in Bally-money. He also anticipates Asquith's response to the Home Rule log-jam.

'... The three kingdoms are on the tip toe of expectation over the statement to be made by Asquith on Monday night. An arrangement between the two front benches was come to that the statement would be made earlier than what it was proposed on the condition that the necessary votes would be passed before the end of the month. It is quite likely that Asquith will offer generous terms but it is just as likely that the Tories, trusting to the chapter of accidents in their favour, will spurn them and there may be rows in the house and one need not be surprised if they egged the mad heads of Ulster to begin a row by attacking all who are suspected of leaning towards Home Rule. That is quote on the cards and possibly there will be an *emeute*. The unexpected however may happen and it may be that the Tories may say Asquith has caved in and that he has practically given a new bill. I hardly think that will occur but there is nobody for the exclusion of Ulster in whole or in part save the scalliwags who go for that with hope of wrecking the parliament act ... .'

D.1792/A3/5/12   **Part of a letter to W. S. Armour from Armour,**

11 March 1914   commenting on the possibility of a compromise settlement of the contentious Home Rule question.

'... Asquith did not propose that there should have been a plebisite of the whole of Ulster on the question of the inclusion or exclusion of the whole of the province. I verily believe that the province by its vote would have gone for *inclusion* in case that was the issue. I think this would have [been ?] a simpler and more effective method of settling the question. As far as I can see the real way of settlement would have been to increase what we may call the Protestant section in the *senate* and slightly increase the representation of the Protestant element in the lower house. However, I may pass from the matter ... .'

D.1792/A3/5/13

Part of a letter to W. S. Armour from Armour, [*page torn*],

19 March 1914

explaining his reasons for deciding not to resign for the present and commenting further on reaction to the Asquith exclusion initiative.

'... [Rev.] Wylie, who had always leanings to Liberalism in a way which kept wrath against him in Coleraine, is turning out in private converse a strong radical. To his credit, he refused to sign the Covenant or touch it with a forty foot pole, though he got postcards or at least one with the usual charitable query, "Are you a Lundy or a Judas or both?". He has had a sharp controversy with his brother John who is wild against Home Rule—his antipathies *in re* anything not squaring with his opinions are fierce—but who admits that if the defeat of the present bill meant the return of the Tories to reign as long as they did before, he would prefer the present bill as it is. He is getting on. I mentioned I think to you my half-formed intention to ask leave to retire in June. Wylie who has himself retired, though a younger man and with many mighty dollars in his purse, tried to dissuade me on the grounds that I should wait at least a year as in that case the Home Rule *imbroglio* would probably be out of the way— settled. Such was the purport of his advice and in one sense there is something in it as to ask now might be construed into a tacit acknowledgement of despair for the future of my country which is far from the case. The whole question is hanging in the balance in the meantime ... .

Save in the political world which is full of acrimonious excitement, everything else seems flat and stale. Asquith has stiffened his back considerably within a week. It was natural as the opposition did not accept the principle of his offer and to give details would have been a waste of time—said details involving a good amount of trouble. It is, as it always seemed, clear that when it comes to the bit, the idea of exclusion of Ulster in part or in whole is impossible as the really thinking Carsonites see that it would spell disaster to Ulster ... .'

D.1792/A3/5/14

Letter to W. S. Armour from Armour,

26 March 1914

commenting on the Curragh mutiny and defending Asquith's handling of the whole episode.

'... The political situation is in a tangle. I have not read the papers this morning but it is clear [J. E. B.] Seeley [secretary of state for war] has bungled the business and will likely have to resign. It is rather a pity of him as it is clear from Morley's speech in the lords that the king interfered in a particular way and Seeley may become the scapegoat. Asquith denies—so I heard your ma reading out—that his majesty interfered in any way but the court has been really at the bottom of the officers' escapade. It is difficult to disentangle the threads of the web but one thing stands out clear that the officers have been guilty of insubordination and their action may lead to consequences for them which will not be pleasant for themselves. The common soldiers may take it into their head to put in for an optimal obedience if they are ordered to put down a strike in the labour world. You had better read Churchill's speech and Lloyd George's ... and in George's specially you will find the inner meaning of the officers' action. The papers are hardly to be depended on as each side gives its own version. The *M[anchester] G[uardian]* was a little hard on Asquith the other day but his card is a very difficult one to play as the court evidently is trying to boss him ... .

I have glanced at the doings and sayings in parliament last night. Asquith has brought the party round an awkward corner with not only success but with a new revelation of govt. strength. That man is a genius in statecraft. Nobody else could have done it. Seeley had to appear in the white sheet but he behaved with humility and it is to be hoped he will not persevere in his wish to resign. After last night I fear [Sir Hubert] Gough and his officers will not be so cocksure of their oratory. The court—not to speak of the king—will feel a trifle small and perhaps will not keep up the stupid intrigues they have been engaged [in] ... .'

D.1792/A3/5/15 **Letter to W. S. Armour from Armour,** [*page torn*],

2 April 1914 further discussing the Curragh mutiny and its allegedly dampening effect on the Unionists; and also his possible retirement at the General Assembly in June. His elders desire him to hold on for another year at least, he claims.

'... This has been *par excellence* the most exciting week politically in my memory but there seems a glimmer of light on the horizon this morning. Asquith's was a stroke of genius in assuming the role of secretary of war. The colonels and their abettors are soberised by this line as it has dawned on them that the government will stand no nonsense. The court—I exclude the king—and the duchesses and grand ladies had been doing their best at social gathering [*sic*] to which officers of all degrees were invited to get the Jackanapes to mutiny should they be ordered for service in Ulster. That helpless politician Bonar Law with a number of others of the Beresford type had done their best to lay down for officers' duty the law of conditional obedience and they had become quite sure that by dropping the sword of [?] into the scale the Ulster covenanters would help to destroy the parliament act and do away with Home Rule. It is difficult to know how far [Sir Arthur] Paget went in carrying out his instructions. He possibly transcended his commands or at least tried to take the edge off his orders. [J. E. B.] Seeley seems to have got a hint from the palace. At any rate he added paragraphs which were harmless in themselves but which assumed a serious aspect in the light of a letter [Sir Hubert] Gough carried off in triumph. [Lord] Morley signed the paragraphs but he did it in ignorance of the letter to Gough and so he did not feel bound to resign as Seeley did—Seeley being bound in honour to do so as [Sir John] French would not withdraw his resignation. The imagination of the fanatics has been running riot and the Tories believe implicitly that the government intended to send troops to attack the covenanters and the Almighty himself could hardly dislodge out of their brains that notion which is absolutely without foundation. They believed that they would be quietly allowed to attack govt. arsenals looting them but they have got a lesson which may be useful. They are not cock-a-hoop these days. I was up at an insurance meeting on Tuesday and Lyons, the grand master of the Orangemen, called out to me across the table—"How do the Ballymoney people receive the news of Asquith's move?". "Some of your friends" was the reply "are a little gloomy over the business". "This government will never resign" said he "until dynamite is applied to them". The faces of several I saw yesterday were far from cheerful. The army *emeute*—or foreshadowed action—has soberised the fire-eaters. The speeches in the H. R. debate for the past couple of nights have indicated the cooling of the volcanic fires. Sir Edward Grey's was decidedly firm but conciliatory and one would not be surprised if some working and workable scheme was not possible. At least even in these [*page torn*] ... the feeling is spreading that the bill will pass and strong language is being ... Protestant home rulers. My name is coming in for a certain amount of abuse ... week wipes out the opinions of the preceding week [*page torn*] ... .'

D.1792/A3/5/16 **Letter to W. S. Armour from Armour,**

9 April 1914 commenting on the position and attitude of the Unionist party and also on the likely future composition of the officer class in the army, in the aftermath of the Curragh mutiny. The letter also includes various items of local news, for example, details of the financial problems being experienced by the local temperance committee resulting from their purchase of a run-down local hotel.

'... The political outlook does not seem too clear as the Tory party is becoming fanatical—their fanaticism increasing as hopes of office are receding. The refusal to contest Asquith's seat is an indication that they were afraid of a worse licking than on the last occasion. I am taking for granted the contest was finally given up today. I have not seen an evening paper. Birrell said truly some months ago that the Tories were always digging graves for their opponents but that they themselves filled the graves they dug. They had put their hope on the army coming to their assistance and now they and the army are receiving a much needed lesson. The officers will not in the future be drawn all from the snobs of society. It is time it was made a real national force and I fancy that will be the outcome of the present muddle. ...

Asquith got a walk over after all and the Tories are priding themselves on their courtesy and patriotism forsooth. Humanity in the average is a curious jumble of contradictions. ...'

D.1792/A3/5/17   **Letter to W. S. Armour from Armour,**

[n.d. 16 April 1914 ?]   reporting the annual meeting of the Route Presbytery and expressing hostility towards Sir Edward Carson's most recent series of public speeches throughout Ulster.

'... The political situation is in *status quo*. Carson is haranguing through Ulster, putting [words ?] in the lugs of the covenanters. His attitude is the Pope's on all questions—*non possumus*. He is trying to keep up the spirits of his dupes by telling them of the help they will get from the civilised world and *gasconade* of that sort. He has not a particle of statesmanship in his composition and therefore rightly belongs to "the Die Hards". He is to be in Garvagh today but many of the farmers will prefer to attend to sowing oats rather than cockle from Carson's bag. ...'

D.1792/A3/5/18   **Letter to W. S. Armour from Armour,**

[15] July 1914   commenting on the current political situation and discussing the possibility of standing again for election to the Queen's University senate in tandem with a Catholic candidate. In the event he decided not to proceed with this idea and since he was not included amongst the four government nominees, he ceased to be a member of the senate.

'... My visit to Dublin was pleasant. They know as little there as any of us about the political situation but Birrell seems to be in an optimistic frame of mind for him as he has had a continuous spell of pessimism. You will see enough about the 12th from the [*Ballymoney*] *F*[*ress*] *P*[*ress*] which has been the quietest 12th for many years. The civil war seems postponed perhaps *sine die*. It will likely take its place with the chapter on the snakes in Ireland which read "there are no snakes in Ireland". The general opinion in spite of spasmodic attempts at the blood-curdling business seems to be that some kind of peace will be patched up though one cannot see much solid foundation for this confident hope beyond the fact which seems to be a fact—that the coffers of the Unionists are running down.

I am thinking of running for the senate of the Q.U.B. again and I am beginning a series of letters. It seems to me that the members of convocation will not allow a Catholic to be on the senate which would mean that the Catholics might make up their minds to get endowments among themselves to make St Malachy's institution a constituent college of the National University. If this took place which is possible, it would be ruinous for Q.U.B. The members of convocation are without vision and where there is no open vision the people perish. I spoke to some of the Catholics to say that if they would run a candidate along with me that we might get both in. In that case as the government has the right of nominating four—one of whom must be a woman—three or four Catholics might get a seat on the senate and thus the present numbers which are scanty enough could be kept up. My idea was that I should help them a little and that they could help me though it was necessary that each of us should in outward appearance seem to have no understanding. Henry—Prof.—seems to think the thing could be made to work. It will entail work but a fight keeps one from blue-moulding. ...'

D.1792/A3/5/19 **Letter to W. S. Armour from Armour, [*page torn*],**

23 July 1914 mainly devoted to describing the circumstances which had prevented his nomination for election to the new Queen's University senate and his feelings about the eight candidates who had been so nominated by the 'wire-pullers' of the convocation of the university. There is also a brief comment about the abortive Buckingham Palace conference on the Home Rule question.

'... it is difficult to understand how far the king is involved in calling a conference which from its personel [*sic*] seemed from the first doomed to end as it has done in an abortion ... .

[*page torn*—he is discussing the eight senatorial candidates selected by convocation] fought bitterly ... against the establishment of the Q.U.B. and now they are anxious to be chauffeurs of the educational motor, perhaps with the intention in the background that they wish to destroy it or attempt to build it on an impossible basis. It is a new thing to find the sworn foes of an institution posing as its friends. They have not allowed or will not allow a single Catholic on the senate, though the result will likely be that the Catholics of Belfast may put St Malachy's as a going concern and get it affiliated with the Nat[ional] University and thus take away at least the third of the students and starve the place so that in about twenty years a commission may be appointed practically to dissolve the institution. It is noticeable that R. M. Jones [principal of the Royal Belfast Academical Institution] was not one of the eight, though the Institution of which he was the head has done more for Q.U.B. in sending pupils of every kind than the eight have done or could do. He is to be sacrificed for his services like some others. I wrote a few letters—not more than a dozen and favourable replies have come from several unexpected quarters but, looking at the matter squarely and without anybody ... I have concluded to do nothing further in the matter for these reasons. The fighting spirit is no doubt strong in one still and even if beaten which is likely I would not withdraw from a fear of that kind. But it would be an expensive business to run as there are 1,100 members of convocation—all of whom would require a letter and it would be very worrying and my health is not naturally and necessarily what it was. As I am thinking of resigning the charge here next June if I live to that time, it would be foolish of me to eat up what strength I have in carrying on a contest which could do me no good. There is a little irony in the situation—life is full of ironies—that the one who fought through good and evil report for the founding of a Belfast university and who during the years on the senate got more changes for the good of the place carried than any other single man should be thrown to the lions. It is the usual fate of those who work for the good of the community. Sir Hiram Wilkinson was anxious that I should stand. He, too, who did so much for the university does not get a place among the eight—that is a little disgraceful but it shows what political rancour can do, though he is a good Unionist but he is not rabid. ...

The cheering of the Irish Fusiliers for Redmond and Dillon at Wellington Barracks beside the palace may open the eyes even of George and remind him that common soldiers have a conscience as well as officers. ...'

D.1792/A3/5/20 **Letter to W. S. Armour from Armour,**

30 July 1914 commenting on the imminence of war in Europe, the government's handling of the Howth gun-running and the Bachelor's Walk incident. He expresses his hostility to the government's amending bill to guarantee special treatment for Ulster when Home Rule is finally implemented. He continues to believe that it is unnecessary as the Unionists are bluffing and that Home Rule, once enforced, would gradually be accepted by everyone. He also discusses the Queen's University senate nominations, reiterating his hostility to the eight senators selected by convocation.

'... The week closing has brought strange almost tragic tidings to our ears—tidings which are stunning. The war which has practically begun may bring about revolutions. [Sir David] Harrel [formerly chief commissioner of the Dublin Metropolitan Police and Irish under-secretary

1895-1902] in Dublin has managed a business which is truly tragic and one which may give him a back seat in social life. Birrell speaks of his action as a mistake: it was rather an act of a lunatic. Sir J[ames] B[rown] D[ougherty] will be in a state of distress as I see the *D[aily] N[ews]* is rather hard on him this morning. I expect with the war on hand and with the revelation that there is one course of action by the police officials for Belfast volunteers and another for the National Volunteers events may compel a settlement of the Home Rule imbroglio in a very short time. The king has not gained much kudos by his action and by his patting on the back of the Ulster rebels. Tomorrow or rather Friday we will know the mind of the cabinet on the amending bill. It will be a useless mistake to proceed with it at all: if the bill [*i.e.* the Home Rule bill] was on the statute book, the excitement in Ulster would die down in a few weeks as no sane person really wants exclusion in any shape. The Tories here have been soberised a deal by the Dublin tragedy as they are beginning to realise that they must share in the responsibility for the events which have taken the public with alarm. ...

[Professor R. M.] Henry was disappointed when I told him that I would not stand as he said Sir Samuel Dill himself and several others were ready to sign any nomination paper. However, I am satisfied with my decision to sit still and seek no further honours of an expensive kind. I have done enough for the place. As I said, it is one of the ironies of life that those—the whole eight chosen—who fought tooth and nail against the establishment of a Belfast university are very anxious to be chauffeurs of the new educational motor and that at least one who advocated the project through good and specially evil report should be relegated to outer darkness. Life has its curiosities but one has to be a philosopher. Boycotting is the sin of sins south of the Boyne but it is the virtue of virtues in the province of Ulster where it is the monopoly of the pious. It is convenient for some to regard the moral law as only a geographical business. It ought to be binding in some quarters but not in others. Such is the will of some of the Presbyterian leaders but they may live to find that they are handling a gun which may kick. I told you that neither [R. M.] Jones nor Sir Hiram Wilkinson was chosen by the provisional government of convocation. As Sir Hiram proved himself a very useful member and as he got my suggestions carried out almost to the letter, I have given notice that at the September meeting he will be proposed as a pro-chancellor and thus get beyond the reach of a few Pharisees to touch him. I wrote him what I proposed to do and he is much pleased. Some fifteen senators will sign or rather have signed the nomination paper so humanly speaking his election is safe. As a Unionist, he is impressed by the fact that those who take the opposite views from him should wish to honour him. No senator has refused to sign but as several of them are away they cannot be reached in time for the notice paper. It is hard for some people to keep out of interfering with things. Several very strong Unionists promised me support and I half believe that if I had kept in the field, I would have pulled through but that may be only imagination. It is no harm to have dreams. They set off life's drab. ...'

D.1792/A3/5/21

Letter to W. S. Armour from Armour,

6 August 1914 in which he discusses his attitude towards the war and towards those within the Liberal party who are opposed to it. He takes some pleasure in the fact that the Ulster question has now been overshadowed by events in Europe and he expresses support and admiration for John Redmond's patriotic stance.

'... This is a time of excitement throughout the empire possibly never known before. Our forefathers doubtless passed through a time of panic in Napoleon's day and of course having no memory of those dark days we cannot compare the present with the past but the kingdom never was so stirred in living memory as it is today. The Ulster question has receded into the background and very few—those only of the baser sort—are thinking of Home Rule or anything else in the presence of a struggle the result of which no one can foretell—a struggle at any rate which will bring untold suffering to millions and which may eventuate in the paralysis of trade and therefore may make many firms topple down bringing famine in its train. Redmond's speech in the H.C. produced such an impression that it is said a special messenger was sent to Buckingham Palace to tell the court its purport and the impression it made on the house. It was almost a stroke of genius, full of real patriotism and a challenge to Sir Edward—a challenge which he did not take up, probably because he feels that he has started a state of feeling in Ulster of a diabolic kind which he cannot control. He is becoming the victim of a policy which was the height of madness. His followers here are whistling to keep up their courage and it is beginning to dawn on them that the Home Rule bill will receive the signature of the king and being on the statute book it will remain there whatever the amending bill may be and what compromise it may contain. The ladder which they dreamed would bring Ulster to [be] the arbiter of the fate of the measure has been kicked from under their feet and they are left lamenting at least inwardly. It is almost certain that with money at 10%, with little possibility for say Ulster either to get in material for carrying on her trade and with no market for her wares, many firms in Belfast—I am speaking only of Belfast—will come down with a crash. What is true of Ulster will be true everywhere, specially in Lancashire, and there are materials for a crash of a widespread kind with untold misery in store for the community. If the war goes on as it seems bound to do there will eventuate a new map of Europe. I do not like Great Britain to be fighting on the side of Russia which is a barbarous power and possibly has an eye to reach some day Constantinople and subdue the whole of the Balkans. For a victory for her with the help of England would mean an attempt in the near future to seize India. On the other hand for Germany to subdue France, Belgium, Holland and it may be Italy would be dangerous for our empire. It is quite possible to take two opposite views of the situation and one has some sympathy with the *M[anchester] G[uardian]*, Lord Morley and John Burns though now that the die has been cast one is bound, even if he thought his country wrong, to at least support the side with loyalty. It is hinted that the route to India may be blocked and that there will be no guarantee for the regularity of letters to and fro. I don't see how that is at all likely but in a state of war the unexpected may happen. ...'

D.1792/A3/5/22

13 August 1914

Letter to W. S. Armour from Armour, 9 Park Terrace, South Shields [home of Max Armour],

commenting on the lack of concrete news about the progress of the war, repeating his own views concerning the necessity of Britain's participation and describing his journey via Stranraer, Scotland, to South Shields, along with Mrs Armour, for a short holiday with Max. He also reviews the war's continuing effect on the Irish political situation.

'... The war has hushed all talk of civil war in Ulster. Redmond's fine speech as the *M[anchester] G[uardian]* points out was worth a Dreadnought to the British government and it is plain from reports from America and the colonies that the feud between the Irish and English is practically ended. It—the war—has unified the English-speaking population of the world. A few hooligans in Ulster may give trouble for a day or two when the Home Rule bill is signed—which signing is likely to take place before the end of the month—but it will be partial and sporadic. Carson's last utterance practically bids his followers in Ulster to keep quiet and to do what they can for the endangered empire. A practically pacified Ireland is the outcome of the Kaiser's madness. Grey's speech and Asquith's—both very clear and strong—left no loophole for dissension in regard to the fact that for honour's sake and for the preservation of the empire, England's duty was to go to the help of France and Belgium and help to roll back the tide of tyranny. A cooler proposition and a more audacious proposal could not be imagined than that of the Kaiser to ask neutrality for England. It was like a burglar's request not to interfere with him when he was raiding a neighbour's house with the silent assertion—when that is done yours will come down in due course. One at a time is all that is asked. He must be really mad and until he is disposed of as Napoleon was, hopes of permanent peace are in vain. The unfortunate part of the business is that our forces are to be ranged on the side of Russia—a tyrranic, barbarous regime and in the event of victory over Germany, India may have to be vigorously defended against the Tsar but the future will have to arrange for the curbing of Russian greed of territory. ...'

D.1792/A3/5/23   **Letters to W. S. Armour from Armour,**

20 August 1914   regretting the absence of hard news about the war,
                                            describing the seige atmosphere in South Shields
because of the supposed threat from the German fleet, praising the skilful landing of the
British Expeditionary Force in France, criticising Lord Kitchener's rather autocratic control
of war news and reviewing the general political situation.

'... The Home Rule business has been side-tracked and with the exception of a few who are
afflicted with a double dose of insanity it is hardly mentioned. In the [*Northern*] *Whig* and
[*Belfast*] *Newsletter* and [*Belfast*] *Evening Telegraph* there are subsidiary articles calling on
the faithful to remain firm but the articles are probably written with the tongue in the cheek.
Lloyd George is coming into his own, even the Belfast merchants are speaking of him as a
financial genius, as one who has saved the commercial citadel. Even the Tories are glad that the
present cabinet is in power as they are beginning to recognise how barren their side is in brains
and therefore in administrative capacity. There has been one of the most peculiar revolutions
in opinion through the king down that has taken place in our history. ...'

D.1792/A3/5/24   **Letter to J. B. M. Armour and W. S. Armour from
                                     Armour,**

16 September 1914
                                            reporting the final meeting of the first senate of the
Queen's University of Belfast at which Armour successfully proposed a motion to appoint
Sir Hiram Wilkinson a pro-chancellor of the university. He again expresses his regret at the
convocation's selection of eight Protestant Unionists to represent it on the new senate.

'... So the first senate is ended. We know the eight convocation has selected but they did not
allow a single Catholic on the senate and thus showed their boasted toleration which is the
essence of an intolerance never manifested before in this world. Ulster is a rare country or
province surely. ...'

D.1792/A3/5/25   **Letter to W. S. Armour from Armour,**

24 September 1914   commenting on war news, on the reaction of local
                                            Unionists to the placing of Home Rule on the statute
book and on the impending retirement of Sir James Dougherty as under secretary of state for
Ireland.

'... Asquith is to be in Dublin on Friday. I was tempted to go up but it is too far and physically
it would not be conducive to health and therefore I will not run the risk. Carson who has
shown how deeply he feels the coming ruin of Ulster in consequence of Home Rule has gone
and got married. He is to be in Belfast on Monday for the anniversary of the Covenant. Some
of the folks in the north are afflicted with sore heads. It is reported in the *Irish News* today
that in two episcopal churches not far from the centre of Belfast several of the worshippers
stamped out when the national anthem was sung. They showed what people were saying about
them that their loyalty was conditional. It is a sign of soreness and pettiness worthy of contempt
but one could expect nothing else from people who have been born without vision. Jas. B.
Hamilton [Ballymoney solicitor and Unionist organiser] is said to be very sore and no wonder
that after all the bouncing about no Home Rule for Ireland, the bill should have got the length
of the statute book where it will remain in spite of Carson. They have got a very bad fall and
they deserve what they will hardly get in a practical form—sympathy ... . It is reported that
Sir J[ames] B[rown] D[ougherty] is to go out of office on the 1st of Nov. and that some man—
an Englishman—[Matthew] Nathan ... is to be his successor. The [*Irish*] *Independent* I hear had
an article yesterday denouncing the appointment on the ground that he was an Englishman and
therefore he has neither the knowledge for ruling Ireland, nor the peculiar sympathy requisite

for managing the Celtic race. There is something to be said for that view but it is not likely to have much weight in government circles. No successor will do as well as Sir J. B. D. who may be retained though contrary to the letter of the rules bearing on the subject. ...'

D.1792/A3/5/26 **Letter to J. B. M. Armour and W. S. Armour from Armour,**

13 October 1914

recounting a visit to Dublin and discussing the circumstances surrounding the resignation of Sir James Dougherty as under secretary of state for Ireland, as a result of the Bachelor's Walk riot. In particular, he attacks the role of Chief Secretary Augustine Birrell in the matter. He comments pessimistically on the fall of Antwerp and the possibility of a total Belgian collapse.

'I forget, *carissimi*, what I wrote you about my Dublin visit but I may add a little even though part of it may be yesterday's dessert. In regard to the report of the commission of inquiry into that Sunday's riot in Dublin, Asquith was in a fix about the personnel of the commission. Lord Shaw he had selected but the Tories were calling out for one of their way of thinking to be on the commission. Sir J. B. D. was asked. He put forward the chief secretary, Malory, who was accepted. Then he suggested Judge Andrews—whose brother Thos. Andrews was one of the prominent leaders of the Ulster brigade. That will do nicely said Asquith and then Birrell was instructed to spur him and if he hesitated to accept, he was to butter him up by hinting that his majesty's government had great faith in his impartiality and judicial fairmindedness. The bait took and the commission set to work. Andrews upset [Sir David] Harrel, who pleaded that the telephone was not working, by asking him straight, "was the under secretary's office just beside your office? Why did you not go there?" That was a poser which boled [*sic*] Harrel quite off his legs. The commission you will have seen came down rather heavily on Harrel and Cuthbert and declared that Sir J. B. D. was free from blame. He (Sir J. B. D.) took up the position from the first that he had no share at all in Harrel's illegalities. The Tories are perfectly furious with Andrews who they fondly believed would shield Harrel and throw a little mud on Sir J. B. D. After the publishing of the report, Sir John Ross, who is an incapable and had resigned rather than face the music, and Harrel's friends got hold of the editor of the *Irish Times* who wrote a fierce attack on Sir J. B. D. I did not see the *Irish Times* but I hear it was rather savage and in the face of a unanimous deliverance by the commission only showed how badly the Harrelites had been hit. Prof[essor] M[acMaster] writes your mother this morning to say that Jack [Galland ?] had told Earnest Osborne that Birrell in the H.C. made such a halting defence of Sir J. B. D. that it was practically a violent attack on him. Birrell is at times with all his good nature rather a weak reed and he certainly ought to have been bound in honour to stand up for his subordinate who had paddled safely through many a storm. Had it not been for the under-secretary's tact and advice master Birrell would not have been able to retain the chief secretaryship so long. The storms on which Sir J. B. D. threw oil would have swamped Mr B[irrell]. B[irrell] is talking of resigning but that it seems to me he cannot do in the meantime. No matter in that case what he would put forward as a reason would be misunderstood. It would be more than hinted at that the cabinet was dissatisfied with his administration—that he had been a failure—his foes have been always harping on that string and that he was trying to put a cloak over his failure by putting his resignation on his wife's health and his desire to return to the green pastures of literature. I think I told you that his exc[ellency] is distressed over Sir J. B. D.'s resignation and would like to retain him as a private secretary. Sir J. B. D. was a mollifying influence between his exc[ellency] and Birrell as the latter two were usually at loggerheads over appointments and general policy. A day's [?] was absolutely necessary and the [?] was in his element as a reconciler. His exc[ellency] is the decentest of men but he is a worshipper of his wife, and Birrell in his heart and by his nature is decidedly antagonistic to her as he fancies with some truth that she is always starting some wild-cat schemes. Nathan, the wise or unwise, will need also the advice of Sir J. B. D. as the former being an Anglicised Jew and a born official with Jewish notions—perhaps with a trifle of Shylock in his veins-will need advice to keep him from pitfalls and trenches from which the Irish will shoot at him. He will be a fortunate beggar if he escapes Irish sharp shooters, at any rate I expect Sir J. B. D. will have a hand on the helm though he is out on pension. ...'

D.1792/A3/5/27   **Letter to W. S. Armour from Armour,**

22 October 1914   discussing the apparent success of John Redmond's
                                       recruiting campaign in Ireland and the reaction of
Ulster Unionists to it; criticising the absence of press comment on Sir James Dougherty's
retirement; and commenting on the death of Dr Anthony Traill, provost of Trinity College,
Dublin. Armour reiterates his unhappiness at the relative absence of war news and expresses
his views on the proposed remodelling of the presbytery boundaries of the Presbyterian
Church in Ireland.

'... Redmond seems in the fair way to squelch the Sinn Feiners and to bring the whole of the
south and west into his fold. The Ulster troglodites are prophesying that his volunteering
campaign will turn out a fiasco but as that is their view, one may discount their gainsayings
and take up Asquith's position—"wait and see"—a very wise motto but quite useless for people
born without the power of vision. ...

I have heard nothing from Dublin about how Nathan is carrying sail nor how Sir J. B. D. is
enjoying his leisure or how he feels without the collar which he wore with dignity. It seemed
rather odd to me that no paper made any reference to the demission of an office which he
filled with a success never surpassed before. Speed the parting guest and welcome the new-
comer seems to have been illustrated. He has got out without a hair turned and in peace. He
will be in something before long. Dr Traill you will see has gone at last. In spite of many
failings, I fancy he did more for T[rinity] C[ollege] D[ublin] than any provost of the past.
He was a good manager. Who will be his successor is not known yet. Mahaffy expects it but he
is too old. One of the Gwynns is mentioned and so is Starkie and even Sir Samuel Dill, who
would do well, but I think T.C.D. would kick wildly against anyone as provost who was not
innoculated with the T.C.D. spirit from breathing its air for long. There is no word as yet
about the successor to McCormick [as clerk of the crown]. Your ma made a fight to get the
shops in Main St[reet] and Linen Hall St[reet] to put up the shutters as a mark of respect for
Dr Traill and succeeded. Mahaffy is reported to have said of Traill that he had an immortal
body, though he was not altogether sure of the immortality of his soul. The Ballymoney
people—the most of them—did not like him as he had the reputation founded on real facts of
being one of the most tyrranical of the landlord party. Many of his deeds were high-handed
but he has gone before a perfect tribunal and we may hear the words, "Forbear to judge for we
are sinners all" ... .'

D.1792/A3/5/28   **Letter to W. S. Armour from Armour,**

29 October 1914   entirely devoted to local, family and war news/
                                       rumours.

D.1792/A3/5/29   **Letter to W. S. Armour from Mrs Jennie Armour,**
                                    [completed by Armour],

[n.d. October/November ?
1914]   in which Armour describes a visitation which he had
                                     made on the previous day to Roseyards Presbyterian
Church and he recounts a speech which he had made in defence of Lord and Lady Aberdeen.
In the speech he had taken the opportunity to indulge in an attack on the anti-Presbyterian
bias of members of the Church of Ireland.

'... We had a visitation in Roseyards yesterday which resulted in praise of [Rev.] Crothers and
his folk. I made a short speech on his exc[ellency] and her exc[ellency], defending the latter
from a private letter some enemy had got hold of and published in which she had accused the
Red Cross Society for using their organisation for Unionist purposes. The [*Northern*] *Whig*
has been strong on the subject. I asserted that her statement in my opinion was perfectly true

as in the distribution of the P.O.W. Fund in this district I had seen the church people who had contributed very little taking possession of the reins *etc.* Even Mrs Crothers told me that what I said was perfectly true about the Dervock committee. I should have liked that the words had been reported, even though I had brought an old house about my head. I rubbed into them the fact that the church folks had made up their minds to keep the Presbyterians in the Arctic regions as in the past—a truth that could not be palatable to Mairs, McCammon, Craig, Crothers and company [all fellow Presbyterian clergymen of Unionist sympathies]. ...'

D.1792/A3/5/30   **Letter to W. S. Armour from Armour,**

5 November 1914   entirely devoted to local and family gossip.

D.1792/A3/5/31   **Letter to W. S. Armour from Armour,**

19 November 1914   commenting on the War Office's mishandling of southern Irish recruiting; indicating that he intends to travel to Dublin to attend the jubilee celebrations of Rutland Square Presbyterian Church; and giving his personal reaction to Birrell's failure to nominate him as one of the government representatives on the Queen's University senate (in the light of the unwillingness of convocation to elect him).

'... The two greatest assets Britain has in this war are Botha and John Redmond—I agree with your point in the last letter *in re* John Redmond. If these two had taken an attitude of hostility, the whole of the Irish throughout the world and all S. Africa would have been real foes instead of stalwart friends of the empire. Both have done and are doing their best, Redmond has a difficult card to play as the Sinn Feiners are being bought with German gold to be pro-German but their efforts, while annoying and throwing a wet blanket in some places on volunteering, will not mean much in the long run. The government or rather the War Office is unaccountably at fault in granting the Ulster volunteers the right to proclaim their motto and refusing a similar right to the Irish volunteers. ...

I am going to Dublin on Saturday to be present on Monday evening at the jubilee of Rutland Square at the request of [Rev. J. D.] Osborne. John Hamilton has arranged a service for me at the viceregal [lodge]. Sir J. B. D. is acting as private sec[retary] to his exc[ellency] and therefore is still in harness. His letter will show you that Birrell has not nominated me for the senate. I have no feeling on the point as it was tiresome and expensive travelling up there once a month and I did a fairly useful day's work there and I did not see what I could do more. One or two on the senate wished me to apply but I refused. They wanted to give Messrs Lowe and Company a back slap for their treatment of me. But I did not heed and I am satisfied to be out of the business. ...'

D.1792/A3/5/32   **Part of a letter to W. S. Armour from Armour,**

[n.d. November ? 1914]   discussing the resignation of Lord Aberdeen as lord lieutenant and the possible reasons for it, making it clear that he was unwilling to take part in any manoeuvering to get him reinstated, since such manoeuvres would be useless in that the government had obviously determined that Aberdeen should go (possibly in conjunction with the Irish parliamentary party). Armour also predicts the removal of Birrell within a short time.

'... This has been a week of entanglements. On Monday a telegram came from Osborne asking me to start for Dublin over their exc[ellencie]s' resignation—a euphemism for compulsory removal. I was up the street and did not get back until it was too late for the train. I telegraphed accordingly and wrote by the evening post saying that I had to be in Belfast on Tuesday and that if there was urgency that he (Osborne) should wire me at the Church House. I think what was wanted was that I should go to London to get [Robertson] Nicoll [editor of the *British Weekly*] to take up the case in the *B[ritish] W[eekly]* —a fishy sort of business. I had told O[sborne] in my letter how I had written N[icoll] on the subject and pointed out that part of the Irish correspondence in the *B[ritish] W[eekly]* was evidently written by N[icoll] himself. Fortunately your ma had copied N[icoll]'s letter which was sent you and the copy was sent on. It clearly dawned on O[sborne] on reading N[icoll]'s letter to me that everything that could be done was done and therefore he telegraphed here on Tuesday that I need not go Dublinward. The telegram was sent on to me at the Court House. He (0) was to write but he has not as yet. I called on Tuesday on Dr Purves and he is clearly of opinion that any interference from the outside now would be useless as he thinks that it is a cabinet affair. I showed him O[sborne]'s telegrams, from one of which it was plain that an interview with Asquith was asked and quietly refused. Purves is not much in love with O[sborne]'s ways of interference. However, it is evident their exc[ellencie]s were the parties originating the telegram to me. Purves and I agreed that their exc[ellencie]s would make a huge mistake if they remained in Dublin, as is intimated, after giving up office. It would show a lack of the sense of dignity and would do them immense harm in the public eye. I am half afraid the Nationalists are parties to the removal. [Lord] Wimborne who is spoken of as the successor—a cousin of Winston's—is said to be on very intimate terms with Joe Devlin, that the latter goes with him to the [?]. Further it is odd that Devlin never replied to my letter in which I pointed out that the removal of the Aberdeens seemed to me an attempt to whittle down the Home Rule measure with a view to make it palatable to the Unionists—a vain proposal as it would mean that the three fourths of Ireland would resent it. That he has not replied seems queer at least and lends countenance to the notion that the Nationalists are a party to the change. I suspect that in a very short time Birrell will go also to break the fall of the Aberdeens. Who his successor may be is not apparent. Some say [Charles] Masterman if he can get a seat—some say Sir John Simon, but I fancy the latter will not give up £17,000 a year for £4,200. ...'

D.1792/A3/5/33	**Part of a letter to W. S. Armour from Armour,**

24 November 1914 describing a visit to Dublin to attend the 'Osborne function', analysing the reasons for the removal of the Aberdeens by Asquith and commenting on their unhappiness at this development.

'... There is a thick cloud over the heads of their exc[ellencie]s'. They have suddenly got notice to quit office and they are in a state of nervous prostration. What is behind it one can hardly say. That unfortunate letter her ex[cellency] wrote, and which was scandalously, contrary to all the courtesies of life, published, will be regarded as the cause but I fancy that is not the real cause. Perhaps it is rather the Irish aristocracy which hates them getting the ear of the English court, or it may be that Asquith wants to change hands so that new men may prepare for the Ulster struggle when the war is over. It is said Birrell will go also but I hardly believe it. Her ex[cellency] it seems to me has complicated matters by her interminable schemes which will ruin her financially and which will die when she departs. His ex[cellency] is sore with Asquith. He did not say so to me but to a chaplain to whom he unburdened himself (foolishly in my opinion) he said, "Poor Archie" [Gordon] is forgotten—Archie being engaged to Mrs Asquith. He was a little hard on Asquith but I said you may be sure it is not Asquith but some pressure brought to bear on him. He seemed to think that as a family they had been hardly treated, Lord Tweedmouth being compelled to resign—the real cause for which was that he was becoming insane and Lord Pentland sent off to India to get him out of political life in England. The truth is that Pentland had not been a success and the Radicals and Munro Ferguson had their knife in him. McKinnon Wood who was forked into his place is not any more a success. It appears, as I hear, that the Aberdeens were sent to Canada because John Morley refused to be chief secretary for Ireland [in 1892] if Lady A[berdeen] was to be in Dublin. However, the cup of their sorrow is very full and I am heartily sorry for them as he is the decentest and most kind of men and he ...'

D.1792/A3/5/34   **Letter to W. S. Armour from Armour,**

3 December 1914   discussing Sir James Dougherty's unopposed return as
                                                       the Liberal member for Londonderry City on 2 Dec-
ember and the attempts of the *Belfast Evening Telegraph* to connect Sir Roger Casement (now
collaborating with the Germans) with those who support Home Rule such as John Redmond.

'... You will have heard that Sir J. B. D. is the man for Derry. His opponent, Goode, probably
conscious that his chances of making a show were slim got an invalid informal paper sent in;
at any rate he ran away. The [*Northern*] *Whig* with its usual meanesss had a nasty note on the
great Woggler, asserting that he was the worst enemy of the Protestants of Derry and of all
Protestants on the globe. The *Evening Telegraph* sent on to Max [Armour] with the request to
put it with two *M[anchester] G[uardian]s* which failed to come here was fairer and milder
without the malicious bitterness of the [*Northern*] *Whig*. It had an amusing article headed
"Ballymoney and Berlin"–an odd combination dealing with Sir Roger Casement and the
Ballymoney meeting, insinuating that we were all traitors like Sir Roger. It is a curious world.
Sir Ed[ward] Carson and Captain Craig coquetted with the Kaiser and brought on the war
sooner that it would have come but that was patriotism in essence. Sir Roger is doing what
they did from all accounts but then that is traitorism pure and unadulterated. Many of the
Orangemen through the north are credited with the wish that the Kaiser should win as they
regard him as the only real Protestant king in the world. Conan Doyle's explanation of Sir
Roger's action that he is off his mental balance is likely true and *The Spectator* says before
condemning him we ought to hear what he has got to say. To identify him with Home Rule–
the Home Rule of Redmond–is a sign of the unscrupulousness of prejudiced partyism. It is
reported that Miss Casement of Ballycastle, his sister, is being watched by the police but that
may be only another form of the thousands of Russians that so many saw passing from
Aberdeen on to Leith and then through England to the continent. ...'

D.1792/A3/5/35   **Letter to J. B. M. Armour from Armour,**

[n.d. 3 December ? 1914]   largely repeating his comments expressed in D.1792/
                                                       A3/5/34 on Sir J. B. Dougherty's return as member
for Londonderry City and Sir Roger Casement's involvement with the Germans. He also
speculates as to the possibility of Dougherty succeeding Augustine Birrell as chief secretary.

'... I send you also a cutting from the *Evening Telegraph* dealing with the Derry election and
funny article on Sir Roger Casement and Ballymoney. Sir Roger has clearly lost his balance but
at the very worst he is doing nothing different from what Sir Edward Carson and Captain Craig
did. Their action certainly brought on the war sooner but with the usual sense of fair play in
the north, they are patriots and he is a traitor. It is also curious that a certain percentage of the
Orange fraternity here is quite pro-German as he, the Kaiser, is regarded as the one Protestant
king in Europe. It is reported that Miss Casement of Ballycastle is under police surveillance.
Perhaps it is a mere tale or myth like the passing of the thousands of Russians. ... I am writing
Sir J. B. D. by the evening post. It is within the bounds of possibility that he may be chief
secretary yet. This is only a surmise but it is not unlikely but that Birrell may go with the
Aberdeens. ...'

D.1792/A3/5/36   **Letter to W. S. Armour from Armour,**

10 December 1914   almost entirely devoted to local and family news apart
                                                       from some further brief comments on the imminent
                                                       departure of Lord and Lady Aberdeen.

'... I wrote Sir W. R. McColl over the Aberdeens who have to give up on the 31st of January.
I enclose his note which has just come in. What is behind the move, it is not easy to say farther

than that it has been an intrigue at the court and in my judgement it is an attempt to whittle down the Home Rule measure so as to make it acceptable—a vain try—to the Ulster gang. Wimborne, a cousin of Winston's, it is thought will be the successor and as Winston [Churchill] nearly upset the coach one may conclude that his hand hs been in it. ...'

D.1792/A3/5/37　　　　　　　　　**Part of a letter to W. S. Armour from Armour,**

17 December 1914　　　　　　　entirely devoted to local and family news. He indicates that he has been 'writing out for K[enneth] a defence of Sir Roger Casement'. Kenneth Armour was by now a student at Cambridge University.

D.1792/A3/5/38　　　　　　　　　**Letter to W. S. Armour from Armour,**

23 December 1914　　　　　　　discussing the progress of the war and further giving his opinion on the reasons for the removal of Lord Aberdeen from the lord lieutenancy of Ireland.

'... I fancy, as I have stated, that the Nationalists are in the business which shows their folly. They will learn their mistake when too late but the affair is theirs. I fear nothing can be done to stay the execution of the *fiat* that has gone forth. ...'

D.1792/A3/5/39　　　　　　　　　**Letter to W. S. Armour from Armour,**

[n.d. 30 December 1914 ?]　　　　reporting that a deputation, including the lord mayor of Dublin, had waited on Lord Aberdeen to ask him to withdraw his resignation; commenting on the changed nature of warfare; and advising William to accept a schools' inspectorship in place of his headmastership if one is offered to him.

'... A deputation consisting of the Dublin lord mayor and King-Kerr from Belfast and somebody from Derry and other places waited on the lord lieutenant to ask him to withdraw his resignation *etc*. He replied diplomatically as he was bound to do in as much as the resignation is only a euphemistic way of putting a notice to quit ... [Rev.] J. D. O[sborne] seems to think that their stay may be prolonged. I hardly think so and if I were in their shoes I would refuse to stay even if asked. That is only my way of thinking. ...'

D.1792/A3/6/

1915

Originals of letters from Rev. J. B. Armour to his wife and sons (principally to W. S. Armour), with the copy of an address to Lord Aberdeen.

D.1792/A3/6/1

[n.d. January ? 1915]

Letter to W. S. Armour from Armour,

commenting on the death of Rev. John Hamilton, senior chaplain to Lord Aberdeen, and again discussing the circumstances of the departure of the Aberdeens.

'... It appears the resolution to change the viceroy was come to in Oct[ober]. Winston Churchill is thought to be at the bottom of it as he wanted to fork his cousin Lord Wimborne into the job. A letter from Asquith was sent to say that as they had been in office for nine years they needed a rest *etc.* and hinting that an appointment was made of the successor. It took him not only by surprise as it came like a bolt from "the blue". Her exc[ellency] wrote even to the king, praying for relief from what was worse than hanging. He replied much in the same way as Asquith's letter indicated. Dr [J. M.] Hamilton and [Rev. J. D.] Osborne got up a farewell note putting forth their services and the regret with which their resignation was received—this was to be signed by any of the Presbyterian chaplains who were willing to sign. I had on Wednesday last a note from John Hamilton asking me to sign and return which I did that evening—probably the last note he wrote. [Rev.] Martin told me that [Rev.] Purves was the only one who had refused to sign—the reason being the way they had treated him on the last visit a fortnight before I was there. He insisted on going to the [viceregal] lodge hours before the time of service, expecting that he would be received with open arms—on that morning Asquith's letter had come and they were so much wounded that they hardly spoke to him and he went back to Donore thinking that he had offended them in some mysterious manner. The reason of the coolness was of course Asquith's letter which had overwhelmed [them]. It is a pity they did not mention the subject to him that day instead of unburdening their souls to Martin who would tell the matter to his brother which meant telling "the Protestant Germans" in Belfast. Still though that was a fatal mistake, it was tactless and small on the part of Purves to refuse to sign. It showed a littleness which is almost unforgiveable. ...'

D.1792/A3/6/5

11 February 1915

Letter to W. S. Armour from Armour, [written from Dublin],

explaining why he had decided to come to Dublin to attend the presentation of a farewell address to Lord and Lady Aberdeen by their chaplains and enclosing a copy of the speech which he had made at the ceremony.

'... I would not have come so far but for the fact that some of the chaplains—Park, Lowe, Montgomery, McKean and D. Taylor refused to sign. Lowe is blamed and perhaps rightly for having published in the [*Northern*] *Whig* the draft of the address he received which was marked private and confidential. This was not playing the game and even Prof[essor] Heron was furious over the scandalous breach of confidence. Martin of Magherally, brother to R. I. Martin, told me that Purves was the only one who refused to sign the address. I told Purves who was quite indignant. He said he signed it and posted it half an hour after he got the document. I am waiting for the Mansion House demonstration on Friday evening. Sir J[ames] B. D[ougherty] is likely to be there. Their exc[ellencie]s are sore over the business and they are likely to make a stupid blunder as her exc[ellency] avers she will return in spirit for the meetings of the different schemes she started. I hardly see how this could be in accordance with etiquette to put it mildly, as ex-governors are usually forbidden to go back to the provinces they have left for years. If they go back, it must be with the permission of the government of the day. Such a course of going back seems to me to be lacking in a sense of dignity and could only lead to complications which would not be pleasant for the parties concerned. However, that is only a detail and I could hope that wiser counsels will prevail. No doubt many of her schemes will collapse without her presence but that is expected. The incoming viceroy and vicereine I hear have practically refused to take up the reins of the schemes her exc[ellency] has set in motion ... .

Osborne read the address and I previously made the enclosed little speech with which his exc[ellency] was evidently much pleased saying that I had always been very kindly and loyal to them and that I had the gift of speaking plainly. He said [?] that he was specially pleased that I had come so far to bid them good bye ... . Their exc[ellencie]s leave on Saturday at 2.30 for Holyhead. They go to Edinburgh to stay with Dr Whyte or possibly some other of that name. They are not going to London meanwhile ...'.

Copy of the speech made by J. B. Armour at the presentation of a farewell address by twenty-one of the Presbyterian chaplains to Lord and Lady Aberdeen.

'Your excellencies, we have met to bid you good bye, not to say farewell, on your demission of an office you have filled longer, with more efficiency and with greater good to Ireland than any viceroys who have had the honour of representing the sovereigns of Great Britain. Your departure is a tremendous loss to our country as you have identified yourselves wholeheartedly with everything pertaining to the moral and physical advantage of our country. Both time and money have been spent by you to promote the health and well-being of the community impartially. You have made many friends of every class and creed who will cherish the memory of your vigour but as in all cases where public progress in beneficial government is inaugurated, you have incurred the wrath and hatred of powerful sections of the social world which detest the principles of democracy and of the government to which you have afforded the most loyal support. "The Hymn of Hate" has been sung against you and one is sorry to say the diabolism of that unchristian carol has been put in motion to slander your personal characters which are deservedly stainless and to belittle and nullify the benevolent and healing measures you have started with such benefit to the poor and the sick. Her excellency's schemes for the health and comfort of the poor have been marvellous and are bearing fruit which shall remain. The very malignancy manifested against you—a re-echo of crucifixion times—by the reactionaries who think that Ireland should be always ruled by the mailed fist rather than by the wand of justice tempered by kindness is the realest testimonial to the worth of your long reign as viceroys of Ireland. As chaplains of a church you were the first to acknowledge as having a claim to public recognition, we heartily testify to your unfailing kindness and courtesy towards us and to the reality of your Christian character. We are tolerably well aware that the end of your rule is also the end of services conducted after the Presbyterian fashion in the lodge. We will not forget your work of faith and labour of love in endeavouring to apply to the open sores of Ireland the leaves of the tree which are for the healing of the nations and we unite in praying that God's benison be with you and be with all who like yourselves have tried to make good of bad and friends of foes.'

D.1792/A3/6/18   **Letter to W. S. Armour from Armour,**

20 May 1915   commenting on the creation of the Asquith coalition government which he regards with some suspicion, especially since he feels that the cause of Home Rule is likely to suffer a setback.

'... This coalition government is a dubious sort of experiment. *The Times* and the papers under its control are very unpatriotic and have been playing into the hands of the enemy. It is almost certain that Kitchener and French have not hit it off. It is within the range of possibility that Kitchener may be sent out to take charge of the armies. There are hints already in that direction and the most curious suggestion of all is that Lloyd George should take his place at the War Office. He has filled many roles in his time and that would be almost the climax of a wondrous career. Then Fisher and Churchill have been at variance—the former thinking that his *ipse dixit* should not be called in question and the latter having decided opinions of his own. How the cabinet will be reconstructed you will know before this note reaches you. It would be the irony of the situation if John Redmond should become chief secretary for Ireland. The Ulster folks would fill all the asylums in a fortnight should that take place. I fancy Home Rule will get a set back in any case. ...'

D.1792/A3/6/19   **Letter to W. S. Armour from Armour,**

[n.d. May ? 1915]   attacking the composition of the new coalition
                                                   government and condemning particularly the inclusion
of Sir Edward Carson in the cabinet, since this is likely to damage the prospects for Home Rule, especially as Asquith and the Liberals are no longer in need of Irish Nationalist support in the house of commons.

'... *The Times* I think I'll slip as it has played the traitor and [Lord] Northcliffe deserves certainly internment at least. He has played the mischief with the [?] and Asquith has shown for once a want of real courage. You will see in the *D[aily] N[ews]* a good article on Northcliffe which hits him off well. The real unforgivable fault of Asquith is including Carson in the cabinet. It will work mischief in every way, disgusting all real radicals and probably putting an end to recruiting in the S. and W. of Ireland. He (Carson) was largely responsible for the war and it is a curious way of rewarding your enemies for mischief done. The Nationalists seem to me to have lost all grasp of statesmanship. Their first stupidity against which they were warned was allowing the Aberdeens to be shunted. That was probably the work of Churchill who shoved in his cousin and said C. has got practical dismissal, though one is sorry for his untoward fate. Then the next mistake of Redmond was the attitude he took up in regard to the liquor bill of Lloyd George. Redmond permitted the Tories to use him to pull the chestnuts out of the fire for them. If he had lain aside, they would have had to show their hand but he fell into their trap and the consequence is he has disgusted a large section of the Liberal party. He may whistle for his Home Rule but it is practically in my opinion shelved as the coalition can now do without him and his merry men and it can whittle down the whole thing so that it becomes a sham and shadow. The taxation when the war is over will be so heavy that the money for running the show will not be forthcoming. Things are in a nice kettle of fish and as for the war one can say nothing beyond this that the flower of the rising generation is being mowed down like grass. ...'

D.1792/A3/6/20   **Letter to W. S. Armour from Armour,**

3 June 1915   still fretting about the establishment of the coalition
                                                   and the inclusion of the Unionists within it.

'... It appears the political cart was upset by [Arthur] Balfour and Winston [Churchill] but what was their hand in the business is not published and there is only rumour. The conferring of the Garter on Kitchener is a slap at Northcliffe and the *D[aily] N[ews]* —a deserved flout. There will be inward grieving over the wound which may fester and lead to a drastic operation. I wrote Sir J[ames] B. D[ougherty] yesterday and I may hear some of the reasons for the coalition. Probably the real reason is that when the settlement comes—some settlement must come—there is to be no room for political recrimination as both political parties will have a hand in the matter and therefore it cannot be a subject for a political campaign. ...'

D.1792/A3/6/31   **Letter to W. S. Armour from Armour,**

11 August 1915   mainly devoted to local and family news, but he also
                                                   comments critically on the Roman Catholic religion
                                                   in discussing a papal plea for peace.

'... The Pope seems to have declared the Vatican pro-German and his talk of peace in his circular is too absurd for discussion. He will not come through the business with credit to the Vatican. One can never really understand the position of Irish Catholics who, in Dan O'Connell's phrase, say we take our religion from Rome but not our politics. It is hard to see how Catholics can believe in the infallibility in religion and the fallibility in politics of the Pope. He is either infallible all round or not infallible at all—the latter of which is perfectly true. It is one form of religion which never appealed to me on any side. That may be a limitation but one in which I rejoice. ...'

D.1792/A3/6/36

Letter to W. S. Armour from Armour,

29 September 1915

includes, as well as local news, an attack on Edmund McNeill, father of the Unionist leader Ronald McNeill, who has just died.

'... Edmund McNeill, father of the banshee—Ronald McN[eill]—has died at the age of ninety-four and more absurd articles about a man never were written than what has appeared in the [*Northern*] *Whig* and [*Belfast*] *News-Letter*. He was the most unconscionable tyrant as a land agent who ever walked on shoe leather. He was known as "desolation McNeill". Instead of dealing fairly with improving tenants, if he had met one of them with a decent coat on his back he clapped on £5 on his rent. If he meets any of his victims in the other world—there were very many—they will give him what he deserves a keel-hauling. ...'

D.1792/A3/6/37

Letter to W. S. Armour from Armour,

7 October 1915

expressing yet again his familiar anti-Anglican views, in this case in response to a speech by Bishop Bernard of Ossory opposing the idea of civil war in Ireland. Bernard was soon to become archbishop of Dublin.

'... You will see from an article in the *Freeman*[*'s Journal*] sent that Bishop Bernard who was a candidate for the archbishopric of Dublin in room of Peacocke has thrown a bomb into the camp of the Ulster folks. Clearly he has put a spoke in the wheel of the fire-eaters in the north who have not given up the notion of civil war should Home Rule be established. Trench, evidently Max's old professor of English in Galway, has come out with a strong letter in yesterday's *Daily Express* backing up Bernard's views. I cannot get a copy of the letter for tomorrow's letter but I may manage a copy for next week. I always thought the Episcopals would throw over the Presbyterians and come in for a big share in the government of Ireland in the future. Wee Henry and MacDermott and co. were roped in to do the dirty work of the bouncing Tories and they will be left high and dry with the only consolation that they did their duty in pounding at the Pope—a barren sort of theology but every man to his taste. ...'

D.1792/A3/6/41

Letter to W. S. Armour from Armour,

24 November 1915

commenting on the European situation and attacking Birrell for failing to appoint Professor R. M. Henry to the Intermediate Education Board in lieu of Professor Todd-Martin, who had just died (since the place had been offered to Sir James Dougherty but he had refused it).

'... I wrote Sir J[ames] B. D[ougherty] yesterday to protest and to say B[irrell] was a lump of putty. He had sworn by all his gods that he would not give the place to T[rinity] C[ollege] D[ublin] but he had done it and that he deserved a kicking. While Sir J. B. D. was in Dublin he (B) could be kept tolerably right but now "the putty" was showing itself. As I told you and told D[ougherty] yesterday in my letter, B[irrell] is obsessed by the theory that no Protestant could be a home ruler: if he professed himself in that way he is either an office seeker or a hypocrite. That seems to be his doctrine—a curious doctrine for one who professes to believe that Home Rule will be the salvation of Ireland. It has been, as I have pointed out, the salvation of the empire already, for if Botha and Redmond—the one getting Home Rule and the other obtaining an act of parliament for it on the statute book—had taken the side of the Germans in the war, the British empire by this time would have been in fragments. ...' [*See also* D.1792/A3/6/42.]

D.1792/A3/6/44

Letter to W. S. Armour from Armour,

29 December 1915

commenting on the cabinet crisis over conscription, the pressure from the press for changes in government and Lloyd George's possible ambition to replace Asquith as prime minister.

'... There may be a cabinet crisis before a week runs over conscription. *The Times, D*[*aily*] *Mail* and [J. L.] Garvin's organ are out to have Asquith's head and think the millenium would come if he was out of the premiership. They are for having Lloyd George as their man, to throw him over in a short time should they manage their game. Lloyd George could put an end to their campaign by uttering a sentence or two but he is entirely as yet silent so the suspicion is growing that he would like to have the chief seat in the new synagogue—if it gets into order. It may be perilous for him for however some Tories may dislike Asquith, they distrust the other more. It is possible that Asquith who has a genius in engineering politically may be able to meet checks without and within the cabinet successfully. It is difficult to see how Kitchener could serve under Lloyd George after the latter's speech on his management of affairs lately. ...'

D.1792/A3/7

1916

Originals of letters from Rev. J. B. Armour to his wife and sons (principally to W. S. Armour).

D.1792/A3/7/2

5 January 1916

Letter to W. S. Armour from Armour,

commenting on the likelihood of the collapse of the Asquith coalition government over the issue of conscription and the possibility that Lloyd George had plotted against Asquith.

'... There seems a likelihood that the coalition government may founder over conscription. As far as one can see the conscriptionists in the cabinet have carried the day. Lloyd George has probably played against Asquith. As far as the returns go as published, there seems no strong reason for conscription. Asquith's unfortunate pledge not to call on the married men to serve until the unmarried were roped in was an instance of weakness on his part and he is being pinned down to the pledge. He may today be able to convince the house on the reasons for conscription but it will lead to disunion, controversy and probably disruption of the government. From the figures published this morning it is not easy to see how so many can be trained for service within a year and a half and one hopes the war will be over before that time. ...'

D.1792/A3/7/12

19 April 1916

Letter to W. S. Armour from Armour,

discussing his application for retirement, the military situation in Europe and the continuing weakness and instability of the Asquith coalition government. He was in the end persuaded not to retire.

'... The government is staggering I fancy. This compulsion business is playing the mischief. Asquith allowed himself to be jostled on to the down plane and it would appear that he is compelled to go down the plane a little farther. Lloyd George is not from all appearances standing to him loyally. It would be the irony of circumstances if Lloyd George should follow Chamberlain and become the leader of the Tories. Life is mixey/maxey [*sic*] at present . ...'

D.1792/A3/7/13

26 April 1916

Letter to W. S. Armour from Armour,

commenting somewhat inaccurately on the Easter Rising in Dublin and on the methods of the 'Sinn Feiners' [*sic*]. He is particularly interested in the possibility that they have been inspired to violence by the example of the Ulster Unionist gun-running episode.

'... What the state of matters in Dublin is one cannot tell as there is not a hint in the paper this morning. Rumour, that false jade, is blowing her horn vigorously but what is below the rumours is in cloud. It appears that Sir Roger Casement with his cruiser has been nabbed—the unfortunate man who turned traitor to his country. Some still believe that he has been a British spy in Germany all the time—a theory which can only be true because it is impossible. The Sinn Feiners have taken a leaf out of Sir Edward Carson's book and like the Ulster men they will not have Home Rule. The Ulster people thought they were doing God service by begging the Kaiser to come over and snatch Ulster from King George and be their ruler. These Sinn Feiners are trying the same by attempting to make Carson's theory run. But Ulster thought it was fighting or trying to fight for the highest Christian principle but of course these other folks who are imitating them are the most wicked people ever seen on the planet. To buy and bring from Hamburgh [*sic*] old German rifles at a dear price, land them at Larne and get motors all over the north of Ireland to take them to Orange lodges was an act calling for a *"te deum"* and was and became a new version of "God save the King". For the other people to copy their example is treason of the most Judaistic type. Human nature is a curious study in the concrete as well as in the abstract. Both parties—the Ulsterites and the Sinn Feiners—are the violent enemies of Home Rule but the one party is the saintly clan, the other belongs to their father the devil. The moral law is becoming a little mixed nowadays. Sir Edward Carson is a hero and a saint but those who take his principles and attempt to yoke them to practical politics are sinners above all the Galileans. By this time you probably know more of what has happened in Ireland than we do as Birrell's statement yesterday in the house has not reached us here. The [*Northern*] *Whig* has only four pages today without a word about the fighting at Verdun or the front in any [?] and without a word about what has occurred in the metropolis or anywhere else. The rumours about the seizure of the P.O. in Dublin and the blowing up of the bridge over the Boyne at Drogheda are probably the figments of imagination without very much foundation in fact. That soldiers are being drafted from the north to Dublin is likely true and that a considerable number of mad people is likely laid up by the heels by this time is also likely a fact—these may be imagined as real occurrences. Beyond that there is nothing certain. To speculate on uncertainties is ploughing the sand ... .

Being up the street I have heard numerous stories. One is likely true that Sir Roger Casement has been taken to London and handed over to the Scotland Yard folks and is in the Tower. He is to be tried for high treason. It appears that the r[ailwa]y at Malahide was broken up, hence his exc[ellency] could not reach Belfast if he had wished but he has plenty to do in Dublin at present. The rumours are many that the Bank of Ireland and the P.O. were seized—that several camps where Germans are interned were stormed and the prisoners liberated—that motor cars, among which one in which Ja[me]s Cunningham was going or one of the Cunninghams, were commandeered by the rebels and that some place about Oldcastle, Co. Meath, has been seized. Some of the papers say that r[ailwa]y communications between Belfast and Dublin will be resumed today. No telegram or letter has come today or yesterday. ...'

D.1792/A3/7/14	**Letter to W. S. Armour from Armour, [completed by Mrs Armour],**
17 May 1916	

analysing the aftermath of the Easter Rising, including Asquith's visit to Ireland, criticising the severity of the military authorities in dealing with those who had rebelled, suggesting the reasons why most of Ireland had not been involved and recounting an argument with an unknown Ahoghill, Co. Antrim, Unionist. He also discusses R. D. Megaw's efforts to associate the organisers of the Ballymoney meeting of October 1913, such as himself, with Sir Roger Casement's treasonable activities.

'... I was in Belfast yesterday again but I saw nobody who could tell me about Asquith's success with the Belfast reactionaries. He could do nothing I fancy with such cattle as they are obsessed with the German idea, applying it locally in the form "Ulster over all", the Germans having a more ambitious programme "Germany over all the world"—a programme which does not seem to work out as speedily and satisfactorily as they expected. The *M[anchester] G[uardian]* takes the only sensible view of the situation. It is well worth perusal. It goes rightly against the severity of the military as it thinks that now the leaders of the Sinn Feiners have got scragged, leniency ought to be shown to the dupes that followed their insane programme. As a Frenchman wrote that the reason why almost no farmer in the south and west had anything to do with the rising. The real cause of that was Gladstone who gave the farmers their freedom and their rights. The Clan-na-Gael in America, suborned by money from the German Americans, engineered the business largely in Ireland. Sir Roger Casement who is clean mad was an agent and syndicalism and Larkinism—these were the prophets of what was called the rebellion. Going up yesterday in the train, [Rev.] Craig of Finvoy came into the carriage. Some ignorant man from Ahoghill was there and he was very vehement against the Sinn Feiners. His doctrine was certainly thorough. He would shoot them every one *etc. etc.*—the usual whine and absurdity of Ulster. I listened patiently until he had cleared what he is pleased to call his conscience. At last I said you have talked more nonsense since you came in than I ever heard in the course of my life. Hear a few words in reply. Sir Edward Carson came to Ireland and proclaimed that he had come to break every law of the land. The Sinn Feiners took up his position and proceeded to break every law human and divine and you have the result in what has occurred of putting Sir Edward's position into practical work. Tell me is the man who proclaimed a policy not responsible before God when the policy is put in operation? Then there was the gun-running at Larne when his followers purchased from the Germans a large quantity of war material. The guns were not to shoot crows but were intended to shoot his majesty's soldiers some day possibly. The Sinn Feiners got guns galore from Germany and they used them with real result against his majesty's policemen and soldiers—where is the moral difference between Carson's gun-runners and the Sinn Feiners? There is [?] of you blame the one party, a just judgement demands blame for the party which set the example. Then the Carsonites wished to take Ulster from King George and make it a province of the Kaiser. The Sinn Feiners wished and intended to make the whole of Ireland a republic under the patronage of the Kaiser. The Kaiserites of Ulster find their policy attempted by the Sinn Feiners—where is the difference in principle? Then you have been severe in a feckless way on Redmond and his party. Well if Redmond and his party had joined the Sinn Feiners, then God help Ulster, it would have been today suffering as much in the way of destruction as Sackville Street is, and further, if Botha had not got Home Rule in S. Africa and if the Home Rule bill had not been on the books, the British government would not possess in S. Africa today one acre in that continent and if the Irish in America and throughout the colonies had not followed Redmond in loyalty, the British empire would be in smithereens at this hour. He ventured to say he did not care—yes, was the reply, you care not for the welfare of the empire if you could only get your subversive policy carried out. He never spoke from that moment until we got to Belfast. I was glad that Craig was present. He never uttered a syllable to support the old fellow. I took the bull by the horns. I sent on the bundle of papers and a letter which appeared in the [*Northern*] *Whig* on Monday by R. D. Megaw. I think a more absurd, stupid, ill-conceived letter never was written. Nobody on the [*Northern*] *Whig* has made any reference to it—a proof of the public estimate of R. D. M.'s views on any matter. I should have liked to get at him for a few sentences but what will gall him most will be that nobody has taken him up either by way of approval or condemnation. There was nothing said by Casement or anybody else at the meeting for which there is any need of apology. If Sir Roger has gone wrong in the mind, we cannot help that any more than we can help R. D. M.'s stupidities. He threw away a great chance for himself and he is now like a rat dying in its hole. I pity him for his persistent folly. ...

The odd thing is that Ja[me]s Chambers K.C. M.P. [South Belfast] is to defend Prof[essor Eoin] McNeill before the court martial. How Sandy Row will look on that is too abstruse a question for the plain man. You will see in due course the trial of Sir Roger. ...'

D.1792/A3/7/15

24 May 1916

Letter to W. S. Armour from Armour, [written from Portrush, Co. Antrim],

discussing likely future political developments in the wake of Asquith's Irish visit and in particular the possibility that the Unionists will have to accept some sort of compromise over Home Rule. He sees hopeful signs that even the Ulster Unionists will, with difficulty, accept this and, as ever, he tends to underestimate the intensity and strength of their feelings.

'... Asquith has come and gone but what he has in his mind to do in regard to the government of Ireland is largely at present his secret. All the Tory London papers with the exception of the *Morning Post* are in favour of some compromise on the Home Rule question which represents a big change in political feeling. It means that the Tory party has come round and that they will not back up Carson in his civil war project under certain conditions. Every sensible man now sees that he had a real hand in the so-called rebellion and it is dawning on many that the mistake of the government was in not coming down hard on the gun runners of Ulster who thought they were doing a good stroke of business for themselves, though it is becoming apparent they were committing suicide as well as endangering the empire. Their sin is finding them out. It is said this morning that a lord lieutenant for Ireland is out of the question and that Wimborne is to be the last. I hardly think that is possible. There must be somebody to represent the king in Ireland, though he may be called by a different name from the present nomenclature. Even Swift MacNeill [Nationalist member for South Donegal] says the Castle system cannot be entirely abolished. It is hard to see how it could. Asquith however has a clear head and he may be able to get Redmond and the party for which Carson stands to agree to some workable scheme. Carson raised the devil in Ulster and it will be difficult for him to cast out the demon he worshipped for a time. There are many in Ulster unamenable to reason as they were so poisoned by whirling speeches that they fancy their prejudices have the sanction of Sinai. However there is a larger element of sanity in Ulster than there was. The archbishop of Dublin—Bernard—represents a vast change in the feelings at least of the Church of Ireland and the fact of [J. H.] Campbell being attorney-general means that he and his party do not intend to abandon the hope of having a share in the future government of Ireland. There is evidence of a new atmosphere in Irish politics but one can say nothing more than "wait and see". It must have been galling to R. D. Megaw that nobody in the [*Northern*] *Whig* referred to his letter in any possible form. There was a letter in the [*Ulster*] *Guardian*—I cannot lay hold of a copy—hauling him up, pointing out that several—such as Davey of the [*Ulster*] *Guardian*, William McAfee [*sic*] B.L. [unsuccessful Liberal candidate for North Antrim in December 1910] and others had volunteered for service to their country but that R. D. M. had contented himself with lampooning such volunteers. The letter pointed out that [R. G.] Glendinning [Liberal member for North Antrim, 1906-10] who was referred to in his precious letter had given two sons to the war but the name of a Megaw had not appeared in the long list of volunteers. If he sees the letter which he is sure to do, he will not keep it as a testimonial to his courage and patriotism. A more foolish letter than R. D. M.'s never appeared and why he wrote it is a mystery only explicable on the ground that common sense was an element wanting when he got the first start for life. ...'

D.1792/A3/7/16

Letter to W. S. Armour from Armour, [written from Portrush, Co. Antrim],

31 May 1916

commenting on the Lloyd George Irish initiative and on the pressure of world opinion on the Ulster Unionists and expressing grave doubts about the policy of excluding Ulster from the jurisdiction of any Dublin parliament, a policy which is increasingly favoured by the Unionists.

'... The public events are disturbing. Lloyd George who was anathema to the Tory mind a few years ago has been appointed unanimously by the cabinet to try to settle the Home Rule quarrel. The fact that Lansdowne, Bonar Law, Balfour, Long and Curzon have agreed to hand over the settlement to the wee Welshman is a proof of the change of feeling that has taken place in English Tory circles over the knotty question. It is said that Asquith told the Belfast reactionaries plainly that the opinion in the United States and all through the colonies was that the question must be settled and that the settlement of the matter would have more effect on the empire and the war than even the loss of the province of Ulster. How they took the plain talk is not known but from the articles in the [*Northern*] *Whig* and [*Belfast*] *News-Letter* it is plain that the Unionists of Ulster are like little boys whistling as they pass a graveyard. The bottom is tolerably well knocked out of their theories and their diatribes against Home Rule sound like the death rattle in their throat. How they can possibly go in for a policy of the exclusion of Ulster passes my dull comprehension when one considers first that at present the representatives of Home Rule in Ulster are one more than the Tories. Then what would become say of the Ulster Bank which has more branches in the rest of Ireland than it has in Ulster and what would become of the merchants as a whole. Because if Ulster says we will have nothing to do with you legislatively, naturally the rest of Ireland will say, "well then we will have nothing to do with you commercially". It seems to me perfectly idiotic and is an outward proof of the barrenness of the Ulster mind in statesmanship. The Ulster folks are up against a stone wall. Whether the question will be raised at the Assembly next week or not, I have no idea. ...'

D.1792/A3/7/17

7 June 1916

Letter to W. S. Armour from Armour, [written from Belfast] ,

expressing sorrow at the death of Lord Kitchener, criticising the acceptance by Carson and the Unionists of the exclusion of six Ulster counties and indicating that the General Assembly has given him leave to retire.

'... We had Sir Edward Carson addressing the [General] Assembly this morning—his appearance was received with heartiness but not with the enthusiasm of two years ago. He did not touch on politics. Yesterday he told his friends that six counties in Ulster would be excluded and that they might accept or reject the offer but the government would do no more. That is a change. Three years ago, "we will not have Home Rule for Ireland". "We will march an army from Belfast to Cork to put down Home Rule everywhere", but now we are willing to give Home Rule to twenty-six counties as a form of Home Rule for six counties. We are progressing. Formerly Ulster was to defend the Protestants in every part of Ireland and now we will only defend the six counties and let the other Protestants starve in Home Rule for ever. That is the new form of manliness. Every man in the six counties save himself and let the devil take the others. A more idiotic policy never was proposed but in the continuous reign of madness one need not be disappointed if insanity gets the upper hand. The proposal has come like a wet blanket on the mad-heads and they are considerably subdued. How it will work out I cannot imagine. ...'

D.1792/A3/7/18

[n.d. June ? 1916]

Letter to W. S. Armour from Armour,

again expressing familiar criticisms of the suggested partition of Ireland and claiming that Sir Edward Carson has been seriously defeated in that he has been forced to abandon his objective of maintaining the whole of Ireland within the Union.

'... Carson seems down in the mouth over the Irish business. It must have been trying for him after all the bombast he has been uttering for the past few years in the key of "no surrender" to have to say that his visit now is the saddest he has had. It is perfectly true as his castle of cards has collapsed. His house was built on the sands. "The rain has descended, the floods have come and the winds have blown and beat upon that house and it has fallen and great is the fall thereof." We will not have Home Rule anywhere in Ireland was the boast but now we will permit it in twenty-six out of thirty-two counties. We will stand up for and defend all Protestants in the south and west, we will have an undivided Ulster in any case but now the people who were to be defended in the three provinces are to be handed over to the wolves, nay Monaghan, Cavan and Donegal are to be outside our rule. There never was such a collapse and there never was anything so stupid as demanding separate government for the six counties. It will be ruinous commercially for the six counties for the tendency will be to exclude the merchants of the six from trading with the rest of Ireland. The city of Derry for example does the most of its business with Donegal and the merchants there are said to be almost in a state of panic about their future. Even those who yelled loudest "no surrender" are frightened. Carson is no statesman, however clever he may be as an advocate and he has been listening to, and going by, the opinions of the mad-heads and simply acting as their mouthpiece. It is reported on all sides that the people of Sandy Row think he has betrayed them and it is questionable whether many of them would go to hear him at a public meeting. At least he has taken good care not to hazard a public meeting at present. There might be in a public meeting a rift within his lute. The delegates from the different centres have left the business in his hands, an indication of the bankruptcy of their blatant statesmanship. They are in a mess and they are awakening to the fact that they have shot their last bolt which has only damaged their own ramparts. ...'

D.1792/A3/7/19   **Letter to W. S. Armour from Armour,**

5 July 1916   commenting on Sir Roger Casement's involvement in
                                                  the Easter Rising which Armour puts down to a loss
of sanity; criticising the report of the Hardinge Commission which he believes was too limited
in its scope and treated Augustine Birrell unfairly; and expressing his conviction that, as a consequence of underestimating the strength of revolutionary nationalism, John Redmond's career
was virtually at an end.

'... Casement, now no longer Sir Roger, has driven his head against a stone wall and is now to be
treated as a felon with a poor chance of being enrolled in the list of martyrs. It is tragedy. His
actions for the last two years can only be explained on the ground of insanity. He is an illustration of a man of mature life yielding to a temptation to a course which could only end in failure
even if for the moment it was partially successful. Young hearts are liable to be carried away
by will-o-the-wisps but how a man of his experience of life could have been so demented is a
mystery. Still his services to the empire and humanity were very real as he had an inborn hatred
of tyranny and cruelty and few deserved better of his country than Sir Roger. It is not likely—
at least I hope so—that he will suffer the extreme penalty of the law but in any case he has
sinned beyond the hope of restoration to public favour. It may be true that his sin calls for
vengeance—it is not possible to question on the evidence the justice of the sentence—but what
good could a broken man's death do to any save to gratify for the moment the passion for
hanging. We remember him in his sanity and found him a very charming guest. Even Susan
[Green, the Armours' housekeeper] was taken by his courtesy. A worthy man who in a crisis
lost his mental balance is the verdict on Sir Roger. I am really sorry for the fate of the man.
The report of the Hardinge Commission on the rebellion is published and seems a very unsatisfactory docum[ent]. The scope of the inquiry was too limited. The Nationalists protested
against it from the first and they are up in arms against the outcome. The *Irish News* and
Freeman['s Journal], I am sorry I could not get a copy of either, are rather savage over the
business. The commission comes down like a hundred of bricks on the head of Birrell but hardly
justly in my opinion. It is true that he is a sort of [camel ?] as a statesman but his position was
very anomalous. The gun running at Larne should have been taken vigorously in hand and the
tower of [Babel ?] should have fallen on the heads of the leaders. Unfortunately the whole
Tory party were then on the side of the Ulsterites and even the heads of the army forgot their
duty as officers and regarded themselves as the tools of a really rebellious gang. Nothing drastic
could be done. Then if they were allowed to bring in guns, drill and form themselves into
volunteers, naturally and necessarily other parties could not be taken by the throat for doing
the same. Redmond and most of the Nationalists took the view that the Sinn Feiners were a
much more negligible party than they really were and so things were allowed to slide on and an
avalanche was the result. His star was one to turn out unlucky. I fancy his days as a statesman
are over. One wonders if he will resign his seat or whether he will face the music. There are
many things in the report, however tersely written, which are questionable and Hardinge has
not raised himself by the effort. I fancy there will be a debate over the business. It will not
make the position of Chalmers—or Chambers I forget which—as under-secretary any easier. The
Nationalists will have their knife in him. I am sincerely glad Dougherty and the Aberdeens
were out of the business. Wimborne must be sore at heart for such an ending to what was
thought a great career. You will see the report in the *M[anchester] G[uardian]* ....'

D.1792/A3/7/20   **Letter to W. S. Armour from Armour, [written from
                                                  Portrush],**

12 July 1916
                                                  discussing the sad impact of the news of the heavy
casualties experienced by the 36th Ulster Division at the battle of the Somme and commenting
on a debate in the house of lords on the Hardinge Commission report and on the possible
consequences for the six Ulster counties, if they are excluded from the operation of Home Rule.

'... Not a drum is beaten today in Ulster—a new thing in the province: perhaps the drumming is a thing of the past. It is said that in parts of Belfast bunches of Orange lilies are tied with crepe, as they were celebrating a funeral. It is a very say day throughout the province as the Ulster volunteers have got a tremendous crushing. They fought like lions but whole battalions are said to be wiped out. The troops are said to have got largely out of hand, rushing past the German trenches which were full of Germans who when they passed turned their guns on them and mowed them down like grass. They have had the glory but the fate of the noble 600 in the Crimea. There is hardly a home here that has not to bewail one dead or badly wounded ... .

Asquith's speech on Monday did not throw much light on the situation. There was a debate in the [house of] lords last night—bitter in some respects but Crewe managed to defend Birrell who has been unfairly dealt with by the Hardinge Commission. He was the victim of circumstances. Colonel [R. C. A.] McCalmont [Unionist member for East Antrim] has a wicked letter in the papers this morning, practically saying that the leaders of the Unionist party have betrayed Ulster and the Protestants of Ireland. He represents the worst element of Unionism and so does many of his party. The Ulster six counties will likely have to pay for their whistle in the exclusion from the Irish parliament. They will come under English rule for which they have been clamouring with the result that conscription will be applied to the six counties. There will be heart burnings in the six counties and there may be a serious revolt against Carson. It will be interesting to watch how things will work out in this extra loyal province. Will the province sing "Halleluliah" [*sic*] over the war situation? ...'

D.1792/A3/7/21   **Letter to W. S. Armour from Armour,**

19 July 1916   describing his attendance at a Co. Antrim insurance committee meeting in Belfast at which he had vigorously attacked the idea of the exclusion of Ulster from the rest of Ireland. 'In less than three years the six counties would beg on their knees to be taken in.' He expresses optimism about the progress of the war and argues that the very heavy losses sustained by the 36th Ulster Division at the battle of the Somme can be largely ascribed to Edward Carson.

'... Carson is largely to blame for the debacle as he insisted that the rank and file would select their own officers with the result that the officers chosen were addressed by their names, discipline there was little and training for war was entirely absent. They thus went into the fray under the men who had no authority and no real control over the men. The officers were mown down and so were the privates. It is hard to read the lists of casualties which are appearing in the [*Northern*] *Whig* and [*Belfast*] *News-Letter*. If the contingents had been put under the care of officers of the army, really trained men who would have stood no familiarity, and if they had been trained as others were, the story might have been different but the facts are very much as I have stated and there is mourning through the province and will be in increasing volume. ...'

D.1792/A3/7/22   **Letter to W. S. Armour from Armour,**

26 July 1916   containing family news and commenting on the government's handling of the aftermath of the Easter Rising and of the political situation generally.

'... The government have muddled and bungled this Irish business most stupidly. They have broken faith with Redmond scandalously. It is hard to know whin mair or what the outlook really is. Even Lloyd George has floundered hopelessly. His speech was about the weakest and least convincing he ever made. Fancy him telling the house that an agreement put on paper could not be drafted into an act of parliament. Devlin put a spoke in his wheel by asking if the agreement was not in the *first* draft of the measure. He had to admit that it was and therefore gave away his whole case. Carson, to do him justice, made the most conciliatory speech he ever made and the best on the occasion. The Nationalists are well out of the business in my opinion and with their party they have secured a new lease of life. What America and the colonies will say over the [?] business one does not know but it may dull the interest of them all in the real problem, how to finish the war with success. Coalition governments never have succeeded in our empire and the present one adds another illustration of the futility of trying to unite oil and water. I see from the papers this morning that there may be another attempt to make another trial but the Nationalists neither care nor will have any more negotiations. Deceived and betrayed once, they will not risk a second betrayal. The real difficulty is to set up some form of government for Ireland during the war in a form which shall not be hateful to Irish opinion. Sykes, a Catholic Tory, is spoken of as chief secretary but who will be lord lieutenant is not hinted at. Lord Derby, with a Tory chief secretary, would be throwing the fat into the fire. Two Tory officials with Campbell as attorney-general would give life and energy to the Sinn Feiners. It would be better for the Liberal party and for the Nationalists if the government of Ireland was not drastically changed during the war. The Home Rule bill is on the statute book for the whole of Ireland without exclusion of any counties. Doubtless there was promised an amending bill but as one amending bill has turned out an abortion with the general change of opinion throughout the empire on Home Rule, it is not likely that Ulster will fare as it expects. Hardly any sane man believes in the good or the feasibility of exclusion of any part of Ireland from the other part. I suspect Carson is in his heart not enthusiastic over the exclusion of the six counties either permanently or temporarily. Of course permanent exclusion is folly. Asquith's point that Ulster would not be coerced is stupidly thin. He might as well say that the brewers, distillers and publicans cannot be coerced to submit to legislation they oppose. It is very good doctrine for landlords but in this world certain classes for the good of the whole must give in. Asquith has wobbled over the business and he has not got out of the hole. ...'

D.1792/A3/7/23 **Letter to W. S. Armour from Armour,**

2 August 1916 again returning to the plight of Sir Roger Casement and discussing Asquith's weakness as leader of the coalition government. He is particularly concerned that the government and administration of Ireland have passed into what he sees as Tory hands.

'... I fear from this day's paper that Casement is doomed. It is a political blunder for though the sentence was just, mercifulness would have been politic. As the *M[anchester] G[uardian]* puts it, Casement living would be of no use to the Germans, Casement dead is worth a battalion to them. The coalition can do nothing right and Asquith is at times too weak. He bungled the Irish settlement and broke faith in an outrageous manner with Redmond. Now nobody knows where we are and [H. E.] Duke's appointment [as chief secretary for Ireland] with [J. H.] Campbell as attorney-general means that Ireland is to be run by the Tories. It may turn out a pretty kettle of fish. The Nationalists are glad at heart that the proposed settlement is burst up. ...'

D.1792/A3/7/27 **Letter to W. S. Armour from Armour,**

30 August 1916 recounting a discussion which he had had with Sir James Dougherty, who was on holiday at Portstewart, Co. Londonderry, about the Casement affair. In particular Dougherty had informed him about the Casement diaries and their controversial contents and Armour feels that it will prove difficult to obtain a permanent place for Casement amongst the martyrs and saints of Ireland.

'... We discussed the Roger Casement business. He told me that the government had seized his papers and among them were confessions of the most unspeakable kind of personal immoralities he had been guilty of in the Congo and elsewhere. Quite a disgusting confession, the reality of which could only prove moral as well as mental insanity. The government had actually offered to his counsel the papers with the idea that they would plead insanity but they refused to consider the matter. Casement was in their opinion a very secondary consideration. His case was of no importance if they could do something sensational for Ireland as the solicitor Duffy was a Sinn Féiner and he selected as counsel a relative of Tim Healy. The client was of no importance—his death was a secondary matter if only they could establish an impossible proposition that Casement could not be held legally a traitor. Sir J[ames] B. D[ougherty] said that for a time the feeling in many members of the cabinet was in favour of a reprieve for Roger. But the murder of Captain Fryatt by the Germans made a reprieve impossible as the outcry in the army and elsewhere would have been universal. Casement's becoming a Catholic in the light of the revelations his diaries contained does not add much glory to the Catholic faith. It is perfectly plain that deviations from the path of honour, such as Casement was guilty of, arise from moral twists. The way of personal purity is the way to moral and mental sanity. I fancy that it will take a great effort to establish Casement among the martyrs and saints of Ireland though there are curious specimens of Irish martyrs and saints in the calendar. ...'

D.1792/A3/7/28   **Letter to W. S. Armour from Armour,**

6 September 1916   again criticising the report of the Hardinge Commission and recounting Sir James Dougherty's attitude towards it.

'... The mistake of the Hardinge Commission was there was nobody on it who knew anything of Ireland. Hardinge had to undergo a slight operation during the sitting and the case was entirely in the hands of Shearman, a talkative man who thinks he knows everything. The commission was worse than useless and its report will soon be in oblivion. Dougherty thought they had made up their mind to sit as a court of *review* in regard to the Irish commission but as he refused to give evidence if that was the intention, they *half* modified their purpose in their report. ...'

D.1792/A3/7/29   **Letter to W. S. Armour from Armour,**

12 September 1916   commenting on the internal dissensions within the Nationalist party in the aftermath of the Easter Rising.

'... The Irish problem is still in the clouds. Redmond and the Irish party are coming in for hard words. There was a meeting on Sunday in Dublin in which several from Omagh took part. Some priest from Carndonagh made a most bitter attack on the Belfast Orangemen which has called forth strong words of condemnation in several nationalist quarters. There was a biting article in the *Freeman['s Journal]* yesterday. I could not get a copy but if I can find a report of the speech published in Monday's [*Northern*] *Whig* you will have it with this. There is an attempt to wreck Redmond. Whether it will succeed or not is another question. Joe Devlin is coming in for abuse from rash and rancorous tongues. Joe will have failed much if he does not give back with interest more than he has got. ...'

D.1792/A3/7/31   **Letter to W. S. Armour from Armour,**

27 September 1916   indicating that Sir James Dougherty, in view of his advancing age, would not stand for re-election as Liberal member for Londonderry City. 'He is satisfied that he has been in the house.' Armour suggests that the Dougherty family are likely to retire to Dublin, though in fact they ultimately stayed in London.

D.1792/A3/7/40

Letter to W. S. Armour from Armour,

6 December 1916

discussing the fall of the Asquith coalition, for which Armour blames Lloyd George, and its likely political consequences.

'... The bolt from the blue has fallen—Asquith has resigned. "The Welshman" has brought that about and one knows not what to say further than that the war over which so much blood and treasure have been spent is likely to give victory for the Huns. The one clear head is cast aside. Lloyd George has cast his lot in with the Tories which has been suspected for over a year would happen. It is clear that Bonar Law, however clever and loyal, can only get a cabinet of third rate men and how they can win is not very apparent. It is likely true that the war department made up of the Bourbonic elements which forget nothing and learn nothing has brought things into a mess and that the navy department under Balfour has not grasped or held the reins tight enough. The situation is full of peril, the horizon being very dark all round. One can only sit in silence and cultivate hope almost against hope, which is an exercise easier said than done. If an election takes place, there will be greater confusion with the likelihood of a new chance for reactionaries. The fat is certainly in the fire. To forecast the future would take the wisdom of one of the Old Testament prophets who is not likely to come forth with a message of supreme wisdom. I fear the ambition of the Welshman has been the cause of the imbroglio. It is reported in the papers that Bonar Law and Carson have made a deal with the Nationalists by which Ulster is to be joined in the Home Rule business for three years—I suppose giving Ulster the right to secede at the end of the term—and that the Nationalists are to yield to some form of conscription. Such is the purport of a statement in the press. It would be the irony of history if the Tories after all their covenants *etc*. should be the party to propose and carry Home Rule. It might turn out true. At any rate Bonar Law cannot form an administration without help from Liberals and possibly Nationalists. ...'

D.1792/A3/7/41

Letter to W. S. Armour from Armour,

13 December 1916

commenting again on the fall of the Asquith coalition and the alleged part played by Lloyd George in that process.

'... The political situation is in a queer mess. Mr Lloyd George will be forgiven if he manages to bring the war to a successful end. The suspicion is general that he has been intriguing against Asquith all the while. ...'

D.1792/A3/7/42

Letter to W. S. Armour from Armour,

20 December 1916

again reiterating his suspicions of, and hostility to, Lloyd George and his new coalition government and accurately forecasting some of Lloyd George's future difficulties with his new Unionist allies.

'... Lloyd George has got into the saddle apparently. I have not read his speech. I hear that *The Spectator* is angry over the change of government and while it gives due credit for the Welshman's ability, it looks with suspicion on the move. *The Nation* takes a similar view and says it is the case of the serpent devouring the lion. [Sir James] Dougherty also takes the same view, saying the Tories in the cabinet engineered the business and expects an election soon as the Tories think they might sweep the country and then they will turn on the Welsh attorney whom they hate and will not forgive probably, unless like [Joseph] Chamberlain he eats up all his former views and joins the reactionaries. ... I would not be surprised if he did as nobody can trust utterly a Welshman. ...'

D.1792/A3/8

1917

Originals of letters from Rev. J. B. Armour to his wife and sons (principally to W. S. Armour).

D.1792/A3/8/1

1 January 1917

Letter to W. S. Armour from Armour,

commenting favourably on the freeing of Irish political prisoners by the new Lloyd George coalition but repeating his accusations of betrayal against Lloyd George personally.

'... The situation in political matters is perplexing. The fact that the government of which Carson is a leading spirit has loosed the Sinn Féiners from jail without conditions apparently has been a grief of [mind ?] to the [*Belfast*] *News-Letter* and the [*Northern*] *Whig* and is a wonderful business. If Birrell had done the job, he would have been execrated but Duke having done it is only a proof of mistaken kindness and policy .... Lloyd George one must say did not play the game and his only place now is with the Tories who will for a time accept him, though possibly they may one day rend him as like the Bourbons they forget nothing and learn nothing. It is a curious team he is leading and it may be "God hath chosen the weak things of the world to confound the mighty". Asquith's star, I don't think has set yet any more than Grey's. ...'

D.1792/A3/8/2

10 January 1917

Letter to W. S. Armour from Armour,

repeating his criticisms of Lloyd George's new ministerial team and expressing his support for the restriction or prohibition of the sale of liquor by the state.

'... I am a trifle doubtful about the success of the wee Welshman as he has gathered a very odd team about him. To fancy that he can win the war with Carson, who was largely the cause of the war from his reckless speeches inciting to civil war in Ireland, as first lord of the Admiralty— with Milner as an adviser who, if his policy in Africa had been followed, would have lost Africa to the empire and therefore would have lost us this war in a few months—with Curzon who is a Tory crank who did mischief in India and with Balfour who by his act of 1904 sold the country to the brewers, distillers and publicans—that seems to me an insane act, a taking the bit in the teeth and damning the consequences to use Milner's phrase, so often repeated within the years previous to the big drive. With you, I have no solid hope that the wee Welshman can win a righteous peace. To set aside two of the finest minds in world at the bidding of the real traitorous press and to choose the shoddy minds may be striking but is not warfare as the Frenchman said of the Crimean battles. If reactionaries can win anything, they have their chance now. Unless the Welshman is allowed to be dictator without any advice from the others, the hope of a solid peace rests on sand. ...'

D.1792/A3/8/4

24 January 1917

Letter to W. S. Armour from Armour,

condemning Woodrow Wilson's pacific views and revealing disenchantment with the *Manchester Guardian* for treating them with some sympathy in a leading article. He expresses his preference for the *Daily Chronicle* which he believes is 'saner and more moral'.

D.1792/A3/8/5

31 January 1917

Letter to W. S. Armour from Armour,

chiefly devoted to war news and to the local activities

of the Temperance League but also briefly mentioning a speech made in Dublin at a reception for Canadian soldiers by the new chief justice, J. H. Campbell, the former Unionist politician, in which he had forecast great changes in Ireland in consequence of 'recent events', much to the delight of the *Freeman's Journal* and the concern of the *Belfast News-Letter*.

D.1792/A3/8/6   **Letter to W. S. Armour from Armour,**

[n.d. February ? 1917]   welcoming President Wilson's ultimatum to the Germans and commenting on the successful outcome for Sinn Féin of the North Roscommon by-election.

'... The Roscommon election is a bad blow to Redmond but a wrong interpretation on it is seen to be taken by the Unionists as it is a strong condemnation of the action of the government which has done nothing to scotch rebellion—nay its action is to encourage it. I sent you the leader in the *Freeman['s Journal]* on the subject. The snow helped [Count George Noble] Plunkett as well as the wild priest O'Flanagan. Will the count as a Sinn Féiner take his seat at all?. ...'

D.1792/A3/8/11   **Letter to W. S. Armour from Armour,**

14 March 1917   criticising Lloyd George's attitudes towards Home Rule and in particular his apparent unwillingness to force Ulster to accept it. Armour feels that Lloyd George has now departed from his Liberal principles.

'... Indeed the Welshman seems very much to be the square stick in the round hole. His speech on the Irish question was deplorable, showing an utter lack of statesmanship. The underground feeling is very much against his utterances which were stupid. If these were his real opinions, it is clear he has burned his boats and cut the connection with Liberalism. Like Lord Milner, he will soon be regarded as a lost soul... . The Welshman will not coerce Ulster but he will coerce the Protestants in the south and west to submit to Home Rule for the other parts of Ireland. It is a pity that the party of which he was leading spirit did not coerce Ulster when it did everything to start civil war in Ireland and was a match put to the pile to start the present war. Had he coerced Ulster then there would have been no Sinn Féin rebellion with all its tragedies and losses. It is easy to say "we won't coerce Ulster" but can we coerce the other parts of Ireland and specially the Irish in the colonies and America. The Irish in America have tied the hand of Wilson for long and may deter him from active part in the war. The bankruptcy of statecraft has been publicly declared by Lloyd George. One might see Asquith back in power again. It is not improbable that we shall see the Welshman's ambition to become prime minister overleaping itself. He is clearly a man strong in words but rather feckless in political action. ...'

D.1792/A3/8/12   **Letter to W. S. Armour from Armour,**

21 March 1917   commenting on the appointment of James Chambers (Unionist member for South Belfast) rather than William Moore (Unionist member for North Armagh until his appointment as a judge in 1917) as solicitor-general for Ireland and on a speech on the Irish question by Lord Northcliffe. He also discusses the Dardanelles report and developments in Russia.

'... [James] Chambers has been made solicitor-general whereat there is a wicked article in the [*Northern*] *Whig* this morning in which the appointment is bitterly attacked. It asserts that the appointment has been made at the beck of [John] Dillon, that Chambers has been disloyal to the Unionists—that he has only taken part in four divisions out of sixty-four and that W[illia]m Moore was the man for the job. The article calls on the electors of S[outh] Belfast to oust him when he re-appears before them which I suppose he must do on his appointment. "We shall see". It is reported that Wm. Moore has got the promise of a judgeship and there is a hint that he may succeed Craig in Belfast whose term of office will soon entitle him to the full retiring pension. It is not unlikely that Moore has got a promise of some decent berth. It is generally believed that [H. E.] Duke [chief secretary] could not give the position to such a fire-eater as Moore. It would have been a sort of scandal and in the present state of Irish opinion it would have done much harm. The [*Belfast*] *News-Letter* does not refer to the subject this morning which shows a trifle of wisdom ... .

Lord Northcliffe's speech at the St Patrick's banquet on Saturday is bound to have a real effect on the Irish question as it is a silent confession that his papers took a wrong view of the situation all along and at the same time a warning to the p[rime] minister that he must "eat the leek" over the stupid speech he made on the question in the h[ouse of] c[ommons]. A more miserable exhibition of statesmanship was never made by any p[rime] m[inister]. It was Carsonism at its zenith of folly and has damaged himself in the opinion of the sensible Unionists in England. Of course the Irish Unionists called out "Halleluiah" [*sic*] as they always do when coercion is part of the English policy. ...'

D.1792/A3/8/14   **Letter to W. S. Armour from Armour,**

4 April 1917   commenting on the possibility of America's entry into the war; criticising Carson's failures as first lord of the Admiralty in the coalition government; and speculating on the likely shape of a settlement of the Irish problem.

'... Carson has not been a success. How long will it be until the public become aware of the stupidity of giving him a position for which he is not fitted. His previous history as in great part the author of the war and therefore of the blood that has been, is and will be shed should have kept Lloyd George for [*sic*] making him one of his agents. Lord Milner and he ought to have been excluded from office ... .

What the government have up their sleeve for the settlement of the Irish business is only guess work so far. There may be a hint in tomorrow's papers but I hardly think so. That they will make an attempt is sure especially as the younger Tories don't want to go to the country without a settlement. The Ulster dead heads are as absurd as ever but they should not count. If the government leaves every county to say whether it is for Home Rule or the reverse there might be only four counties in Ulster voting against and that would settle the business of exclusion. Those who agree with us are not excited over the matter as time is on our side. ...'

D.1792/A3/8/16   **Letter to W. S. Armour from Armour,**

18 April 1917   describing a visit to Magherafelt on the previous day to attend and speak at the annual synod meeting and discussing the comments made by one of his clerical colleagues about increasing Presbyterian disillusionment with the political attitudes of the Church of Ireland.

'... I learned afterwards from [Rev.] Shaw—a decent sort of Unionist who has never been bitter—he is a stout, decent kind of man with the picture of kindly nature written across his frame—that it is beginning to dawn on the Presbyterians that the Church of Ireland is ready to betray the Ulsterites as that church is quite ready to make a deal with the Nationalists which is not unnatural seeing that possibly the largest contingent of their churches and members is scattered through the other three provinces. It is a striking confirmation of Shaw's theory that in the General Synod of the Church of Ireland yesterday in Dublin, no reference was made to the Home Rule question. ...'

D.1792/A3/8/17

Letter to W. S. Armour from Armour,

25 April 1917

commenting on the progress of the war and the continuing failure of the government to solve the Irish problem.

'... A solution for the Irish *imbroglio* has not been found. It has got to be solved—the Romanoffs of Ulster are holding out but there are signs that they must give in a little further. Carson stands in the way. I expect Lloyd George has not the courage to cast off Carson and to propose a real solution. However, what he may propose will be a step forward to a working hypothesis. The end is not yet but it will come soon I think. ...'

D.1792/A3/8/18

Letter to W. S. Armour from Armour,

[n.d. April ? 1917]

ridiculing Unionist support for opposition to any kind of partition of Ireland by the Catholic and some of the Anglican bishops and again severely criticising Carson and Lloyd George.

'... The Irish question is not settled and may not be. The business is complicated as the Catholic bishops with three Protestant bishops have come out strongly against the partition of Ireland in any shape or form. The Belfast folks apparently are rejoicing that the Catholic bishops are against Home Rule. It is odd to think that these people who all their life have been denouncing the bench of bishops as the great enemy of Ireland are now regarding them as friends. It is clear that if an alliance with the devil would help them to carry their prejudices to victory they would hail him as an ally. I fear the p[rime] m[inister] is a failure. It is reported that it was through the machinations of Carson that Asquith was ousted from the premiership and that is the reason why Carson got such a position in the government—a position he with his record should never have had. The omens are pointing to the possibility of Carson getting the sack. The Nationalists are suspecting that Lloyd George is their real enemy. If he does not satisfy them with his scheme they will turn against him. One's faith in his statesmanship is waning and he may come a cropper. ...'

D.1792/A3/8/19

Letter to W. S. Armour from Armour,

2 May 1917

speculating as to Carson's possible resignation as first lord of the Admiralty; suggesting that the government is unlikely to introduce a radical Irish settlement but that it is under pressure from President Woodrow Wilson to take some action; and condemning the idea of Ulster exclusion.

'... The submarine warfare is becoming threateningly severe and though there is no panic, it is likely that the Admiralty will get a keel-hauling soon and possibly Carson will resign on the plea that he disapproves of Lloyd George's projected settlement of the Irish question though the real reason will be that he has been a failure at the Admiralty. He may, as some papers suggest, not be responsible for the failure but it is apparent that nobody could have done *worse*. The Irish proposed settlement is postponed until next week as the p[rime] m[inister] has had to start for the continent. Some serious disturbances have arisen among the allies. The noon day of victory has not come yet. To expect much from the p[rime] m[inister], surrounded as he is by reactionaries on the Irish settlement, would be snuffing up like the wild ass the east wind which is never a flattering business but it may be a stage in the settlement. It is expected that Balfour has got a strong hint from [Woodrow] Wilson that the thing has got to be ended as it is important for his success in America as the Irish have always been Democrats and have a big following there. ... The Belfast papers are writing as if Ulster was being betrayed by its friends which is a sign that their flag will have to be lowered considerably. The *Irish Times* is against the exclusion of Ulster and that represents the views of the Ch[urch] of Ireland in the south and west. The cross-currents are many. The gulf stream which was thought to flow entirely on the shores of Ulster is being considerably deflected as the sun of Toryism is not shining with its former vigour. ...'

D.1792/A3/8/20   **Letter to W. S. Armour from Armour,**

10 May 1917   commenting on the Sinn Fein success at the Longford
                                                    by-election and on the influence of Archbishop
Walsh's letter opposing Home Rule, and anticipating the government's new Irish policy initiative.

'... The Irish business is in a bad state. The Longford election is awkward for the Nationalists and is the same for the government. Archbishop Walsh's letter, which was cowardly and evidently shows that Catholic bishops are against Home Rule as we always thought, settled that election. I would like to hear Joe Devlin's opinion on that particular letter. It would be a vigorous string of epithets. It appears the heads of the government proposal will be given this evening to the Redmondites and the Unionists. These may not suit either party and therefore a settlement is not possible at present. ...'

D.1792/A3/8/21   **Letter to W. S. Armour from Armour,**

23 May 1917   discussing the government's proposed Irish Convention
                                                    and the reactions of various political groups, including
                                                    the Unionists, towards it.

'... The Irish problem has advanced a very long step ... . The Die Hards have advanced much. Lord Lansdowne has said that Home Rule has advanced so far that it is impossible to turn it back. That is a big confession for him to make. Carson also in spite of his saying that he will never desert Mrs Micawber is evidently about to advise the Ulster [Unionist] Council to take part in the convention. At least something will be attempted and possibly much will be done. The p[rime] m[inister] has also given up the *non-possumus* attitude. He has eaten the leek practically and the young Tories are anxious for a settlement. ...'

D.1792/A3/8/22   **Letter to W. S. Armour from Armour,**

13 June 1917   commenting on the war situation and on the death of
                                                    James Chambers, Unionist member for South Belfast
and recently appointed solicitor-general for Ireland; assessing who will be Chambers' successor; evaluating the career of William Redmond who has been killed in action; and briefly analysing the composition of the Irish Convention.

'... Passing to local affairs we have heard with great regret of the death of Ja[me]s Chambers— M.P. for S[outh] Belfast and lately appointed as solicitor-general for Ireland. He was very able and very decent and humanly speaking his foot was on the ladder for a position on the bench at no distant date. It appears that the weather about the time of his appointment was very cold and he got a chill on the day of his re-election for S[outh] Belfast. The chill developed into mumps and then into pneumonia. He suffered excruciating pain. The two diseases were too much for a frame worn by hard work and the end has come. The [*Northern*] *Whig* at the time of his re-election wrote a very unfair article on him, calling practically on the electors to give him the sack. It was an outrage on the amenities of ordinary life but the electors gave no heed to its covert suggestion. There will be the usual intrigues for his successor. I wrote at the time to W[illiam] Moore expressing my hope that he might get the berth but he did not. He has a small reputation as a lawyer. The government could not dare to give him the place when two really competent lawyers like Chambers and Denis Henry [Unionist member for South London-derry] were in the field. [H. E.] Duke, the pompous chief sec[retary] will be in a new fix. Henry, being a Catholic though a Unionist, may have to stand aside again as I am sure at the present time, the government would not wish to have both law officers R.C.s. I fear the chief sec[retary] could not appoint Moore for the two reasons—that he is not well up in the law, his reputation at the bar being low, and further because he has been so violent as a politician, irritating the Nationalists whenever he got on his legs. Chambers was wiser in his generation at least in a matter of this kind. We must wait and see ... .

Willie Redmond's death in the battle has made a great sensation. The house of commons broke its rule in his case—the P.M., Asquith, Carson, Devlin were fine in their eulogies on a really great figure. His speech in the h[ouse of] c[ommons] on his return from the seat of the war was conceived in the best of spirits and did much to take the edge off the opposition to Home Rule. For repartee in the h[ouse of] c[ommons] he had no equal and some of his sayings nudged in during debate not only gave infinite pleasure but will live and be repeated. He was, with his wife, very kind to Sara Wallace on her journey to Australia, took her with him to big meetings and kept your humble servant's name before the audiences. He was a marvellous figure and perhaps the dead which he slew by his death were more than he had slain in his life. The news has come that Bonar Law's son is a prisoner with the Turks. The personnel of the convention has been given but the chairman has not been named. That is the difficulty. Some are suggesting [A. J.] Balfour, as the latest convert to H[ome] Rule. Asquith would be better but the Ulsterites would naturally prefer the former. You will see the way the convention has been arranged. ...'

D.1792/A3/8/23

Letter to W. S. Armour from Armour,

20 June 1917

expressing his doubts about the wisdom of releasing the Sinn Féin prisoners arrested after the events of Easter week 1916, though he sees it as an indication of how flexible the Unionist members of the coalition government have become. He also comments on the progress made towards setting up the proposed convention.

'... You will have seen that the Sinn Féiners condemned for the part taken in the Dublin rebellion have been released unconditionally and they on their return are quite as violent as they were. The papers with the exception of the *Morning Post* were in favour of the action of the government and perhaps it was wise. The one striking thing is that Law, Carson and Curzon were in favour of it which shows how far they have travelled on the political pathway. One is in a way glad that Asquith was not P.M. Had he been he would have been denounced as a traitor, a friend of murderers and worse than the Huns. The Tory papers of Ireland, as it was the act of Law and Carson, have eaten the leek with wry faces it is true but they have eaten it quietly though the leek is not very conducive to ordinary digestion. It is useless to speculate on the result but one hopes that the future will set its seal to the wisdom of the act—though it is hard to justify it on the ground of morals. The R.C. [bishops?] yesterday appointed four of their bench as members of the convention. The chairmanship of the gathering has not been fixed. Perhaps it may be Asquith who as a statesman would be the best possible choice. Will the release of the rapscallions give a fillip or set back to the Sinn Feiners is the question on which opinion is much divided—some holding that it is sure to increase the number very largely and some holding *contra* ... the election in Clare will be a barometer. The letter of Archbishop Walsh which decided for Sinn Feinism is said to have been written not by Walsh but by his assistant, as it is reported that Walsh is suffering either from senile decay or softening of the brain. That is the opinion of some who think they ought to know. At any rate the letter seemed to be rather the original violence of the man who, in early days of his career, a Catholic land-lord called a spoiled attorney. The Catholic bishops as a body are not in favour of Home Rule: that is tolerably clear. ...'

D.1792/A3/8/25

Letter to W. S. Armour from Armour,

11 July 1917

discussing the progress of the war and commenting on the South Longford and East Clare by-elections. He again expresses the hope that Sinn Féin's advance may have been halted, especially since it had not opposed M. L. Hearn's return for South Dublin. In practice Joseph McGuinness and Eamon de Valera won both seats for Sinn Féin.

'... The Clare election came off yesterday—we may not hear the result before the evening but I fancy—I hope—[Patrick] Lynch [the Irish parliamentary party candidate] may sail in. If so, the Sinn Féiners will be a waning force. The fact that they did not face a contest in S[outh] Dublin is a sort of mark that they are not so confident as they were. The Unionists in Longford voted for Sinn Féin which shows a state of morality among them very despicable. I think they will have voted in Clare for Lynch or at any rate abstained. The Sinn Féiners must be getting money from some quarters but from where is not apparent. Somehow or other I feel the Germans cannot be emptying their gold into any part of the world. It is reported that the curates in Clare who were favourable to Sinn Féin were ordered into retreat during the election but that the retreat of the priests, who are thought to be favourable to the Nationalists, was over for them before the day of election. That is the report which may or may not be true. ...'

D.1792/A3/8/27   **Letter to W. S. Armour from Armour,**

27 July 1917   expressing admiration for Alexander Kerensky's
                                                provisional government in Russia, reiterating his
hostility to Sinn Féin and commenting favourably on the opening of the Irish Convention in Dublin under Sir Horace Plunkett's chairmanship.

'... The convention was to meet this morning and one would like to cherish the hope that some satisfactory settlement may result therefrom. Sinn Féinism seems carrying everything before it but it is thought—possibly rightly—that there is a divided counsel and that they are beginning to distrust each other. The way of conspiracy is beset with difficulties and as for their part one may be sure that they will betray one another and that their republic is a rather remote dream. A few months will prick the bubble. ...'

D.1792/A3/8/28   **Letter to W. S. Armour from Armour, [written from
                                                Carlingford, Co. Louth],**

15 August 1917
                                                detailing his return from a holiday in South Shields
with Max Armour and also describing Carlingford and its environs; commenting on the resignation of Arthur Henderson from the coalition government because of Lloyd George's unwillingness to allow Henderson to attend the international socialist peace conference at Stockholm; and repeating his familiar views about Sinn Féin.

'... The war is ploughing on without much sign of a termination in the immediate future. The labour world here is in a state of excitement. [Arthur] Henderson's action is hard to explain. He has been trying to ride two horses which cannot go abreast. His position in the war cabinet became impossible. It is possible that the labour vote will continue to be on his side but not to the same extent. There may be a landslide. The Stockholm meeting may never take place. Sinn Féinism is still flourishing but its zenith has been reached and it may come a cropper soon as its aims are impossible. ...'

D.1792/A3/8/35   **Letter to W. S. Armour from Armour,**

30 October 1917   indicating his increasing frustration at the growth of
                                                Sinn Féin and laying the blame for this on the British
government's repressive policy in 1916 and its subsequent willingness to release unconditionally the internees in 1917.

'... It was a mistake to be so severe on the Sinn Féiners, court-martialling them, and then a bigger mistake in letting them out without binding them to be quiet. The English government by its stupidity created Sinn Féinism and now it is in a helpless position with regard to the "the infant [*sic*] terrible", [H. E.] Duke [chief secretary for Ireland] is a pompous creature and Lloyd George does not seem to have the statesman's gift. We are in a sort of maelstrom and the power of vision is very dim. ...'

D.1792/A3/8/36   **Part of a letter to W. S. Armour from Armour,**

13 November 1917   containing war news and hostile comments on the Bolshevik revolution in Russia which he believes is 'a pricked bladder'—Lenin he dismisses as a man 'bent on betraying his country for the sake of German gold', who deserves to hand on a rope. He also advocates that tough action should be taken against Sinn Féin, which he believes is on the wane.

'... The government is beginning to deal sensibly with Sinn Féin. It was time. The Waterford meeting turned out a fiasco for the Sinn Féiners. You may hear of many of them in the near future shot down. They have been too tenderly dealt with up to the present. ...'

D.1792/A3/8/39   **Letter to W. S. Armour from Armour,**

11 December 1917   rejoicing at the capture of Jerusalem, especially since it may act as 'a wet blanket on the Leninite crew in Russia'; praising John Morley's memoirs, despite Morley's agnosticism; and engaging in a further attack on Edward Carson's record in the coalition government.

'... I fancy Carson's berth is a little shaky. His speech in which he ran foul of [Woodrow] Wilson about the League of Nations will put the P.M. in a fix. Carson has been the bane of the empire and to his name there has to be added—the father of Sinn Féinism. ...'

D.1792/A3/9

1918

Originals of letters from Rev. J. B. Armour to his wife and sons (principally to W. S. Armour).

D.1792/A3/9/3

22 January 1918

Letter to W. S. Armour from Armour,

commenting amongst other things on the resignation of Edward Carson from his post in the war cabinet of the coalition government, which he interprets as the harbinger of an Irish settlement based on the forthcoming Irish Convention report.

'... The news today is the resignation of Carson which was long overdue. I fancy the inner reasoning of the job is that the cabinet at last has made up its mind to deal with the Irish question when the convention has given in its report. It is not likely according to reports that an agreement has been arrived at as Ulster blocks the way and Carson wants to pose as a leader of Ulster. The mistake was in giving him a place in the cabinet at all. Milner, Curzon and Carson —especially the first and third ought to have been kept out of the councils of the nation. Their previous record was not good. There is a letter in the papers on the subject but tomorrow we will have a varied account of the meaning of the episode. I did not read the [*Northern*] *Whig* on the subject as anything in the [*Northern*] *Whig* on matters political is irritating in the extreme. ...'

D.1792/A3/9/7

12 March 1918

Letter to W. S. Armour from Armour,

recording the death of John Redmond and paying tribute to him. He also speculates on a likely successor should H. E. Duke, the chief secretary for Ireland, retire. Duke in fact left office on 2 May 1918 and became a lord justice of appeal, with the title of Baron Merrivale. His successor in Ireland was Edward Shortt, who was in turn replaced by Ian Macpherson on 13 January 1919.

'The past week has been full of tragedy, my dearest. The death of Redmond is a tragedy in its way, a fine man really done to death by the ferocious hate of those for whose well-being he devoted his life and his undoubted gifts. If the half of the things that have been said over the man dead had been said over the man living, he might have been still in the flesh and the cause for which he fought might have been a success. Nothing could have been finer than the words spoken in the h[ouse of] c[ommons] or in all the newspapers of every political colour. Justice has been done to him as an orator, a statesman, a man of honour and a conciliator. Is it too much to hope that what was said of Samson may be true of him, "the dead which he slew at his death were more than those he slew in his life"? Let us hope that will be the case but to exorcise political like any other kind of hatred is rather difficult. The Ethiopian cannot change his skin or the leopard his spots, then may they also do good that are accustomed to do it. The old feuds hushed over his grave will break out again perhaps more fiercely but they will not vex his spirit any more. I see his son Captain Redmond is to stand for Waterford. He is evidently the best man that could be selected and it will be interesting to watch the contest between him and the Sinn Féiner. I sent in the bundle today the *Freeman*['*s Journal*], *Irish News*, [*Irish*] *Independent* with their accounts of his death and the *Freeman*['*s Journal*] of today giving an account of his funeral. The best article on his death that I have seen is the article in the *M*[*anchester*] *G*[*uardian*] and the *resume* of his work by a correspondent. They are all worth perusal. The picture of the group when through young Gladstone and you he gained a real victory in the head quarters of the Tories [Oxford Union] is about the most interesting photo he ever had taken ... . It was a great victory the general and his lieutenants gained on a memorable field. Reports are frequent that [H. E.] Duke is giving up the chief secretaryship and retiring to the position of master of the rolls. He has done no better than Birrell who was abused in all the moods and tenses by the northern papers. They have not a word of commendation for

Duke who will go off unwept from the Castle. It is said [Ian] Macpherson, a Scotch Presbyterian, a radical and the most capable of under-secretaries is to be the successor. He may possibly [be] treated like [Admiral Lord] Jellicoe and retire a defeated man, though able if he got a fair chance. The Tory element is too strong in the cabinet for a radical to succeed. ...'

D.1792/A3/9/12   **Letter to W. S. Armour from Armour,**

24 April 1918   commenting on the hostile reaction to the suggestion that conscription be extended to Ireland. Armour is particularly incensed by the attitudes of the Roman Catholic hierarchy and John Dillon and by the attempts of Irish nationalists to secure President Woodrow Wilson's sympathy and support.

'... Ireland you will see is in a state of frenzy over conscription. The bishops have thrown off the mask. Most of us knew that they were in heart deadly opposed to Home Rule and now they have come out into the open. They have embraced Sinn Féin. [John] Dillon is too much of a mad-head and too little of a real statesman to guide a party in a crisis. [Joe] Devlin has a leveller head. The mayor of Dublin is resolved to go across and interview [Woodrow] Wilson. Some say he should not get a passport but that would be foolish. Wilson is level-headed and would likely tell him straight that he could not listen to a man who is agitating to get the soldiers American and Irish murdered in thousands by the Germans while he and his party refuse to take part in winning the war which is of more importance for liberty and civilisation than the case of unreasonable Irishmen. As for the mayor's desire for an independent nation, he would likely say America spent millions of men and rivers of blood to keep the southern states from seeking to be an independent nation and that he has no notion of reversing the policy of the American republic for the sake of the Irish bishops. The government has bungled the business from first to last and has shown itself barren of common sense. Is it riding as some think for a fall? ...'

D.1792/A3/9/13   **Letter to W. S. Armour from Armour,**

30 April 1918   criticising the Lloyd George coalition and predicting the return of Asquith and Sir Edward Grey to government, since 'government by the Northcliffe papers has been tried and is found wanting'. He comments on the impending departure of H. E. Duke, the chief secretary for Ireland, and on the other changes likely in the administration of Ireland, and he expresses the hope that the influence of American opinion will modify the political attitudes of the Irish Catholic hierarchy.

'... There is no light on the Irish situation. The Home Rule bill, if introduced, will do little good as the Irish members will not take any part in the matter. [H. E.] Duke goes and [Edward] Shortt, a radical, comes in his place it is said—with Lord Midleton or Lord French as lord lieutenant. It is difficult to see what they can do. However, it is possible the Irish hierarchy will have to modify their attitude as the American press as well as the leaders of the Irish in the States are coming down heavy on them. The bishops hated Home Rule as they have always been at heart on the side of the Ulsterites. Extremes meet. ...'

D.1792/A3/9/15   **Letter to W. S. Armour from Armour,**

28 May 1918   expressing a much more favourable view of Lloyd George than heretofore; praising President Woodrow Wilson; and engaging in a violent attack on Sinn Féin. Armour welcomes the government's decision to intern leading Sinn Féiners for participation in the alleged 'German plot'.

'... The internment of the Sinn Féiners was a big stroke. The only mysterious thing about it is if, as appears, the government knew of [the] beginning of the intrigue with Germany, why did it release the prisoners? Why did it not put down its foot and say—not a man or woman of them will get out save on the condition that they will behave in Ireland? Of course the Nationalists and Sinn Féiners are saying that the evidence of their guilt does not exist and if it does, it should be made public. At least they may say they hate the Germans but those are only words, though the facts are they are doing everything they can to break down America and the allies as a whole [John] Dillon made the stupid mistake of entering into a conference with de Valera, therefore giving up the principle of constitutionalism and sanctioning anarchy. There is a moral twist in the mentalities of Dillon and now he is going to be beaten with his own rod as the Sinn Feiners are bent on contesting Cavan and will probably beat his candidate. A party led by a statesman and gentleman, as Redmond was, does not throw over its principles at the bidding of a few fools and moral maniacs. One can see little light on the Irish problem. The lord mayor of Dublin is not likely to go to America. He might not get back safe and if he did Wilson would put a flea in his ear. America will not stand the destruction of its citizens Irish and American through the action of a wilderness of lord mayors of Dublin who are bent in their hatred of England on scoupering [*sic*] the liberties of humanity. They say they do not like the Germans but their gospel is a gospel of hatred as their motto is "God straffe England". ...'

D.1792/A3/9/19   **Letter to W. S. Armour from Armour,**

18 June 1918   commenting critically on the attitude of the Nationalist party towards Sinn Fein and on the appointment
of the Unionist lawyer, J. H. Campbell, as lord chancellor of Ireland.

'... The Irish question is in the clouds. One can see little light as the majority of the Dillonites while repudiating the Sinn Féiners are showing leanings in that direction—that is they are practically taking them up and insisting on an open trial for them. The policy they are pursuing seems a trifle mixed in its moral bearings. Balfour's policy of "coercion" seems to be renewed but with what result is another matter. The appointment of [J. H.] Campbell as lord chancellor is hard to defend save on what the *Freeman['s Journal]* calls "the triumph of Carsonism" which is a little ominous for the future. We can only wait and see but the vision is not altogether the vision of daylight. [Rev. J. D.] Osborne says he (Campbell) is converted, if so wonders will never cease. ...'

D.1792/A3/9/22   **Letter to W. S. Armour from Armour,**

27 August 1918   gleefully commenting on J. H. Campbell's declaration
in favour of Home Rule and condemning Edward
Carson's letter to President Wilson, which had denounced Irish nationalists for their attempts
to influence the president.

'... I sent off a bundle of papers yesterday. You will find the declaration of [J. H.] Campbell, the lord chancellor, in favour of Home Rule—an utterance which has almost driven the northern papers crazy. He is regarded as a traitor willing to betray the ark of the covenant. As we were away, I could not get some of the papers dealing with the speech—only subscribers get their papers but you have the short article in the *M[anchester] G[uardian]*. Yesterday T. P. O'Connor gave a heavy counter-blast to the Carson letter to President Wilson—which is very ably done and which I got to enclose in the bundle along with two or three items including Viscount Grey's letter on the League of Nations. Carson and his entourage denounced the nationalists in all the moods and tenses for daring to write to the president but they have adopted the tactics of the other side. T. P.'s blast is well done and is worth reading. The northern papers here only give a very few lines to the manifesto. The *M[orning] Post* holds that [J. H.] Campbell should resign which I fancy he will not do. It is possible that he may have made his speech with the permission of some members of the cabinet. He could hardly have spoken as he did without feeling that he was expressing views which were the views of some of the ruling powers. ...'

D.1792/A3/9/28   **Letter to W. S. Armour from Armour,**

10 December 1918   violently condemning Lloyd George for abandoning
                                    the radicalism of his early career and adopting a
dictatorial approach to politics. Armour sees the Labour party as the only possible hope for
radicals in the future. He also comments on the election prospects in North Antrim and Ulster
generally and in particular on Carson's decision to relinquish his Trinity College, Dublin, seat
in favour of Belfast's Duncairn constituency. In North Antrim Peter Kerr-Smiley comfortably
defeated the Sinn Féiner, Patrick McCarry (9,621 votes as against 2,673).

'... I quite agree with what you say about L[loyd] G[eorge] but he is practically working to be
a dictator and wants a nominated h[ouse of] c[ommons]. "Limehouse" he leaves far behind
and he is associating not with colleagues but with those who will use him for their own purpose
and then turn on him and rend him. The only hope one can have now of righteous legislation
is practically in the Labour party. ... The *M[anchester] G[uardian]* is wobbling a good deal
and seems to have modified its old policy. It praises L[loyd] G[eorge] and puts in a few doubts
about the outcome of his policy. The cartoonist in the *Westminster [Gazette]* felt the war a
wet blanket on his ability but he has jumped into the saddle again and his cartoon in last
Saturday's is of the old stock. I take it you have it sent you. William Stuart [the potential
Liberal candidate for North Antrim] reneged at the last moment and now we have [Peter]
Kerr-Smiley [Unionist] and a Sinn Féiner [Patrick McCarry] in the field. Carson is in full flow,
but if the temperance and other parties about Belfast like his policy and reasons for it, they are
mightily easy to please. Trinity College was tired of him and practically gave him the go-by. ...'

D.1792/A3/9/29   **Letter to W. S. Armour from Armour,**

17 December 1918   commenting on the 1918 general election (in which
                                    some women were voting for the first time) in Ulster
in general and in North Antrim in particular. Peter Kerr-Smiley had held the seat for the
Unionists against Patrick McCarry (Sinn Féin). He also attacks the Unionist arguments in favour
of the partition of Ireland and advances reasons which he believes will prevent it from coming
to pass.

'We have got into the doldrums now that the election is over. The lot is cast into the lap and
the disposing thereof depends on the ballot boxes which may in one way be regarded as at
heart the possession of the Lord. No election in my memory was ever so quiet as was Saturday's.
A considerable portion of the community—perhaps it might be called the respectable part,
though others would call it the Home Rule party—did not vote. A few excited females—
Mrs R. A. McElderry, the Boyds and Mrs Stewart and the Pattersons—a number of dafties
were out haling [*sic*] men and women into the Tory camp. We got doubtless a good deal of
private abuse for refusing to take part with the Pharisees but that did not hinder our sleep or
interfere with our digestion. "Eat and let the parties rave. They are filled with idle spleen.
Rising, falling like the wave. For they know not what they mean" was the motto. Every old
woman in the Roddenfoot was taken in motor cars to save the empire and keep out a Papish,
though if they had been in S[outh] Derry they would have had, with their Orange brethren, to
vote for Denis Henry—one of the Pope's brigade. It is a topsy-turvy world in truth. ...

The elections are a leap in the dark. Little interest was taken in it in most places but women
were to the fore in some districts. Joe Devlin according to reports has been elected by a large
majority [in the Falls division of Belfast]. Dillon according to Sinn Féin has been snowed
under but his backers think differently. It appears the Unionists expect to pull off, owing to the
fact that the Nationalists and Sinn Feiners are in the field, four seats but the Unionists pledge
themselves against the partition of Ireland. God has made the island one and they object to the
attempt of Carson to divide it. The boat which carried the Carson crew has hidden rocks ahead
of it and it may be wrecked between two seas. The Church of Ireland—one need not speak of the
Presbyterian community—will not stand without a very strong protest about being cast over to

the tender mercies of those Carson regards as wolves. The merchants of the north would not care to have as their field for merchandise only some five counties. The banks will fight shy of a scheme which would practically close up the branches outside the five counties. The lawyers would hardly like to be closed out of the Irish courts and be compelled to take their cases to England and Scotland—that is in cases of appeal as quarter sessions courts run by Irish judges would have to be appointed for the work of these courts. One can understand the cry "No Home Rule" for Ireland, but the cry for partition reaches the bottom of absurdity—that in my opinion cannot carry. I suspect [President Woodrow] Wilson to get rid of difficulty, or one form of it in the [United] States, will insist that L[loyd] G[eorge] and his cabinet will be compelled to put in force some modifications of the act that is on the statute book. Wilson is getting a fine reception in France. He will be a sort of dictator of the terms of peace, though in his own country it may be difficult to get the ¾ths of senate and congress just enthusiastically to have the terms agreed on. Things in Germany, Austria, Portugal and other places are at present wrapped in mystery and one can say nothing about the outlook in these places any more than in Russia. ...'

D.1792/A3/10

1919

Originals of letters from Rev. J. B. Armour to his wife and sons (principally to W. S. Armour).

D.1792/A3/10/1

7 January 1919

Letter to W. S. Armour from Armour,

reiterating his usual criticisms of Sinn Féin; commenting on the views of Ian Macpherson (chief secretary for Ireland until 13 January 1919) and in particular on Macpherson's argument that Asquith was responsible for the failure to resolve the Ulster crisis of 1912-14.

'... The Irish stew has still too much pepper in it. The Sinn Féiners are becoming more intolerably unreasonable and are ready to regard murder as the effective weapon of their warfare. Things are out of joint and nobody apparently seems born to set them right. [Ian] Macpherson is a decent, able man but he has sold himself to the Tories and reactionaries. His speech at Inverness the other day was stupid. His attack on Asquith shows that he knows no more about the past than he does about the present. Carson in his attempts to stir up civil war had then the whole Tory party on his side and had got from Bonar Law the assurance of the help of the whole party in his crusade for civil war. The government was powerless at the time and therefore it could not clap Carson and [General Sir Hubert] Gough in jail which should have taken place. In the state of feeling that bold step could not be taken. Asquith need not be blamed any more than Lloyd George who was part of the cabinet. It is easy for Macpherson to find a scapegoat but it is hardly respectful to his chief to take a swipe at him. The policy pursued was as much the present p[rime] minister's as Asquith's. To go to Inverness when the truth is not known and to bubble out his spleen is hardly the honourable way of playing the game. ...'

D.1792/A3/10/2

28 January 1919

Letter to W. S. Armour from Armour,

discussing the major strikes in Belfast and Glasgow and their significance. He speculates as to how Carson and his victorious Unionists will react to the widespread industrial unrest.

'... The Labour world is in a state of revolution and Belfast which is regarded as the new Jerusalem is worse than any place else with possibly the exception of Glasgow. Everyone seems to be out on strike for forty or forty-four hours a week. How that would ultimately work is not clear. If it became universal in the empire, I fancy Germany, France, Austria and the Balkans, where the hours have always been longer than anywhere else and will be, then those countries will come into a state of prosperity. The whole situation reads to me an attempt of the Labour world to indicate that if the prime minister has established the Tories as masters of parliament, Labour is giving notice that reactionary legislation will not be tolerated. The cabinet cannot be easy in its mind at present with so many problems of difficulty rising around them. It will be amusing to watch what the Carson gang, boasting about their victory in Belfast, will do. They will be faced with the problem—ye cannot serve God and Mammon, that is you cannot please the workers and their masters at the same time. With gas cut off, trains not running and everything in confusion, the outlook is confusing. ...'

D.1792/A3/10/4

12 February 1919

Letter to W. S. Armour from Armour,

recounting a discussion with Lady Pirrie in the Midland Hotel, Belfast, about the significance of the ongoing strikes. He also comments further on the embarrassment which they have caused to Sir Edward Carson and the other Ulster Unionist leaders.

'... We discussed the strike and passed on to politics. I suggested that the strikes everywhere in full swing or in a threatening state were partly the result of the coalition majority. The Labour party expected double the number of seats they got and the strikes were to remind the coalition and cabinet that they would be a thorn in the side of the gov[ernmen]t unless legislation was carried on democratic lines. Sir Edward Carson has been knocked into a cocked hat. Neither he nor one of his followers who got in dare open their mouths over the strike. They have been faced with the question—"ye cannot serve God and Mammon". They dare not take any side for if they took one side they would offend the other ... . They have got a bad fall and are speechless. It is questionable if there was an election next week if one of them would be returned, though they were singing a *te deum* over their marvellous victory. All the beaten candidates took the platform during the strike on the side of Labour. There are searchings of heart among the inhabitants of what is thought to be the new Jerusalem. The soldiers returning are very discontented, I hear, and there are signs of incipient mutiny. The Ulster contingents are very bitter, I hear, against their officers who were incapable, cruel and cowardly. I heard several stories to that effect in the smoking room yesterday. Colonel [R. C. A.] McCalmont, [Peter] Kerr-Smiley and possibly Ja[me]s Craig—though they have been returned to parliament are among the most unpopular. ...'

D.1792/A3/10/6	**Letter to W. S. Armour from Armour,**
4 March 1919	condemning those in the United States who support Irish independence and denouncing the principles of

Sinn Féin as unchristian. He also attacks the Catholic hierarchy for their support of Sinn Féin.

'... There is little light on any of the public questions. Balfour seems fairly hopeful that peace on fair terms may be reached in a few months. The Irish question has been taken up in the United States senate and a deputation was to meet Wilson before sailing for Europe again. The result of the interview has not reached the public yet. I fancy Wilson can hardly be very favourable at heart to what the deputation wants. He can hardly go in for Irish independence in the light of the facts that America went to war for four long, decimating years to keep the southern states from getting independence and the pro-Germanism of the three fourths of Ireland and the fact that they refused to take their part in a war for liberty and humanity—these facts will keep him from enthusiasm for men whose policy has been the contradiction of every Christian principle. Sinn Feign [*sic*] which means for ourselves alone runs in the teeth of all the Christian principles hitherto accepted. The Catholic bishops are getting uneasy. They have begun to see that the policy of getting rid of the Nationalists has landed them with practically no voice in the house of commons. They are speaking of the policy of Sinn Feign [*sic*] as insane. The de'll help them, they deserve no pity. ...'

D.1792/A3/10/9	**Letter to W. S. Armour from Armour,**
6 May 1919	largely devoted to local news but he does again reiterate his opposition to the establishment of an independent Irish republic.

'... The Tory English papers are distressed that Lloyd George is to have an interview with some American Irishmen on the Irish question. He will hardly commit himself very far. By his seeing them at all, he is rousing the hopes of the Sinn Féiners in Ireland. The idea of an Irish republic is rather fantastic. ...'

D.1792/A3/10/12	**Letter to W. S. Armour from Armour,**
10 June 1919	describing the events of the General Assembly and discussing the precarious position of Lord French,

the lord lieutenant of Ireland. He also analyses in some detail the East Antrim by-election which had resulted in the defeat of the Unionist candidate, Major W. Agnew Moore, by George B. Hanna, an idependent Unionist and Orangeman, who had stood as a protest against the unrepresentative nature of the East Antrim Unionist Association. Hanna polled 8,714 votes to Moore's 7,549 and the Liberal, Charles McFerran Legg's 1,778.

'... The speech of Asquith last week has settled French and he cannot be tolerated much longer as the representative of the king in the government of Ireland. His day is over. Kitchener has been vindicated finally. Asquith's speech had a most artistic ending, a letter read without a comment. The East Antrim election has produced tremendous excitement. Carson's nominee received only forty-one per cent of the electors, [G. B.] Hanna a much larger percentage. Carson will not feel easy in mind. He may cease to be the figure head of the Ulster Unionists. The *Irish News* has a strong article on the subject. I could not get a copy of the paper or of the *Freeman['s Journal]*—they were all sold in an hour. It will be interesting to watch developments, especially as all the speakers on [W. A.] Moore's platform told the audience if Moore was not elected the deluge would ensue. All the M.P.s who spoke for Moore harped on that string and the string is [broken ?] whereat there are tears in many quarters, not crocodile tears by any means. The [*Northern*] *Whig* and [*Belfast*] *News-Letter* are laying comfort to their souls—if they have any—that [G. B.] Hanna is against Home Rule—cold comfort when those who voted for him repudiated the leadership of the great Sir Edward. I am sorry that I am not able to send you copies of the nationalist journals. They are in a state of ecstasy over the event. The other organs are in a state of heart mourning—"serve" them right. ...'

D.1792/A3/10/16   **Letter to W. S. Armour from Armour,**

6 August 1919   gloomily analysing the current industrial unrest and forecasting 'red ruin' and government bankruptcy. In particular he feels that Lloyd George is making serious mistakes in giving in to some of this pressure. 'Reds' are obviously lurking under beds, even in Ballymoney!

'... Things seem drifting to bankruptcy. With the strike of the police or attempted strike, with the threat of direct action on the part of the strikers to put an end to parliamentary rule and the introduction of revolution and dictatorship—with the coal and railway strikes—with the millions spent on ruling Ireland—with the millions spent on payment of thousands who will not work—why should they when they get for loafing about as much as they could get as workers—with the continuous expenditure in all state departments—there are the signs of red ruin and the breaking up of laws. L[loyd] G[eorge] may have gained the war but is likely to ruin the peace. You will find an attack upon him by Lord Askwith among the papers sent. It has much foundation. It is curious the *M[anchester] G[uardian]* and few of the papers—none in the North here—referred to the attack. It will however silently tell. L[loyd] G[eorge] is an opportunist who gives to those that ask more than they ask to have a quiet life. That is not statesmanship as he will find and is finding by the bye-elections [*sic*]. ...'

D.1792/A3/10/18   **Letter to W. S. Armour from Armour,**

3 September 1919   containing local news; defending British rule in India; attacking Edward Carson for threatening the government on the Irish question; and alleging that the Unionists are the unconscious allies of the Irish Roman Catholic hierarchy.

'... Carson is about again and is threatening the government and trying to bring back the feeling which eventuated in the gun-running. He and his entourage have been hand in glove with the Catholic bishops and we have the result of their statesmanship. *The Spectator* has returned to the Ulster question again but the great organ I fear is going in for impossibilities. The p[rime] m[inister] like the sphinx has not given a word and nobody seems to guess what line he may take. ... An election must come soon but when is unknown and the question is "will the co-alition be able to maintain its ground?" Perhaps it may with a skeleton of a margin .'

D.1792/A3/10/21   **Letter to W. S. Armour from Armour,**

5 November 1919   describing a visit to Finvoy Presbyterian Church, Co. Antrim, and commenting on the government's mis-handling of the recruitment of Irishmen from outside Ulster to the armed forces during the war (they were not permitted to form separate units as the Ulster recruits were).

'... [G. K.] Chesterton has published a book which the *M[anchester] G[uardian]* reviews and he takes up the point I urged on Kenneth [Armour] of how the War Office put a stopper to Redmond's desire that Irishmen should enlist for the war. The result of stupidity was that Irishmen did not enlist and became madly pro-German. The government is largely responsible for the Irish situation from what they did not do and for what they did do. ...'

D.1792/A3/10/24   **Letter to W. S. Armour from Armour,** [*page torn*],

3 December 1919   commenting on the introduction of a new Irish education bill and the likelihood of its rejection by the Catholic hierarchy and attacking the hierarchy in general for their contribution to the creation of Ireland's problems.

'... The Catholic bishops have a grave responsibility over the present state of Ireland and it may turn out afterwards that the opinions they have winked at may be directed against them-selves. I hardly think they are quite easy in their minds over what is taking place. ...'

D.1792/A3/10/26   **Letter to W. S. Armour from Armour,**

23 December 1919   assessing the significance of the attempted assassin-ation of Lord French, the lord lieutenant of Ireland, and commenting critically on the terms of the proposed Home Rule bill for Ireland.

'... The attempted murder of Lord French has created a sensation and followed as it has been by the wrecking of the [*Irish*] *Independent* newspaper office shows the diabolicity of the crew which stops at nothing. No opinion on the situation is worth much as one never knows what a day may bring forth. Things have nearly reached the climax and perhaps the boil may burst. One is sorry that a few more were not shot. ... We live in a strange country and in strange times. I have not looked at Lloyd George's harangue about the contemplated Home Rule bill but it seems a bad form of settlement and it will likely meet with opposition from most parties in Ireland. It is marking of time. Possibly it is a preparation for a general election which may come soon. ...'

D.1792/A3/12

1921-1927

Originals of letters from Rev. J. B. Armour to his wife and sons (principally to W. S. Armour).

D.1792/A3/12/4

28 September 1925

Letter to J. B. M. Armour from Armour,

discussing the unwillingness of the congregation of Trinity Church, Ballymoney, to have Max Armour as his father's successor and his (J. B. Armour's) reaction to this.

'I feel fairly after a little brush in the church a week ago. I announced that I had preached my last sermon to them and that I appeared for the last time in that pulpit and never again save when some absolute necessity arose. Then thanking the congregation heartily for their kind loyalty to me for fifty-six years, I said that a certain thing occurred at the meeting on Wednesday which for twenty minutes gave me excessive pain. Then I launched forth on the gratuitous insult they had hurled at me through you—an insult which I hurled back on them as it was offensive if not malignant. I pointed out that they had the impudence to put your name not among the four they had selected and that you would be asked if one of the four could not come. ... After giving them a few sentences of indignant truth I said I was sorry for the necessity of talking in this way but [?] for the circumstances that made it imperative on me to defend your honour and my own. I have never feared the face of man and I could not allow a few Solomons and self-made saints to attempt to ruin the opinion which I and the Manse folk had done much to build up. Keep quiet. It will do you more good than harm—write no letters to anybody on the subject.'

D.1792/A3/13

1892-1924

Originals of letters from Rev. J. B. Armour to Jane MacMaster (the sister of Professor James MacMaster, Armour's wife's brother-jn-law.)

D.1792/A3/13/1

[n.d.]

Letter to Jane MacMaster from Armour,

containing birthday greetings and family gossip.

D.1792/A3/13/2

17 July 1892

Letter to Jane MacMaster, Leopold Ward, St Thomas's Hospital, London, from Armour,

retrospectively analysing his role in the 1892 general election in North Antrim, in which he had campaigned on behalf of W. H. Dodd, the independent Home Rule candidate, and also evaluating the effects of these events on his family and himself. Written at the top of the letter is a pencilled comment by Jane MacMaster, presumably intended for William S. Armour: 'I didn't "burn" but I can trust it to you and being still in a cot—you don't remember those days'.

'I am in bed—the wife and weans are out at church. I am dead in body but as undaunted in mind and I hope as clear as ever I was, which according to those here does not indicate any superfluity of mental lucidity. I have been through Hades for the last fortnight and now I have got back to purgatory—not an exhilirating place but one has to make the best of his *locale*. The wife stood the fire like a brick and was very heroic all through. The shot from the big guns did not frighten her in the least but I am a little afraid that she may get irritated with the gad flies of social life here. After a battle you know the "clegs" come in swarms and though their bite is not deadly it is tantalising especially when one cannot make a swoop down on them to brush them away in a heap.

To begin my doleful story, I fear that I have offended all your relatives—Sara excepted—and specially the College St[reet, Londonderry] people [Professor James MacMaster and family] by giving [Thomas] Sinclair a deserved dressing. I handled him as delicately as the circumstances allowed but to touch the sacred name of Sinclair is an unpardonable offence in the eyes of Mr Prof. It is one of the conditions of political warfare and I must accept the inevitable fate with as little grinning as circumstances allow. Then every "cad". and every Liberal Unionist from Dan to Beersheba are charging their guns. They have certainly expended a good deal of Billingsgate already and if they have not exhausted their spite and malignity, it is because their quantity immeasurable. I have fallen on evil days and evil tongues but I feel free and I have no regrets and am untroubled in my conscience about cutting my connexion with a party that I served to the best of my small ability and which is proving itself a party of spite, vulgarity and meaness. At least this is so if the magistrate of Church St[reet, Ballymoney—William Hamilton] is a representative. His spiteful speech published in the [*Belfast*] *News-Letter* first and three days after in the [*Northern*] *Whig* and then his vulgar letter which appeared without a word from me in the meantime, reveal a sense of honour and justice which I hope for the sake of this race are only possible in Church St[reet] B[ally]money. I was handicapped in this way—the papers which published the attack would admit nothing from me. However, I gave Field a dressing at the great public meeting for his windbaggery, which he will not forget for a few days and the letter—a short one in the [*Northern*] *Whig*—left his worship of Ch[urch] St[reet] a spectacle of pity. He had not the grace to withdraw a charge when it was proved to be false and he had not the courage to accept that challenge he threw out and which I took up in terms very favourable to himself. The public here—at least the better part—laughs at his cowardice and I have done with him. [James B.] Dougherty as you know was beaten [in North Tyrone] and the cup of mine iniquity was filled by going to speak for him. I am very sorry in one way about his defeat but I would have despised myself forever if when he asked me I had refused to go, though it was to get pelted by some of the mud flung at him by some of the

meanest men which ever degraded by their presence and vile language social life. The spiteful-
ness of Leabody and the impudence of Dickey—I do not speak of Henry who owes D[ougherty]
a grudge—prove how really small souls they are. I once described Leabody as a Nihilist half [?]
and as a socialistic tailor ready to stick his shears into his neighbour if it suited him and I have
no wish to modify this judgement after his performance. If those gentry represent Unionism,
as it is called, the thing ought to be hewn in pieces and burned out of sight in the interests of
civilisation. It has existed too long and the fatuity of preserving that monstrosity is worthy of
a ship of fools. I love Dougherty and admire him intensely and I hope you will acquit me of
folly in saying a word for a maligned but worthy man. The fight is over now—the reaction has
to come. I know bonds and imprisonments—I speak in metaphors which is the sign they say of
a weakened brain—await me but none of these things move me. I will stand on my feet, I hope,
until the last and I leave the future in the hands of God. Several in this church have been
annoyed by my action and whatever be the outcome of the present unhappy struggle, I believe
good will result therefrom ... . This stupid letter you will burn when read, that is if you have
time or inclination to read through a note which is written as a safety valve. ...

P.S. It is Monday morning. We are thriving and in good health. I don't care to send this but the
master [Mrs Armour] says let it go. Burn it and you will do a favour to me. I am making
speeches all the time—in and out of sleep. My brain cannot rest.'

D.1792/A3/13/3	**Letter to Jane MacMaster from Armour,**
22 January 1895	entirely devoted to gossip about the MacMaster family.

D.1792/A3/13/4	**Letter to Jane MacMaster from Armour, [written on Queen's College, Belfast, notepaper],**
18 June 1895	mainly containing local and family news but com-

menting briefly on the appointment of James B. Dougherty, Armour's friend, as assistant
under secretary for Ireland by the Rosebery Liberal government.

'... J[ames] B. D[ougherty] is fixed and to outward seeming well fixed at last. Mrs D[ougherty]
and her friends will not think so badly of Home Rule now. I hear Mrs D[ougherty]'s brother is
such a wild Unionist that he would scarcely mention J. B. D.'s name and certainly never
mentioned H[ome] Rule without swearing, of course in the mild Toddian way. He will be
reconciled now, I fancy. The appointment has given great satisfaction and to none more than
to your humble servant. ...'

D.1792/A3/13/5	**Letter to Jane MacMaster from Armour, 3 College Avenue, Londonderry.**
19 June 1902	discussing Jane MacMaster's application for a vacant

matron's post in Dublin and enclosing a letter from Sir James B. Dougherty assessing her
chances of success. The letter also includes some gossip about the proceedings of the General
Assembly.

D.1792/A3/13/6	**Letter to Jane MacMaster from Armour,**
20 June 1903	commenting in considerable detail on the Presbyterian General Assembly debate on the Unionist govern-

ment's university reform proposals. Armour defends his abandonment of his previous preference for mixed or undenominational education in favour of denominationalism.

'... I think I sent you all the newspapers, favourable and unfavourable over the business. I am not very thin in the skin and therefore do not mind a little currying. It was a fine hour or two. I was in good form and certainly they listened and the Petticrew party is in a state of despondency at the result. The outside world is rejoicing that a turn is being made. The moderator was the most pained man in the house as he has committed himself to the official gang and in his heart he feels sore—with himself, I think. *The Witness* article today is too stupid and outrageously unfair to trouble about. They have been talking all the time as if I had abandoned what they call the principle of the church on matters educational and was going in for expediency. That is the very reverse of the fact. Petticrew and his motley party wish to enforce what they call their principle on everybody else but the ⁹/₁₀ths of Ireland utterly refuse to accept it and because Petticrew and his followers cannot get their principle *universal*, therefore they will cut its throat and let it perish. My point is this—you cannot force your principle on everybody— the trend everywhere now-a-days and in Ireland for the last thirty years has been in the direction of denominationalism—the government came into power on the denominational ticket; they have endowed the ritualists of England with the sanction of the General Assembly; they have introduced the denominational principle in primary education; endowing denominational houses for the training of teachers; there are two schemes for the endowment of a denominational university, Balfour's and the commission's. It is too apparent that either the one or other is bound to come—I prefer Balfour's as it is direct, straightforward, but to save the principle for which we contended—go to Balfour and demand that he will set up and endow properly one university in Ireland where ecclesiasticism will not be the ruling factor in education. You have a right to claim that your principle will have a chance for existence; you have no right and you have *no power* to enforce it on everybody. So you will be able to see that my position is designed to save undenominationalism in higher education while theirs is the gambler's position, because we cannot get what we think right universally established, we will throw up the sponge and let our principle perish in the fight. However, they are sore and admit now—though with tears—that their game of all or nothing is all up. The sane part of the community is with me and there is great private satisfaction that I was defeated only by Ali Baba's forty thieves. As I told one of them afterwards, that vote is Hasdrubal's head thrown over the wall, Hannibal may pick it up and meditate thereon for it means he has had his Cannae but we will have at no remote period our Zanna. ...'

D.1792/A3/13/7　　　　　　　　　　**Part of a letter to Jane MacMaster from Armour,**

29 November 1907　　　　　　　　containing some comments on the visit of Augustine Birrell, the newly appointed chief secretary for Ireland, to Ballymoney and Londonderry. These reveal his hostility towards the 'intriguers' amongst the Ballymoney Liberals and his anxiety to persuade Birrell, through his private secretary, to rely on the advice of Sir James B. Dougherty on Irish matters.

'... I wrote a long screed to the wife in reference to the Birrell show here and perhaps you heard what was written. I forget where I left off as I had much to say, becoming a trifle garrulous in old age. At any rate this episode has had many commentators since and you will be astonished to hear that the honours of the occasion are divided between the cabinet minister and this mansite. The intriguers have had the wisdom to hold their tongues though perhaps their meditation like the psalmist's is not sweet. Since writing the master, I fell in with the two priests again and more pleased men you have not met. One said the phrase—the Sadducees believe there is no resurrection—for Ireland was particularly true if a trifle biting. But to hear the rustic cackle of our boring which might be taken as the great wave that echoes round the world and go to Derry for a [?] may be a relief. The Prof. [James MacMaster] will tell you about B[irrell] at Magee [College] omitting no particulars. The luncheon was good and well attended but the speaking was poor—Todd having gathered all the expectant lawyers into the presence of the great panjandrum. B[irrell] spoke well but I omit further comments on what was the least interesting part of the wanderings of Ulysses. I ventured to have a serious private talk with B[irrell]'s sec[retary], an interesting youth called Ilingworth, said to be an M.P. of some place. I thought of having a private haver with B[irrell] himself but it occurred to me that the private sec[retary] was the best basis for operations. I told him that Mr B[irrell] was necessarily ignorant of many things in Ireland he should know—that he was entering on a very ticklish job—that in some Liberal quarters already fears were arising that he might be a failure—that personally it would be a great grief to me if he failed and that I was speaking entirely as one who had no private axe to grind. You will kindly, said I, advise Mr B[irrell] to take almost no step in his administration without consulting Sir J[ames] B. D[ougherty]. First—that Sir J[ames] B. D[ougherty] knew more of Ireland than any man about the Castle—that he was the wisest head by far in that place—that he might be relied on to give not only sound advice but advice which, if acted on, would prevent many a mistake, major and minor—that [Edward] Bryce [Birrell's immediate predecessor] had got himself into several holes. ...'

D.1792/A3/13/8

28 May 1908

Letter to Jane MacMaster from Armour, [written from Portrush, Co. Antrim],

commenting on Ulster Unionist hostility towards Augustine Birrell's Irish universities bill and especially on the opposition to it in the General Assembly, led by Rev. MacDermott, Dr Park and Thomas Sinclair.

'... The Hon. Tho[ma]s has asked me for dinner which I hardly expected as he can stand any amount of butter but does not like anything in the way of pepper applied to him. The Sinclairites do not know that they were going for the very thing the Jesuits would like—the destruction of the bill as the said Jesuits fear that Birrell's measure within the near future will be disastrous to the Catholic church. Extremes always meet in the long run. ...'

D.1792/A3/13/9

28 November 1908

Letter to Jane MacMaster from Armour, Brook's Private Hotel, 33-4 Surrey Street, Strand, London,

describing a visit to Oxford for a medical examination which has confirmed that he has a heart condition, albeit 'nothing serious'. The specialist has advised him 'to go it very easy which as I have told you is difficult to carry out'.

D.1792/A3/13/10

[n.d. 1909 ?]

Letter to Jane MacMaster from Armour, [written on Royal Portrush Golf Club notepaper],

describing a visit to Dublin in his official capacity as chaplain to the lord lieutenant and his stay with Sir James Dougherty at the under secretary's lodge. He also gives his views on the proposed link up between Magee College, Londonderry, and Trinity College, Dublin, which he sees as essentially a victory for the Anglican enemy.

'... We talked at the under sec[retary]'s on many subjects and we had a crack on Magee and Trinity. The longer I think thereon the more insane and suicidal the policy of the Magee people appears to be. They give everything and get practically nothing. Dougherty read me an extract from a letter from Birrell which I give you *in strict privacy*. President [Thomas] Hamilton [of Queen's College, Belfast] had written Birrell to suggest that Birrell should answer the charges which the Magee people were making against him by getting some friend to ask a question in the h[ouse of] c[ommons] put in such a way that he could confute the slanderers. B[irrell] wrote back—I will not bother. My hide is as thick as the hide of rhinocerous—they may say away, they are not worth bothering about. Then he added—"I had a letter from the provost of T.C.D. chuckling over the idea of T.C.D. raiding the Presbyterian hen roosts". That is the situation: whatever advantage there may be, if any, Trinity will reap it, getting for every degree at least £22 and likely at the end of five years when [Provost Anthony] Traill is in his grave— the arrangement is to be overhauled in five years—Trinity will insist on terms which will be impossible for Magee to comply with and then it will be left high and dry—a mere high school. The folly of the transaction is beyond description and why or how John Cooke lent himself to the project surpasses my comprehension. Birrell, to do him justice, appointed Cooke and Lea-body as members of the senate. The man in the street will hardly conclude that proved his hostility to Magee. They were appointed not on personal merits but as representing Magee. As honourable men, it seems to me they are bound to resign their seats for it would out Herod the Jesuits for two Presbyterians to hold office in an institution they were endeavouring to weaken. That view of the case had not occurred to D[ougherty] and when I put it in this way he added, "Cooke is under great obligations to the present government as he was selected as lord lieu[tenant] of the county". You may not say the gov[ernmen]t selected him, said I, *you* did it and nobody else. I had written D[ougherty] a year before Sir Hervey [Bruce, the previous lord lieutenant for Co. Londonderry] died to say that in case of Sir H's death, Cooke ought to get the berth. He replied by saying he would keep the matter in mind. I am half inclined to send to some of the papers an interview on the whole subject. An interview seems better than a letter but my difficulty will be to keep from peppering the tents of a few Zulus. They deserve fully a little scalping and they may get it. The whole business is the act of traitors to Presbyterianism. It will weaken the northern university and hand it over to other denomi-nations and surely the common sense view ought to be, "No matter how you came into existence, it is our duty as Presbyterians to make the most of you and to see, as we are the larger sect, that we keep you on lines which are right". I have no time to swear further. ...'

D.1792/A3/13/11   **Letter to Jane MacMaster from Armour,**

12 January 1909   commenting on several books which she has sent to him and on the modernist movement in the Roman Catholic church.

'... It appears to me looking at the movement dispassionately that it will come to little in the meantime but it is possibly the first rumble of an earthquake which if not in our day at least in the future may shiver the Catholic church. Generations before the Reformation there were protests against the teaching and actions of the Vaticanists and the latter squelched the begin-nings of Protestantism within the church and tried to end them by almost diabolic means. But truth like murder will out some day and as reforms were impossible from within, this rupture made them possible without. It has long appeared to me that things in Catholicism—perhaps I should say Roman Catholicism as many Anglicans claim to be Catholics—a claim which never appealed to me—are silently working in the direction of a crisis which may not come for fully a century but which is bound to come, for Romanism, or for the matter of that high churchism, could not possibly be squared with Christianity as revealed in its outlines in the teaching of the founder of our faith. A series of regularly ordained priests with the doctrines flowing there-from is a thing outside the pale of Christ's Christianity. ...'

D.1792/A3/13/12   **Letter to Jane MacMaster from Armour,**

25 April 1910   recounting in detail a visit by Armour and his wife to Dublin to attend various viceregal social functions and to enable both Mrs Armour and himself to be officially presented to Lord and Lady Aber-deen. Apart from a description of the viceregal court, 'the peepshow in Dublin', he also includes some comments on the developing scholastic philosophy issue in the convocation of the newly created Queen's University of Belfast.

'... I sent you a paper, I think, from which you saw that my warfare is not over and that the pagans who opposed me all these years are still on the rampage against Q.U.B., pretending they dislike scholastic philosophy. They packed the meeting with their groundlings paying the fee to qualify many and consequently there was a large contingent there in obedience to Thomas Sinclair's whip. The manses throughout Ulster were almost all empty on that Saturday. A *Benjamin* Moore had sent in resolutions he was going to propose and I had thought of answering them and prepared slightly accordingly but in the [*Northern*] *Whig* of the day before the

Hon. Thomas [Sinclair] issued his manifesto and laid down his proposals. It was then apparent that the divining rod or cup to guide the assembly was not to be found in Benjamin's sack. I chaffed him privately on the matter. The Hon. Thomas [Sinclair] made his speech much on the same lines with which the General Assembly had become familiar through constant repetition for thirty years. Then Benjamin followed by reading extracts from Green, Kant and Huxley—he did not read Huxley's view of the Gadarene swine. Then I started before a rather hostile audience. You have no idea of the difficulty of speaking in such circumstances. One feels he is buffeting with tremendous waves. I got through the Tory papers say with less success than usual but in my opinion quite fairly. [R. M.] Henry spoke after me and made a really firm speech as he knew the inner aspect of the case which I only knew partially and by accident. Then followed Adam Duffin, I think, who took care to dissociate himself with the mover of the amendment, how said mover will [survive ?] after that is a problem ... then Irwin, MacDermott, Davey who rather put his foot in the business—then a man McGowan and then the vote. There must have been at least 150 who did not vote—sitters on the fence of whom Jones with the tear in his voice was one. You have seen the vote therefore I need not dwell thereon. The chancellor [Lord Shaftesbury] was really strong in the direction of the amendment but he is a [?] the majority says and therefore should not count. The whole thing is a vote of censure on the privy council. Sinclair is a land leaguer when the law is not in accordance with his notions. ...'

D.1792/A3/13/13   **Part of a letter to Jane MacMaster from Armour,**

13 January 1914   recounting family news and the events at a number of meetings which he had attended and commenting further on the debate about a possible political compromise on Ulster.

'... There is nothing new on the political situation. The idea of excluding Ulster or part of Ulster is the maddest proposal ever made and if carried out would ruin Ulster as it would endanger the safety of the Protestants elsewhere as the Ulsterites would persecute Catholics and Protestant Ulsterites [*sic*] and thus provoke reprisals in other parts of Ireland. ...'

D.1792/A3/13/14   **Letter to Jane MacMaster from Armour,**

17 March 1914   indicating his desire to retire in the not too distant future, although he wishes to see the Home Rule question settled first; mentioning an invitation to attend a Nationalist banquet in London, to be presided over by John Redmond; and discussing in some detail Asquith's offer of temporary exclusion for Ulster on a county option basis.

'... The papers are a little exciting these days. Asquith's speech last night is one he only could make. In my opinion he has put the Tories in a fix. F. E. Smith was clamouring for the exclusion of what he called homogeneous counties and now Asquith says in a particular way "agreed" and Bonar Law and Carson are in a fury. It is not likely that they will accept the proposal. It would be a bad thing for those counties—in a way ruinous as the other parts of even Ulster not to speak of the rest of Ireland would naturally say "well you refuse to come [ather ?] with us politically, then we refuse to share our commerce with you". The Ulster counties are dependent commercially on their neighbours and cannot live alone. Derry would be in a nice position as a deal of its trade is with Donegal. Looking at the matter from a business point of view, "the Tories" want Ulster, by excluding it in whole or in part, to commit suicide. But they are not sincere in wishing even the exclusion of the whole. Their whole design is to upset the parliament act. From a Protestant point of view, it would be calamitous as the Tories, if they had control of Ulster which they would have, would give Catholics and Protestant home rulers no quarter and therefore by their intolerance would stir up the Catholics in the south and west to harass in a hundred ways the scattered Protestants. This was written up to this point on Friday. Now the public has had Asquith's explanation last night. He is clearly hardening on the points

I

which is very popular as friends of the government were beginning to get alarmed that he was selling the pass. Churchill's speech has aroused the enthusiasm of the folks here as elsewhere as it is without doubt a cabinet resolve. Bonar does not seem to have been particularly tactful last night—he seldom is. It is too soon for him to bang and bolt the door against any and every form of compromise. The Belfast people in their hearts, from indications given by commercial travellers, are secretly in terror lest the counties should be excluded as they know on commercial grounds it would be a blow to business. If providence should arrange that any form of exclusion should be agreed on, I fancy the old text would be illustrated—"I gave them their desire but sent leanness into their soul"—said soul of Ulster being tolerably lean already. Now to turn from matters of the great world to local items—there is a Methodist minister in Portrush called Atkinson who is suspected of Home Rule tendencies as many of the young parsons of the Methodist views are. He has to go from Portrush partly on that ground and partly because he is credited with the zeal for spoils which in Weslyan circles are not regarded as signs of spirituality. ...'

D.1792/A3/13/15

5 July 1914

Letter to Jane MacMaster from Armour, [written from the viceregal lodge, Dublin],

describing a visit to Dublin in his capacity as one of the lord lieutenant's chaplains. The account includes his description of the reaction of various individuals to the current state of the Home Rule crisis.

'... His exc[ellency] is not going to the house of lords this week unless he gets a special summons from [Lord] Crewe [the Liberal leader in the house of lords]. He does not like the amending bill in any shape and, if he dare, he would like to vote against it. [Sir James B.] Dougherty who was at the service says Birrell is quite hopeful of a settlement though he does not give the reason of the hope. ...'

D.1792/A3/13/16

29 November 1914

Letter to Jane MacMaster, [Stoke-on-Trent], from Armour, [to be forwarded to W. S. Armour],

largely devoted to an analysis of the circumstances surrounding the resignation of Lord Aberdeen and a description of Armour's attempts through Joseph Devlin and John Redmond to prevent it. He also mentions that Sir James Dougherty, the recently retired under secretary of state for Ireland, is to be the Liberal candidate in the impending Londonderry City by-election, following the death of the sitting Liberal member, David Hogg, and that Dougherty may have to face a contest with the Unionists. Much of the letter covers the same ground as D.1792/A3/5/34. Jane MacMaster was at this time matron of the North Staffordshire Royal Infirmary, Stoke-on-Trent.

'... I was in the metropolis last Sunday preaching at the lodge and waited on for the jubiliee of Rutland Square [Presbyterian Church] and the same jubiliee of [Rev.] J. D. O[sborne]—a big meeting with an interminable number of speakers in a church building which seemed planted at the North Pole. ... Their exc[ellencie]s are badly in the dumps—*this is strictly private*—as they have got notice to quit and give up the office which they have filled fairly well and hardly know the real reason for their short notice to bundle out. His exc[ellency] is very sore and so is her exc[ellency] as it means the collapse of a number of schemes she has started and which have cost her much money and said schemes are almost certain to collapse. The real reason is that the Irish aristocracy has been intriguing against them at the court of St James where they were no favourites of Ed[ward] VII, and George and his [wife ?] have the same feelings toward them as King Ed[ward] had. The war has started a wave of anti-democratic feeling which bodes ill for the future and they are feeling first the effects of the incoming tide. Possibly the public will set it down to that letter her exc[ellency] wrote, a letter whose publication scandalously broke all the courtesies of social life—insinuating clearly that the Red X Society was being run for Unionist political purposes. I see a nursing magazine you sent on Saturday is down on the letter. Well in my opinion the statement in that letter which was published for [mean ?] purposes is perfectly true—*Pace* the nursing magazine. I am on the P.O.W. Fund for the looking after the wives and dependants of soldiers and sailors and I see the Tories about here, and specially the miserable members of the Church of Ireland who contributed little in money, have grabbed the machinery and are working it for all its worth for their own contemptible ends. I got on the local committee through the moderator of Assembly nominating me for the co[unty] committee but I am the fly in the ointment. It was only at the point of the bayonet that I got the priest of the parish on the local committee and that little squireen Leslie who speaks in a tone like a snared rabbit would not tolerate the idea of Julius Caesar [Mrs Armour] getting on though he filled the local committee with every beggarly Episcopalian he could name. I pity her exc[ellency] for she has spoken in what was intended to be secret an open factual truth, though of course the Pharisees with which Unionism is filled are turning up the whites of their eyes as if the Lord's annointed were anything but the essence of everything that was righteous. I wrote a note on Saturday to Joe Devlin to tell him to inform John Redmond that the notice to quit served on their exc[ellencie]s was the beginning of an attempt to whittle down the amending bill when it comes up so as to strangle his measure, hinting that to betray those who had stood to him all these years to please his foes was not playing the real game. I advised him to get Redmond to put down his foot and not suffer intriguers at court to spoil his innings. I don't know what action if any he may take but he can if he likes put a spoke in the wheel. I quoted part of W[illia]m's [Armour] letter in which he said Redmond was the greatest asset of the British empire at present as his speeches in parliament had made the nationalists of India loyal. Botha and he together are the best assets of the empire. If Botha had followed de Wet, S. Africa would have been lost and if Redmond had taken a different attitude all the Irish in America and the colonies would have turned against Britain with a result disastrous. Their exc[ellencie]s—especially his exc[ellency]—seems sore over Asquith who had told him years ago that he (his exc[ellency]) would cease to be l[ord] lieutenant the day he (Asquith) ceased to be premier. I told him that Asquith had probably nothing to do with the business, it was pressure from without that forced Asquith's hand. He agreed to that view but still he is sore. Her exc[ellency] thinks that Birrell will go too, though Sir J[ames] B. D[ougherty] does not think so but I have the belief that to break the fall Mr B. may go. At least he has been talking at times in that way and possibly pressure of which Sir J. B. D. knows nothing may have been brought on St Augustine. We must wait and see. His exc[ellency] says that after all those years of service to the state he will go back even poorer than he came— which I can very well believe as her exc[ellency] delves into schemes which however good in intention have dipped deep into their purse. I see they are beginning to think that Lord Tweedmouth was shabbily cast off but the real reason was that he was taking softening of the brain and his speech in the lords on the death of C[ampbell] B[annerman] was so hideously inept that he had to go. Lord Pentland in their opinion was cannoned to India to get him out of the Scotch secretaryship. This is now a grievance. I made rather a false move by saying, "Oh he was kicked upstairs"—a saying for which I could have bit my tongue as it occurred to me that he himself might as a solace to wounded feelings get a step up in the peerage, though surely the earl of Aberdeen is a higher title and more historic than the marquis of Aberdeen as he has little chance of being created a duke. Their exc[ellencie]s went to Osborne's fete and sat it out. It was whispered that they were anxious to hear my speech—possibly someone was trying to pull my leg. At any rate I gave them a lift. After two or three sentences on J.D.O. and his church, I proceeded to say that the Rutlandites ought to be grateful for the unprecedented honour conferred on them as it was the first occasion in Presbyterian history that a gathering of Presbyterians was attended by the viceroy and vicereine and probably when they laid down office it would be the last. Then I stated in vigorous phrase that for the first time in Irish history Presbyterian parsons were allowed to preach in the v[ice] regal lodge as they had always got the outside of the door into the charmed circle and possibly, likely the old state of things would return. Then after a few sentences on the character of his exc[ellency] and the real work he had done impartially during his tenure of office and *their loyalty* to our church, I pointed out that her exc[ellency] had started many projects for the good of Ireland—one of which had resulted in nearly a half million of wages—I said doubtless they were maligned by a horde of Philistines, a plentiful stock on Irish soil, but when the Philistines were dead and forgotten their exc[ellencie]s would be remembered in the future as real benefactors of

Ireland. I thundered out a good deal in a very short time and part of the audience agreed by plentiful "hear, hears" but you may be sure Baxter, Park and several others must have thought the speech was the muttering of a judgement on them.

Having delivered my soul, I left to go to Killiney to stay with the Doughertys and found that her ladyship and he had gone to dine at the lord chancellor's. They returned about 12 o'clock and Sir J. B. D. and I havered on until nigh 2 o'clock. I learned then that he was to be the candidate for Derry in the room of Hogg. He was half inclined to think that some of the 'Prentice Boys might jump the [gun ?] and insist on a contest though the respectable Tories were agreeable to observe the compact entered into—not to contest any seat during the war. There is talk of somebody coming forward but I fancy his candidature will end in a bottle of smoke ... . Sir J. B. D. is in very good form and as always the night spent there was for me pleasant. He talks to me freely. I called on the new under-secretary, Sir Matthew Nathan. His exc[ellency] requested me to do so and was to be there at 3 o'clock to introduce me. He did not turn up but he sent a message to the Jew to see me. I had ten minutes with him and talked on various points. He is evidently able. He took his oath for the privy council in Jewish fashion with his hat on. Dougherty told him afterwards that he ought after oriental fashion to have put off his shoes. He did not follow Moses in that respect. It is not thought that he will stay long in Ireland. He bought Sir J. B. D.'s motor for £100. He is not married but he keeps at the lodge six maid servants. What one man has to do with six maids I cannot tell. It is a big house to be sure. I think his private secretary lives with him. ...

It is reported this morning that somebody called "Good" is to give Sir J. B. D. a run for his money. I hope he will not be encouraged but the Derry Christians are a peculiar people and silently "Good" may be promised backing. ...'

D.1792/A3/13/17   **Letter to Jane MacMaster from Armour,**

21 December 1914   conveying family news and trying to defend the con-
                                              duct of Sir Roger Casement in defecting to Germany.
He also repeats the views which he had expressed in his letters to William Armour about the significance of the removal of Lord and Lady Aberdeen.

'... I had to write him [Kenneth Armour] a letter to be sent to some man in Cambridge about my views of the escapade of Sir Roger Casement in Berlin as reported in the papers. It is curious that every report from Berlin about Britain is regarded as a pack of lies but a report reflecting on a political opponent is a sort of 11th commandment from Sinai. I pointed out the fact that Sir Roger had gone in June to America six weeks before the war to get the Washington gov[ernmen]t to arrange for the continuance of the mails from Ireland by Queenstown. As Sir Roger is a diplomat, it is probable that the Washington government which hopes to have a hand in making peace ultimately sent him on a mission to Berlin to watch for an opportunity of giving the president a chance for his design. It is impossible to think that Sir Roger went as an Englishman. Had he done so, he would have been stopped at the frontier and if he succeeded in getting through he would have been interned. It is likely that he had an interview with the German Foreign Office but as they were cocksure that England would be made a province of Germany, it is not improbable that Sir Roger, too wise a diplomat to say that is not very likely, asked in half irony, supposing that takes place what will you do with Ireland and the Foreign Office there, believing firmly that Sir Edward Carson's talk of a civil war in Ireland would take place, said, oh we will regard Ireland as an independent state. Then I wrote something like this—supposing that the worst construction is put on Sir Roger's action, how can he be regarded as a traitor when Sir Edward Carson and Captain Craig, who were anxious to make Ulster a province of Germany, were applauded as the pink of patriots. Why should they be regarded as patriots and the other as a traitor? It is beyond question that the war came sooner than it would have done but for the heroics of Sir Edward and his entourage. When people set a house on fire the [event ?] of an attempt on their part to try to put the fire out is a trifle meritricious. I wrote a letter which he was to use or not use as he thought right. ...

It is impossible to interfere effectively in the matter [the removal of the Aberdeens] ; the *fiat* has gone forth against the Aberdeens. I think it is a court intrigue engineered after the manner of the Curragh business by the Irish aristocrats and Unionists who hate the present government intensely and have wreaked their vengeance on their exc[ellencie]s. It is a pity but what can one do? ...'

D.1792/A3/13/19   **Letter to Jane MacMaster from Armour,**

26 March 1917   commenting on the appointment of James Chambers,
                                               Unionist member of parliament for South Belfast, as
solicitor-general for Ireland and on Unionist reaction to it. He also notes with some pleasure
that Lloyd George has had to modify his views on the Home Rule question.

'May it please your glory, great Queen Jane, I enclose you Sir J[ames] B. D[ougherty]'s last letter with the funny article from the [*Northern*] *Whig*, headed "John Dillon's choice". The editor calls on the electors of S[outh] Belfast to evict Chambers but at the meeting on Friday of the committee with Sir W[illiam] Crawford in the chair, it was agreed to that no opposition was to be offered to Chambers' re-election and further it was added that his selection as solicitor-general was made with the full approval of the Irish Unionists. From this it is clear that John Dillon's choice is the choice of the Irish Unionists. It is hard on the [*Northern*] *Whig*. The [*Belfast*] *News-Letter* made no remarks on the selection. Perhaps you will see in the *Morning Post* a letter from [Rev.] John MacDermott. He is the essence of the Die Hards. It is difficult to find out what he means. At any rate it is trying for one of his mental outlook to find that the Welshman had to eat the leek a few days after his "no surrender" on the Home Rule business and that Bonar Law who egged him on has had to announce that an attempt is to be made to get the question settled. The Russian revolution has had a hand in the matter as it may have a hand in bowling out the Kaiser from Germany. ...'

14 April 1892   **Letter from Rev. J. D. Osborne, 16 Mountjoy Square, Dublin, to Rev. J. B. Armour,**

supporting the candidature of W. H. Dodd in North Antrim, as read by Armour at a meeting at Ballymacwilliam, 29 June 1892. Source: *Ballymena Free Press*, 30 June 1892.

'I saw W. H. Dodd last night and had a talk with him about North Antrim. I sympathise with your position there, and if my opinion is worth having, I believe that you have done the right in asking him to stand as an independent candidate. I am as thoroughly Unionist in my convictions as ever I was since the controversy began, but I see no reason to fear that Dodd will ignore that cause. On the contrary, I believe that his presence in parliament would have an important moderating influence upon the statesmen with whom he may be associated. Besides that, he is a Presbyterian and I trace our iniquitous treatment in the matter of Presbyterian representation to our miserable failure in proper self-assertion. Thus, it seems clear to me that without independent men such as he, advocating at St Stephens the abolition of castle bureaucracy and freedom for the tiller of the soil, the desires of Presbyterian Ulster outside Belfast will find no adequate expression in the house of commons. Further than that, surely the strong temperance convictions of North Antrim merit a better representative than a gentleman indentified with the traffic to which we rightly attribute the worst woes of our country.'

Anti-Home Rule pamphlet which originally appeared on 3 November 1887 and was republished on 6 September 1894 in order to discredit J. B. Armour. (Ballymoney Library special collection, U/A BMO 1315106.)

To the tenant farmers of North Antrim

Beware of the so-called reform meeting. It is a Home Rule meeting as much in the interests of the tenant farmers as a licensed victuallers meeting would be in the interests of temperance. The wire-pullers from abroad urged, contrary to advice here, a meeting for Home Rule. A few carpet-bagging politicians out of a job came to the north to advice [sic] the tenant farmers to commit suicide to save themselves from slaughter. Your refusal to purchase the halter at their bidding has so stirred the gall-bladder of these discarded apologists of crime that they have gone away praying that they may have the chance, in the days of terror they threaten, of acting as the hangman for all who will not become perverts. New orders have come 'can you not gild the pill for those northern brutes by calling it a meeting for land reform!' Hence a meeting is to be held by an entirely new company, but you are invited to hear the old tune rechristened.

Before you walk into the trap think of a few facts. To go in for Home Rule is to postpone land reform for ten years. The wire-pullers wish to teach you a new lesson on matters agricultural. 'Your woes have come', they say, 'because you insist on the exploded doctrine of putting the horse before the cart. Put the cart before the horse and everything will go straight.' Be not deceived, if Home Rule comes it will mean you will get rid of the harpies of landlordism for the vultures of Parnellism. 'Do the tenant farmers of Ireland think', said Parnell, 'I would take off my coat for them.' If they do, they are fools. The judicial rents, as you know to your cost, are oppressive—they are legalised robbery. Who are responsible for them? Who saddled these burdens on your backs? Earl Spencer and Trevelyan mainly. They ransacked every Tory rent office in Ireland to find reactionaries to defeat the land act and rob you, appointing one out of every ten commissioners favourable to the tenant, knowing that he would be powerless to save you. Ask one of the promoters of the meeting how his name was received by Spencer and his gang when he was a candidate for a commissionership. His just, overwhelming claims were flouted—he was politely bowed out by Spencer. Will he deny that Spencer and Trevelyan did their best to ruin the land act? They conspired to rob you to save the landlords. They have ruined the landlords in robbing you and now they wish to betray you with the kiss of Home Rule. These Ethiopians have not changed their skin.

Tell the lawyer loons who come to boast of their want of principle, that they will never crawl to the bench by your degradation. Bid them go straight to the camp to learn there the lawless code of injustice and intolerance which Parnell's judges will be expected to administer, should his reign of terror trouble for a season our unhappy country.

Tell Dickson that he was revered and trusted by the tenants when he was true to himself. When Gladstone hated him, you respected his manliness; when Spencer traduced him you stood up for him, but now that he has fallen so low as to be a worshipper at the shrine of the Manchester martyrs, you must bid him good-bye until he recovers his lost virtues. Ask him to deny that Parnell privately, and without solicitation, promised him support in his contest in Tyrone, and was the first to denounce him as a government hack, and to start a Home Ruler in opposition. Does he now advise you to submit to the troglodytes who boast they keep no treaties? Has the Dickson whom we trusted joined the troglodytes too? Tell the Methodist parrot of Portadown that you dislike cant, and cannot hear him traducing his co-religionists.

Gladstone was one of the best friends of the tenants. We grant this more heartily than any of his present henchmen. But he is now the avowed foe of the farmers of the north. His land bill, introduced in connexion with his Home Rule abortion, would have saddled nine-tenths of the northern farmers with an oppressive judicial rent for all time to come. The farmers of the south and west alone were to get free, because they had learned the use of dynamite. His speech against the leaseholders was brimming with hatred against their claims. He has not spoken for years without pouring contempt on the men of the north. Will any of the promoters of the meeting deny these facts? He is now dropping the mask. A year ago he said the minority would have their lives and liberties guaranteed by the British crown. At Nottingham last week, he said 'the minority need not be afraid to entrust their lives and liberties to their Roman Catholic countrymen'. Shades of Knox and Ridley and Latimer hear this! Tell Mr Gladstone and his idolators that the English government may have the right to cast you off, but they have no moral right to transfer the keeping of your lives and liberties to any power on earth. Be true to yourselves, and don't walk into the trap, even though baited skilfully by Walker, Hemphill, Dickson, Shillington, known now as the notorious ratters.

Post-script—6 September 1894

More appropriate now, especially about the rats.
Oh wud some power the giftie gie us,
To see ourselves as ithers see us;
It wud from money a blunder free us,
Like those of a turn-coat preacher.
    After Burns, by a Celtic professor from Magee College.

Ballad published in the *Ballymoney Free Press* of 24 November 1887.

The Unionist Handbill

List while I tell the story of the handbill
Was issued 'gainst the meeting to discuss a land bill:
'Twas morn within the town, or rather village,
While thronged its busy streets the sons of tillage,
Driving their cattle to the market hill,
A sight was witnessed caused each heart to thrill,
In middle of the road, before the gate,
The mud-compeller stood in solemn state,
A sheaf of leaflets, grasping in his hand —
The guardian angel of this hapless land
Boldly he stood, regardless of the rush,
Wielding his truncheon, *videlicet* brush,
Scattering the leaflets like the autumn breezes
Which sadly sigh among the browning trees;
But these stray leaves from off the tree of knowledge,
Gave but faint signs of love acquired in college,
Some did not read them, for they felt quite sure
'Twas pills of Holloway or Warner's Cure;
He touted for, but as he handed them to sharps and flats,
One of the latter said 'twas 'Rough on Rats'.
This trivial error sure was little matter;
'Twas immaterial between rats and 'ratter'.
Alas! those groundlings ne'er a moment thought
That with great truths its every line was fraught
The 'warning voice' did charge them one and all
On no account to enter the Town-hall,
But turn a deaf ear to those insidious talkers
And boycott all the Dicksons and the Walkers.
Counched in chaste language, 'twas a dreadful crusher,
The style so polished smacked of Peter Usher.
Yet why it failed I know not, its concocters
I'm told were dust men, learned divines, and doctors.
Yet, after all, I think this holy howl
Was largely due to Rev. Blattergowl
Now surnamed Troglodyte, who wields the pen
When met in council Gotham's wisest men.
To each collaborator I'll be fair,
And give to every one his proper share;
While the first rank is taken by theology,
We can't o'erlook the claims of physiology;
For the 'gall-bladder' comes within its scope,
But 'bilious bellowings', we fondly hope,
Was never spoken, 'een in wild bravado,
By that 'light of science', our own dear 'Sangrado'.
'Shades of Knox and Ridley', no Ruskin and Carlyle,
What learned professors e'er had such a style.
This wondrous leaflet published by Brown,
Sneers at the parrot brought from Portadown;
But any parrot is preferred you know
To the coarse croaking of a common crow,
But change of tone denotes a change of views.
He now in Tory dove-cot softly coos,
In the fond hope to find a resting place

Where he may shine by gear, if not by grace,
Alas! his hopes are built upon the sand,
Tho' he on Tory platforms takes his stand;
We all remember how in by-gone days
From him the landlords got scant meed of praise,
But why this change? each one asks aloud
In one and all the office-seeking crowd;
The sacred cause of Union they reply
For Queen and country we're prepared to die.
But, let us tell you, times may yet be worse,
If 'loyal' patriots from the public purse
Are not rewarded, is the almighty dollar
To go to rebels; while a polished scholar
Is forced with sighs to move the ambient air,
Heart sick with waiting for 'a vacant chair',
And other patriots of less condition
Yearning for places on the Land Commission
Ignored their claims with a contemptuous shrug,
In northern markets loyalty's a drug.

Ballymoney Unionist

Resolutions submitted to the General Assembly of the Presbyterian Church in Ireland on Wednesday 15 March 1893 by the Committee on the State of the Country. *General Assembly minutes*, viii, 470-74 (1893).

1.   That we declare anew our devoted loyalty to the person and throne of her gracious majesty Queen Victoria.

2.   That we reaffirm our strong attachment to the constitution of the United Kingdom of Great Britain and Ireland, and express our determination to resist every attempt to destroy the legislative union at present existing, and our firm resolve to maintain unimpaired for ourselves, and our children, the heritage of citizenship which we now enjoy. We protest against any proposal to thrust us out from the protection of the imperial legislature, in violation of repeated assurances that the liberties and interests of the Protestant minority were safe in the hands of the parliament of the United Kingdom.

3.   That having carefully examined the measure at present before parliament, entitled 'a bill to amend the provisions for the government of Ireland', we are amazed at its revolutionary character, and strenuously oppose its enactment by the legislature for the following among other reasons:

(a) Because the measure seriously imperils our civil and religious liberties, inasmuch as it would deprive us of the protection of the imperial parliament and government under which our persons and property are safe, and our religious freedom is secure, and would force upon us instead an Irish legislature and executive controlled by men declared to be 'marching through rapine to the dismemberment of the empire', whom a special commission found to be 'guilty of a criminal conspiracy', and who have supported, and still attempt to justify, the iniquitous and criminal organisation of the Land League, the plan of campaign, and the system of boycotting. Since the imperial parliament has in the present generation abolished religious ascendancy in Ireland, placing all denominations on an equality, we are painfully surprised that a project of law should now be entertained, under which one race, party and creed would always dominate, and which would inevitably result in a new religious ascendancy in Ireland, of a most objectionable character. Our conviction as to this result is amply confirmed by the arrogant claims of the Roman Catholic hierarchy to control the members of their church in the exercise of their political rights, shown by recent election proceedings in the two divisions of the county of Meath.

(b) Because the provisions which the bill contains for the protection of minorities against misgovernment and sectarian domination are illusory in themselves, and would be incapable of application in the face of a hostile majority. In the opinion of the Assembly, no securities can be devised which would safeguard the rights and privileges of minorities under an Irish legislature as they are safeguarded under the imperial parliament. Under the provisions of the bill ample scope is afforded for the indirect endowment of Romanism out of the general taxes of the country, and under its provisions small Protestant minorities might be deprived of state education for their children, except under conditions subversive of their faith.

(c) Because the bill proposes momentous changes in the constitution of the United Kingdom, to which changes the Protestants of all the churches and many Roman Catholics, comprising over a third of the population of Ireland, and representing the intelligence, education, wealth, and industry of the country, are determinedly hostile; and because no advantages would be derivable from an Irish legislature and executive which could not with more certainty and safety be obtained from the parliament and government of the United Kingdom. The measure cannot, therefore, 'afford contentment to the Irish people, important relief to parliament, and additional securities for the strength and union of the empire', but on the contrary, is calculated to embitter the hostilities of conflicting creeds and parties in this country, to add to the difficulties of the imperial legislature, and to encourage the disloyal to seek the complete separation of Ireland from Great Britain.

4.   That the Assembly is strongly of the opinion that the land question has long lain at the root of Irish discontent, and that the time has come for the abolition of dual ownership, which only the imperial parliament can with justice effect. The Assembly is persuaded that a measure enabling every tenant-farmer to become, on equitable terms, the proprietor of the land he tills, combined with a proper scheme of local government, would go far to satisfy all reasonable demands, and would be free from the evils that would follow the creation of a Home Rule parliament in Dublin.

5.   That the General Assembly earnestly exhorts the members of the Presbyterian church to continue to cultivate forbearance, peace, and goodwill towards their fellow countrymen of every class and creed, and to exhibit calmness and patient reliance upon the most high in the present eventful crisis.

6.   That the General Assembly recommends that in all the churches Sabbath, the 26th day of March, be observed as a day of humiliation and prayer, when we shall confess our sins, and entreat the most high to avert the dangers with which the church and the country are at present threatened, and to extend his kingdom throughout the entire land.

7.   That copies of these resolutions, signed in the name of the Assembly by the moderator and clerk, be transmitted to her majesty the queen; the lord lieutenant of Ireland; the prime minister; the chief secretary; the marquis of Salisbury; the duke of Devonshire; Mr A. J. Balfour, M.P.; Mr Joseph Chamberlain, M.P.; and the Irish Unionist members of parliament.

8.   That a petition embodying the resolutions, and similarly signed, be presented to both houses of parliament, and that the Committee on the State of the Country be empowered to send deputations to wait upon the prime minister, members of the legislature, and speakers to address public meetings in Great Britain, and in such other ways as they may deem desirable oppose the passing of the Home Rule measure.

APPENDIX E

Amendment submitted to the General Assembly of the Presbyterian Church in Ireland on Wednesday 15 March 1893 by the Rev. J. B. Armour. *General Assembly minutes*, viii, 470-74 (1893).

Whereas, under the existing system of government in Ireland, the offices and honours of state have practically been monopolised by a small section of the community, and the members of this church have been excluded from that share in the administration of public affairs to which they are justly entitled, the General Assembly of the Presbyterian church is of the opinion that a thorough reform, which will give to Ireland such a measure of self-government as is consistent with the unity of the empire, the supremacy of parliament, and the protection of minorities, is desirable and necessary. The Assembly, therefore, instructs the government committee to examine carefully the government of Ireland bill now before the house of commons, and to take whatever steps may be necessary to secure that the provisions of the bill shall, while giving an adequate measure of self-government, afford at the same time full protection to the rights and interests of this church. And whereas this church is deeply interested in the welfare of the cultivators of the soil, who constitute by far the largest part of the membership of the church, and who are in circumstances of unparalleled depression, and in many instances of extreme suffering, the Assembly hereby directs the government committee with all convenient speed to urge upon her majesty's government the necessity for prompt and adequate measures of relief by a reduction of the judicial rents, which have become oppressive through the fall in prices and the diminished productiveness of the soil, and for a final settlement of the land question at the earliest moment by the abolition of dual ownership upon such terms as, while giving to the landlord the full value of his property in the soil, shall also protect the interests of the tenant, and enable both the farmer and labourer in the future to live and thrive.

Presbyterian memorial to W. E. Gladstone, July 1893.

To the Right Honourable William Ewart Gladstone M.P.
First Lord of the Treasury.

We, the undersigned members and adherents of the Presbyterian Church in Ireland, hereby express our heartfelt gratitude to the Right Honourable W. E. Gladstone for the great benefits which his splendid statesmanship, as leader of the Liberal party, has already conferred upon our country; our sympathy with him in his present efforts to secure the better government of Ireland; and our determination to co-operate heartily with our fellow-countrymen of every class and creed in order to make a measure for local self-government in Ireland a practical success.

We further record our conviction that an urgent necessity exists for an immediate revision of judicial rents, in accordance with the depressed state of agriculture, which, while saving many from a crushing burden, will also provide an equitable basis for a measure to abolish dual ownership in land, by which alone a final settlement of this Irish land question can be achieved.

The new covenant presented by Captain J. R. White, D.S.O., to a meeting of Protestants of Ballymoney and the Route in the Town Hall, Ballymoney, 24 October 1913.

Being convinced in our conscience that Home Rule would not be disastrous to the national well-being of Ulster, and that, moreover, the responsibility of self-government would strengthen the popular forces in other provinces, would pave the way to a civil and religious freedom which we do not now possess, and give scope for a spirit of citizenship, we, whose names are underwritten, Irish citizens, Protestants, and loyal supporters of Irish nationality, relying under God on the proved good feeling and democratic instinct of our fellow-countrymen of other creeds, hereby pledge ourselves to stand by one another and our country in the troublous days that are before us, and more especially to help one another when our liberties are threatened by any non-statutory body that may be set up in Ulster or elsewhere. We intend to abide by the just laws of the lawful parliament of Ireland until such time as it may prove itself hostile to democracy, in sure confidence that God will stand by those who stand by the people, irrespective of class or creed, we hereunto subscribe our names.

THE ARMOUR FAMILY

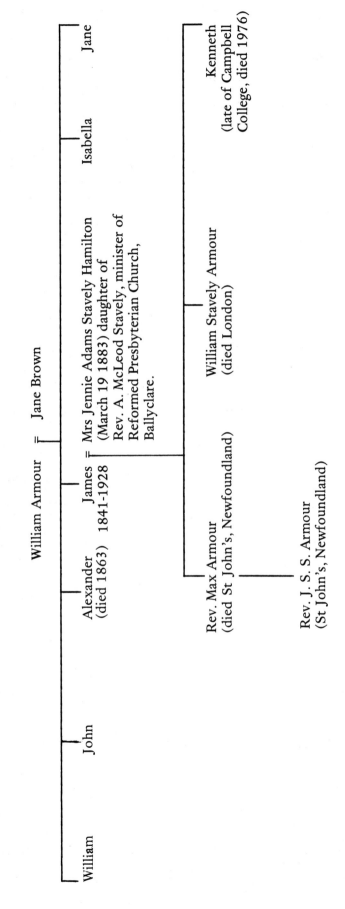

William Armour = Jane Brown

William

John

Alexander (died 1863)

James 1841-1928 = Mrs Jennie Adams Stavely Hamilton (March 19 1883) daughter of Rev. A. McLeod Stavely, minister of Reformed Presbyterian Church, Ballyclare.

Isabella

Jane

Rev. Max Armour (died St John's, Newfoundland)

Rev. J. S. S. Armour (St John's, Newfoundland)

William Stavely Armour (died London)

Kenneth (late of Campbell College, died 1976)

Index

Printed for Her Majesty's Stationery Office by The Universities Press (Belfast) Ltd. Dd. 8804775 7/85